MW00607589

Praise for *The Synchronized Univ*

"I give this significant work my <u>highest recommendation</u>. It is a landmark book that deserves wide recognition."

 -- Dr. Eugene F. Mallove, Editor-in-Chief, <u>Infinite Energy Magazine</u> in book review

"<u>It is a great work in every sense</u>…Your book is very timely. It covers all the relevant ground, and gives reliable data on many subjects where data is hard to find. It will be of great use as a reference. Also, being well written, it will be a pleasure to read."

--John Michel, author, *The New View Over Atlantis*

"<u>Physicist Dr. Claude Swanson has written a superb book</u> on the subject of paranormal research, experiments and theories. Topics included in this masterful book include: prophecies, remote viewing, extra-sensory perception, psychokinesis, group consciousness, cell-to-cell consciousness, levitation, teleportation, out-of-body experiences, adepts, and near death experiences. Each subject is presented with remarkable clarity, a historical overview, relevant diagrams and insightful observations into what appears to be going on…

"*The Synchronized Universe* maintains an impressive overall sense of purpose while covering a vast range of subject matter, and brings it all together in the riveting final chapter in which Swanson presents the Synchronized Universe Model (SUM), to describe how consciousness influences the physical world…

"<u>I give *The Synchronized Universe* my very highest recommendation!</u> It is ideal for anyone seeking a logical, scientific theory to explain and predict paranormal phenomena."

--Cynthia Sue Larson, <u>www.RealityShifters.com</u>

"I am swamped with required reading, but I just had to 'leaf through' that book! I was thrilled that he had summaries at the end of every chapter, so I was able to at least read those. When time permits, I will go back. It is amazing how he was able to connect all the learning (and books) that I have done since I was a teenager. What a great resource book for me to have in my library! WOW...what a brilliant man!"

--Deborah, Phoenix, Arizona

"Claude Swanson is an amazing man. I am deeply honored to call this scientific genius my friend. I absolutely loved his book, *The Synchronized Universe* and was inspired by his vision and passion so evident within these pages. Enjoy this wonderful paradigm stretching book. It is invaluable!"

--Dr. Richard Bartlett, developer of *Matrix Energetics*.

"Due to its comprehensive and exciting subject matter, Swanson's book is a real page-turner, with neat summaries at the end of each chapter... This book is a pleasure to read, to share, and to donate to your local school and public libraries."

--Camille James Harmon, *UFO Magazine* Book Review

"Dr. Swanson in his important book, *The Synchronized Universe*, reveals that some physical theories may have to change to accommodate solid ESP findings. He shows us these data down through the years through words, pictures and graphs...One needs to get out on the edge of what is known and design research which will provide additional information. I believe Dr. Swanson is that kind of researcher and he certainly shows strong evidence in his book why it will be necessary to change some of our theories in order to expand our knowledge."

--Janet Lee Mitchell, Ph.D., author of *Out-of-Body Experiences, A Handbook*

--Dr. Swanson has allowed us to join his inspired and inspirational research into life's mysteries. This unique contribution brings worlds together and offers a next step in our human education."

--Rabbi Michael Shapiro

"Once again, Claude Swanson brings to the forefront a brilliant manner of looking at the future of universal knowledge. I highly recommend this book as a <u>must-read</u> for anyone who seeks to truly understand the truth of the world we live in; a world where what we consider real and what we consider supernatural are merging. The paranormal is no longer hypothetical - it is a quantitative science."

--Dannion Brinkley, best-selling author of *Secrets of the Light: Lessons from Heaven*

"*The Synchronized Universe* is a well-written and exciting presentation of the latest scientific evidence proving the existence of the paranormal. Swanson's suggestions about how present physics can be modified to understand and explain some of these strange phenomena may go a long way to healing the ancient split between science and spirituality. The implications of this book are far-reaching."

--Brad Steiger, best selling author, *Mysteries of Space and Time*

"*The Synchronized Universe*, by physicist Dr. Claude Swanson, Ph.D, provides a revised model of Quantum Mechanics that supports the evidence for ESP as well as a model for UFO propulsion. In my opinion his model effectively bridges the traditions of ancient mysticism and modern science. Kudos to John Schuessler for inviting Dr. Swanson to the MUFON Conference."

--Dr. Leo Sprinkle, Life Member, American Association for the Advancement of Science, Professor Emeritus, University of Missouri.

"*The Synchronized Universe* has laid a powerful scientific foundation for our next quantum leap in science and human understanding. It appears that the industrial and technology revolutions will soon be dwarfed by this greater grasp of natural laws and our abilities as a human race. Kudos to *The Synchronized Universe*…"

--Rick Nelson, Director, Paranormal Research Forum

THE
SYNCHRONIZED
UNIVERSE
NEW SCIENCE OF THE PARANORMAL

by Dr. Claude Swanson

Poseidia Press
7320 North La Cholla
Suite #154-304
Tucson, AZ 85741

www.synchronizeduniverse.com
Third Printing - Revised and Updated

First Printing 2003
Second Printing 2005
Third Printing 2009

Library of Congress Control Number: 2009943162

Category: Science/Spiritual

ISBN: 978-0-9745261-0-2
New Edition: ISBN: 978-0-9745261-2-6

ATTENTION CORPORATIONS, UNIVERSITIES, COLLEGES, AND PROFESSIONAL ORGANIZATIONS: Quantity discounts are available on bulk purchases of this book for educational, gift purposes, or as premiums for increasing magazine subscriptions or renewals. Special books or book excerpts can also be created to fit specific needs. For information, please contact Poseidia Press, 7320 North La Cholla, Suite #154-304, Tucson, AZ 85741. For full ordering information, see last page, page 307.

Poseidia Press
7320 North La Cholla, Suite #154-304
Tucson, AZ 85741.

Printed and bound in the United States of America.

DEDICATION

To my parents, Claude V. and Sarah-Ellen (Dolly) Swanson,
I dedicate this book in love and gratitude.

PERMISSIONS:

The author wishes to thank the following for permission to reprint selections and illustrations in this book:

Rosalyn Bruyere, for material and illustrations from *Wheels of Light* (Bruyere, 1994)

Dr. Elmer Green, for illustrations from *Beyond Biofeedback* (Green, 1977)

Dr. Dean Radin, for graphs from *The Conscious Universe* (Radin, 1997) and other scientific publications.

Drs. Robert Jahn and Brenda Dunne for several graphs from *Margins of Reality* (Jahn 1987a) and their paper "Engineering Anomalies Research," published in JSE (Jahn, 1987b)

Dr. Harold Puthoff for several graphs and figures including one from "Experimental Psi Research: Implications for Physics*,"* (Puthoff, 1981)

Dr. Russell Targ, for illustrations from his paper "Remote Viewing at Stanford Research Institute in the 1970s: A Memoir." (Targ, 1996) and others.

Charles Russell Bull for kind permission to use his photographs, including the cover photograph.

Dr. William Tiller for a graph and an illustration, from his book *Science and Human Transformation* (Tiller, 1977)

Dr. Mark Thurston, for kind permission to use a quote from his book *Millenium Prophecies, Predictions for the Century from Edgar Cayce*, (Thurston, 1997) in the Introduction.

Uri Geller for permission to use two photographs from his book *The Geller Effect* (Geller, 1986).

Dr. P.M.H. Atwater, for a quote from her book *Future Memory* (Atwater, 1996)

Carol Sabick and F. Holmes "Skip" Atwater, for their kindness in taking and providing photographs of the Monroe Institute.

Cleve Backster for two graphs from his book *Primary Perception: Biocommunication with Plants, Living Foods, and Human Cells* (Backster, 2002)

David Blaine, for permission to use a still image from his film *Fearless* (Blaine, 2001)

Dr. Rene Peoc'h, for permission to reprint graphs from his scientific publications (Peoc'h, 1988; Peoc'h, 1988a; Peoc'h, 1995)

Dr. James Spottiswood for permission to reprint his graph from (Spottiswood, 1997)

Dr. Jeffrey Mishlove, for permission to use an image from his book *"The PK Man: A True Story of Mind Over Matter,"* (Mishlove, 2000)

Dr. Jack Houck, for permission to reprint a graph from (Houck, 1986; Houck, 1996)

Paul Dong, for permission to use photos from his book *China's Super Psychics* (Dong, 1997)

Dr. Roger Nelson, for graphs published by his Global Consciousness Project web page, at http://noosphere.princeton.edu/terror1.html and http://noosphere.princeton.edu/groupmedit.html (Nelson, 2003) and other publications (Nelson, 1991; Nelson, 1996)

ACKNOWLEDGEMENTS

This project began in 1985 when I realized that current physics was overlooking some important phenomena. My quest to understand these mysteries has led me on a wondrous journey. Along the way I have been helped by many gifted and generous people. One of the first was Mietek Wirkus, a skilled healer and teacher, who demonstrated to me the reality of "energy healing." I am also grateful to Gladys Davis, Edgar Cayce's lifetime secretary, who was Chief Librarian of the ARE library when I began my quest. She offered useful suggestions and much needed encouragement. I am grateful to Erica Lerner, an early guide in my exploration, and Martin Wolf, who helped in the exhaustive and exhausting early forays to libraries as we mined the scientific literature to develop a comprehensive picture of older research.

I am grateful to Rich Berry, who offered me valuable advice on organizing this book, at a time when the amount of data seemed overwhelming. When I followed his suggestions, the myriad topics of anomalous science seemed to spontaneously organize themselves into manageable volumes and chapters. I am also very grateful to Paul Perry for helpful suggestions and encouragement in this process.

Dr. Janet Mitchell offered me valuable leads and some hard-to-find research papers which were crucial in understanding the "out-of-body" experience. I am also grateful for discussions with Ingo Swann, Joe McMoneagle, Dr. Elmer Green, Dr. William Tiller, Dr. Courtney Brown, Dr. Dean Radin, Dr. Hal Puthoff, Dr. Keith Harary and Dr. Eldon Byrd, among many others, who contributed to my understanding of these subjects.

I am grateful to William Swanson for his willingness to conduct experiments on the Backster Effect, and for his valuable suggestion that it was important to retain the discussion of a possible theory along with the empirical data on paranormal effects. I am also very grateful to James H. Swanson for valuable financial and publishing assistance, and to Alexandra and Marian Swanson for their encouragement in this long process.

Charles Russell Bull is a gifted artist and photographer, as well as a tireless researcher and friend. He contributed the unusual photograph on the cover of this book, and has been a source of encouragement and valuable suggestions during this project.

Other friends who have provided much appreciated help include Jan Briski, who contributed invaluable editorial assistance and advice, as well as Donnie Fields, Melanie Green, June Fritsch, Buzz Mattingley, Charles Bynum, Dr. Kathleen Damiani, Fran Kreer, Patricia Patterson, Patricia Swanson, Thelea Gray, Shana Schultz, Ron Russell and Dr. Simeon Hein. To these and the many others who have helped on this journey, I offer my heartfelt gratitude.

COVER CREDIT

The photograph on the cover was taken by Charles Russell Bull. It was taken at night focused on the lit back porch of a "haunted house." There was no one on the porch at the time the photo was taken. This is a house I have visited many times, and where many strange phenomena have been recorded and photographed. The dark semi-transparent figure is about the same size as a person and has a distinct, twisting, "vortex-like" appearance upon close examination. Note the clapboards on the house behind the vortex. They appear to be twisting upward, as though light from them has been anomalously bent as it passed through the vortex (Copyright Charles Russell Bull, 2003).

TABLE OF CONTENTS

THE SYNCHRONIZED UNIVERSE

INTRODUCTION

The Hopi Prophecy

The prophecies of the Hopi are said to come from Massau'u, their spiritual teacher for the age. Ancient Hopi prophecies were handed down on stone tablets accompanied by an oral tradition of interpretation that was passed on by the elders of the community.

Certain of these prophecies concern events near the end of this current age in the Hopi framework of history. Some seem to have been fulfilled, including the coming of the automobiles and telephones-"horseless chariots" that would roll along "black snakes" across the land, and "cobwebs" through which people would speak over great distances.

Among the prophecies is a petroglyph, or rock carving, that depicts the Hopi Life Plan Prophecy. In part, it shows two horizontal timelines, the top one representing our modern technological, materialistic society and the bottom line depicting the Hopi's own world of attunement to natural forces. Along the materialistic lines are the figures of human beings with their heads detached from their bodies, an apt image for contemporary men and women whose intellectual self and feeling self are so often disassociated.

Also shown in this prophetic petroglyph are two vertical lines that connect horizontal timelines. One of the connecting lines - symbolic of the opportunity for materialistic society to reconnect with the wisdom of the Hopi - is placed, logically just before a pair of circles which interpreters decipher to be the two world wars. The second vertical connector comes after the images for these two great wars, at approximately the time in which we now exist. Thus, there is the opportunity, but not the certitude, for technological society to join with the wisdom of the ancient ones. If not, the Hopi life plan prophecy depicts yet another period of great destruction. -- Quoted from (Thurston, 1997)

The Conflict of Spiritualism and Materialism

This message from the Hopi underlines one of the great conflicts of our age: the separation between the spiritual world and the materialistic world. In Western societies, science is accepted as the final authority on the materialistic world. Scientists take the place of priests in medieval times, telling us about the age of our universe, how it was created, the nature of matter, and even the nature of life itself. The spiritual world has been relegated in the West to periodic rituals and diminishing Church attendance in the older established religions. There has been a backlash from fundamentalist religion, which challenges the scientific world-view head on, but is often viewed by the establishment intelligentsia as extremist and atavistic.

1

There seems to be no place in science for a God, and no place in religion for modern science. The two seem to be in conflict on all the main points. Religion requires miracles. Science requires the universe to follow laws. Religion and science each have their explanation for how the universe began, but these bear little resemblance to one another. They each offer a theory for how humans came to be on the earth, but the miraculous instantaneous creation of Genesis bears little resemblance to the slow evolution from one-celled animals described by Darwin. This split is confirmed by a 2001 Gallup poll, which revealed that 33% of Americans believe in the Theory of Evolution while 57% adhere to Creationism.

At every point there seems to be a deep disagreement. Scientists who are religious resolve this by compartmentalizing their thought. They simply will not think about the contradictions. The deeply religious often bear a deep suspicion or even a smoldering hostility toward science. This schism widens over matters of abortion, public prayer, genetic engineering, and numerous other matters of public debate.

As the Hopi prophecy makes clear, man cannot continue to exist in this divided state. The spiritual and the scientific sides of human wisdom must communicate. Science affords modern man with enormous power. This power can be used for good or evil. Often the long-term consequences are not even apparent. Science cannot always answer such questions. Religion has known for eons that a higher wisdom is available. Man must learn to seek guidance on a higher level, in order to use these new tools wisely. If he does not learn to listen to spiritual wisdom, the new tools of technology will become weapons, and will lead to our destruction. This, I believe, is the intent of the message of the Hopi.

But this does not imply that organized religion, as it is presently constituted, has all the answers we need. Just as science has drifted to an extreme position in which spirituality plays no part, so modern religion has evolved into fragmented, factious groups, often judgmental and condemning of others, and often having lost connection with the original spiritual beliefs of their early founders. Too often, churches and governments have made common cause, and become instruments of aggrandizement for one another. Too often, churches have modified their teachings to accommodate wealthy benefactors or powerful monarchs and dictators.

There are now hundreds, if not thousands, of different religions in the world, each with its own minute distinctions of ritual and catechism, conflicting gods and conflicting dogma. How can a modern look at this chaos of belief ever conclude that deep, satisfying truth can be found here? This is the response of the Western scientific minded, but it is often also the response of the disillusioned, disheartened faithful who continue religious ritual more out of habit than out of conviction.

Universal Truths
There is a resolution to this dilemma. There is an answer to what seems to be a hopeless question. It is possible to resolve the disagreements between science and religion. There is, after all, only one universe, and only one ultimate truth. Present day science has only PART of the answer, and present day religion also has only part of the answer.

A closer examination of the world's religions reveals that, beneath the conflict and cacophony of dogma, there are certain universal truths. It is these universal truths which make religion powerful and satisfying to people. They may have different names for these truths, but in each religion, there is prayer and meditation, and these are powerful and healing. In each religion, an afterlife of some form exists, and a soul which survives the death of the body is an article of belief. In every religion there is a belief in superior beings, invisible, but very wise, to whom one can communicate.

A scientist who has studied this, Dr. Charles Tart of the University of California, states:

> *"Thousands, if not millions, of people alive today have had the experience of existing outside the space of their physical bodies for a brief period and experiencing this separated state as* <u>real</u>*, not as a dream or imaginary experience. A typical consequence of such an out-of-body experience is on the order of 'I no longer* <u>believe</u> *that I have a soul, or that some part of me will survive death, I* <u>know</u> *it!' "* (Rogo, 1983)

There is no place in modern science for a view such as this. Modern science does not allow for the possibility of the soul, or invisible beings, or have any laws of force which can account for the power of prayer. But what if modern science still has a few things to learn? What if present-day physics is leaving out a few important truths about the universe, as well?

This seems to be the case. There are many phenomena which have been proven in the laboratory, and yet which mainstream physics steadfastly refuses to admit or recognize. Why? Because if it did, it would turn the present world-view of physics upside down. But there is good news, too. It would bring a golden age of new discoveries and new technology, undreamed of today. And it would bring modern science and modern religion much closer to healing the ancient rift which separates them.

Scientific Revolution

Evidence has rapidly accumulated over the past three decades that our present scientific theories are badly broken. Science is on the verge of a revolution as far-reaching as the one a century ago that introduced relativity and quantum mechanics. The mounting evidence for this revolution has been largely ignored by "mainstream" scientists, even as it has grown more convincing. The study of scientific revolutions (see Kuhn, 1962) indicates that they are never easy nor smooth. The scientific establishment ignores or actively opposes the new evidence as long as it can.

Modern quantum theory was initially discovered by Max Planck, who later received the Nobel Prize for it. But he was opposed by the scientific establishment of his day, and became so embittered that he later remarked, referring to these establishment scientists: *"Science advances funeral by funeral."* Today it has been largely forgotten that Charles Darwin, who advanced the Theory of Evolution, endured white-hot hatred from opponents, who felt he was attacking the Bible's version of creation.

And few today realize that even Albert Einstein, the widely hailed genius of twentieth-century physics, was very slow in being recognized. His Theory of Relativity encountered very little acceptance for many years, and seventeen years later, when he received the Nobel Prize, it was for his work on the photoelectric effect and "other contributions to theoretical physics." Even then, his revolutionary theories of space and time were not accepted by many physicists.

Four hundred years ago, the intellectual establishment had more persuasive methods of preserving the old paradigm. When Galileo advanced his new theory of gravity and acceleration, which contradicted Aristotle, the Church threatened him with torture on the rack if he did not recant. He recanted.

Copernicus, who discovered from meticulous measurements that the earth revolved around the sun, not vice versa, prudently waited until after his death to have published his revolutionary conclusions. And Giordano Bruno, who proposed that the stars in the sky were other suns much like our own, and might have planets just like our sun does, was offered a choice: publicly renounce his theories or be burned at the stake (Mendoza, 1995). He held to his truth, and was incinerated as a lesson to those who would challenge orthodox beliefs.

Today, orthodoxy in science is maintained in more genteel ways. Ideas and results which challenge the prevailing viewpoint are simply not published in the mainstream journals, no matter how prestigious the credentials of the scientist or the care with which the work is done. The distinguished astronomer Halton Arp decries the present state of scientific publishing:

> *"The tradition of 'peer review' of articles published in professional journals has degenerated into almost total censorship. Originally, a reviewer could help an author improve his article by pointing out errors in calculation, references, clarity, etc., but scientists, in their fervid attachment to their own theories, have now mostly used their selection as a referee to reject publication of any result that would be unfavorable to their own personal commitment...The press, of course, only reports news from established academic centers that have a strong financial and prestige interest in glorifying the status quo. The result is that real investigative science is mostly now an underground activity."(Arp, 2000)*

As a result of these conditions, many scientists are unaware of much of the evidence that has accumulated, which indicates that the present scientific paradigm is broken. What are some of these phenomena which modern physics wishes would go away? Until recently, physicists were dreaming of the "final theory" and thinking themselves very close to achieving it. In the face of such confidence, what reason is there to believe that the present scientific edifice is about to undergo a radical face-lift?

First of all, there is "dark matter." This should be embarrassing to physics. For almost six decades, billions of dollars have been spent colliding elementary particles together in "atom smashers," high-energy accelerators. The outcomes of these experiments became the basis for our modern theories of matter. They were used to predict the kinds of particles which can occur in the universe. And now, suddenly, physicists have to admit that between 50% and 95% of the matter in the universe is of some <u>unknown</u> type that is <u>not</u> predicted by their theories. They know almost nothing about this form of matter. To quote Princeton Professor of Physics Jim Peebles, "It is an embarrassment that the dominant forms of matter in the universe are hypothetical..." (Scott, 2002)

There is also evidence that our theory of gravity, called General Relativity, has some glaring weaknesses. Anomalies have been observed in Foucault pendulums during solar eclipses. They veer off in strange directions during such events. (Saxl, 1971; Allais, I and II, 1959) These anomalies are large and have been well-documented. They cannot be explained by current physics. Instead they have been ignored.

Another example is the furor over "cold fusion." Most Americans believe the cold fusion debacle in the late nineteen-eighties was an example of either bad science or fraud. They are unaware that over 100 laboratories around the world duplicated and verified the results of those experiments! Among those are five U.S. national laboratories. They are unaware that one of the hasty studies conducted at MIT, which supposedly disproved cold fusion, has been discovered to have doctored its data, and that its initial tests also confirmed the reality of cold fusion (Mallove 1991, 1997; Bokris, 1999).

The average scientist or citizen would be even more surprised to learn that EPRI, the large, non-profit research institute funded by the nation's electric utilities, conducted an extensive $10 million dollar evaluation of cold fusion. Their conclusion is that cold fusion works:

> *"This work confirms the claims of Fleishman, Pons, and Hawkins [the inventors of cold fusion] of the production of excess heat in deuterium loaded palladium cathodes at levels too huge for chemical transformation...Further, excess energy exceeds that of known chemical processes by two or more orders of magnitude."*
> (Mallove, 1997; EPRI, 1994)

Likewise, the United States Navy recently completed its own painstaking evaluation of this technology. After all, it would certainly be useful for submarines and ships. Their conclusion: "...we do know the existence of Cold Fusion phenomenon through repeated observations by scientists throughout the world." (Szpak, 2002) These very positive evaluations of cold fusion never received any press coverage, while the "debunking" result of MIT received the highest level news attention.

Cold fusion is a technology which directly threatens a large and powerful industry (oil) and this may explain, in part, the intensity of the opposition it experienced. But it also presented a phenomenon which does not fit in with present theories of physics, and thus presents a challenge to orthodox science.

These examples are from the "hard sciences." Even more dramatic conflicts are seen in the areas of consciousness studies and paranormal effects. "Paranormal" is often viewed as a pejorative term, but it usefully categorizes a broad class of phenomena which defies the present scientific paradigm, and for which there is good scientific evidence.

One of these is "remote viewing". This is a process by which a person goes into a light trance and can describe distant objects or events. It has been demonstrated to be successful in a two-decade program conducted by the U.S. military. Despite public disclaimers that it did not work, there is overwhelming evidence to the contrary, as we will see in Chapter 1. How it works is a mystery which defies our present understanding of space and time, and of physical laws.

Part of the power of remote viewing is its ability to examine targets which are truly "remote" in space and time. One of the great anomalies of this new science is that time and distance do not seem to matter. The target can be ten feet away or ten thousand miles away. And even more surprising, a target event in the past or in the future can be examined just as easily and accurately as one in the present. The consciousness of the viewer seems able to "go" there with equal ease.

This completely violates one of the cardinal laws of contemporary physics, that of "causality," which means that cause must precede effect. And yet solid and statistically valid evidence has accumulated which proves that this law does not hold for remote viewing (Jahn, 1987, 1992).

During such experiments, at the location of the target a strange and anomalous energy has been seen and measured in some cases. Early evidence suggests that some form of energy or "consciousness" can actually travel to the site being remote-viewed, and causes measurable disturbances (Osis, 1980; PRC, 1982; Yonjie, 1982; Hubbard, 1987). This is an unknown form of energy which defies present physics, but may hold the key to consciousness and to many kinds of psychic phenomena.

Similar, possibly related, anomalous forms of energy have been documented in haunted houses, where they have been photographed on hundreds of occasions. They often appear as rapidly moving orbs, and create measurable magnetic and electrical anomalies, further supporting the notion that these energy forms are in some sense "real." Could these energy forms, which carry consciousness and survive death, be the human soul, or some aspect of it? Is our science on the verge of a breakthrough which will enlighten us about our own immortality?

These are just a few examples of areas in which serious scientific research is uncovering facts which violate modern physics. They suggest that the present scientific model is limited, and has left out some important phenomena. It may be that, when physics begins to acknowledge these new phenomena, it will evolve into a more advanced, comprehensive and enlightened system of knowledge.

Professor Willis Harmon of Stanford University has called this the "Third Scientific Revolution," because it goes far beyond the discoveries of Newtonian Physics at the dawn of the Renaissance, and the Einsteinian-Quantum revolution one hundred years ago. The new revolution deals with consciousness and subtle forms of energy which have, until now, been neglected by western science. To quote Professor Harmon:

> *"The fundamental insight behind the 'Third Scientific Revolution" is the view that the existence of states of higher organizational complexity cannot be understood merely through lower-level laws and system-components. The self-organizing properties of matter and of life cannot be fully explained in terms of the physical sciences and molecular biology; completely new fundamental principles will be required." (Harmon, 1995)*

Some of these new discoveries will lead to new inventions and technology which will revolutionize our world. Science is learning that "empty space," for example, is not so empty after all. It is filled with energy. (Boyer 1969, 1975; Puthoff, 1989; Cole, 1993) This energy can be tapped to produce clean, abundant, cheap forms of power which can replace fossil fuel, relieve us of our dependence on oil and save the environment.

The energy in the vacuum may be manipulated to produce miraculous new forms of propulsion. The "physics of *Star Trek*" seems more like science and less like fiction every year (Millis, 1999; Haish, 1997; Puthoff, 1997). We are discovering that parallel dimensions and higher dimensions, long the domain of speculation by theorists, may be quite real after all. And some of the energy forms in the vacuum may be key to understanding the paranormal effects which are being discovered.

In these books, we review the large number of phenomena which have now been established experimentally as real, and yet which violate present day physics, or at the very least pose a serious challenge to it. Our thesis is that it is time for physics to begin to seriously address these breakdowns in conventional science.

From this, a new scientific revolution will result, with a much deeper understanding of the universe and our place in it. Scientists today work on the "Unified Field Theory" and call it the "theory of everything." And yet, they are not aware of, or even trying to explain, broad classes of phenomena which have been proven to occur in our universe. Without including these, a correct unified field theory can never be found.

At the end of this volume, after reviewing some of this evidence, we shall offer some suggestions about how such a new theory might be constructed. It is far from the final word on such a complex and ambitious project. But we offer our ideas on the shape of the "new" physics as a sort of "prelude," in the spirit of "here are some ideas that might work."

This is a voyage into a new era of science. Like Columbus, we know that the world is not flat. It still may be dangerous to tell others that. Old beliefs die hard. But there is an exciting, much larger, world out there, waiting for the "new physics" to sail into it. It is an exciting world with undreamed-of possibilities.

Types of Evidence
In the early days of a scientific revolution, the evidence is always incomplete. Just as during the time when electricity was first being studied, it is seldom possible to rely solely on rigorous scientific experiments. Before there was a Michael Faraday in his laboratory, meticulously measuring and quantifying the electric and magnetic force so accurately, there was a Benjamin Franklin with his kite in a thunderstorm. And before that, there were five thousand years of people walking across carpets on dry days and receiving electrical shocks. Before the rigorous scientific research came the anecdote, the story, the example.

Because we are at an early phase of this paradigm shift, it has not been possible to back up every phenomenon with rigorous scientific experiments. Either the experiments haven't been done yet, or they haven't been published in the open literature. In many cases, modern science does not even know how to measure these strange new phenomena. Photographs can be made, electrical measurements recorded, but these are only clumsy attempts to document some of the results of the phenomena. They do not get at the heart of the force itself.

Appropriate instruments to measure paranormal phenomena will probably evolve as our understanding of the phenomena evolves. This is how it was with electricity and with gravity, as well as with the nuclear forces. Until we reach that stage, it is important that we include a liberal sprinkling of anecdotes and accounts by credible individuals of their anomalous experiences. These experiences are like Franklin and his kite. They demonstrate that a phenomenon is there, and that it has certain general characteristics. It is the first step in developing a scientific understanding.

There is a sufficiently large body of such first-person data by highly credible witnesses that it should not be discounted. These data provide important clues which can help science to feel its way to a more systematic and rigorous approach in the future. Like the spark that shocks someone who touches a door knob, it only takes a few such cases by reliable witnesses to indicate that there is a force involved which we do not understand.

Unfortunately, in the beginning of a paradigm shift, most scientists have no interest in conducting experiments on these "outlandish" topics. They know that if they do, they will lose their funding, be unable to publish, and may even find their academic careers in jeopardy.

Control of research funding has become highly centralized, with the U.S. government controlling most pure research money. In some cases this money is controlled by groups of scientists with vested interest in their own long-standing research areas. In other cases, military secrecy prevents controversial new, potentially powerful technologies from being funded in an open, public forum. Scientists along with the American public have been educated to view these areas of anomalous research with contempt and ridicule, which further compounds the difficulty in addressing these phenomena with rigorous and unbiased scientific analysis. All of these factors contribute to the absence of a completely satisfying scientific study of these topics.

Personal History - How I Got Here

From my earliest childhood, I remembering always wanting to know "Why." I was curious about how the universe worked.

In High School, I met my first real scientist, Dr. John Mrgudich, a wizened electro-chemist from Europe, from the "old world." He imparted to me the romance and adventure that the quest for knowledge can be. He suggested that I keep a journal, and asked what I would name it. I said I would name it "Why."

I went to college at M.I.T., one of the foremost schools of science in the world. I really thought that I would learn the secrets of the universe there. I encountered the *Feynman Lectures in Physics*, which were then only two years old. These wonderful textbooks by the great physicist Richard Feynman fired my imagination. Feynman thinks and teaches from the perspective of intuition. I learned that the intuitive understanding of the world must come first. If you have an intuitive understanding of a new idea, the science will follow.

From Feynman I learned that it is OK to visualize. I used to spend hours watching, imagining in my mind, the motions of an electron, trying to understand the dynamics. In later years I learned that this is called "remote viewing," but in those days I was just trying to understand on an intuitive level.

At M.I.T. I first came across "Mach's Principle." It really came from a freshman physics course by Professor Anthony French. We were studying "centrifugal force." This is the force that pulls your arms outward from your body when you spin around. The interesting thing about this force is that you only feel it when, from your perspective, the stars in the sky are also spinning. The thought occurred to me: "What if the motion of the distant stars is really the <u>source</u> of centrifugal force?

I made some simple calculations to show that this was a reasonable idea, and took them to the teacher. He was impressed and told me about Mach's Principle: that all the local forces can be attributed to the motions of distant matter. This was one of the key ideas which drove Einstein to develop his theory of General Relativity, which is our present theory of gravity.

From Ernst Mach, the German philosopher and scientist after whom the "mach number" is named, came the idea that the smallest local force is intimately tied to the motions of all the other particles in the universe. I really liked this idea. The universe was connected. It offered a way to explain things at a deep level.

But Mach's Principle got lost in Einstein's Theory. In his final theory of General Relativity, objects experience inertia and centrifugal force even when there are no distant stars, no "distant matter." So it actually violated Mach's Principle. In those days, few physicists seemed to be very concerned. In the nineteen-sixties, scientists were discovering a new elementary particle every week, it seemed, in bigger and better atom smashers. Theorists were on the hunt for the ultimate theory of the very small. They didn't seem to believe that the very large, the universe, the distant matter, played a role.

When I arrived at Princeton for graduate school, I discovered there was a split among physicists. Some studied the very small things, and were called particle physicists, or "high energy" physicists. They felt that electromagnetism and the strong and weak nuclear forces were the ones that were important. Others studied the very large, and were called gravitational theorists or cosmologists. They worked with galaxies and the universe, and the force most important to them was gravity.

In the late sixties and early seventies, this split existed. The two groups used different equations and addressed very different problems. Their philosophies and outlooks were different. The Holy Grail was unified field theory. It would unite these theories and these world views into one coherent picture. But it seemed a distant dream in those days.

I felt then, as I feel now, that one of the keys to healing this split is Mach's Principle. If the physicists who study the very small realized that their tiny particles were interacting moment to moment, nanosecond to nanosecond, with every other particle in the universe, then there could be no separation between the large and the small. The processes would be intimately linked. This was my intuition, and I spent many years working on a theory to implement it.

However, most of this research has been done "on the side." Since graduate school, I have made my living doing more practical physics, "applied physics." I have consulted for government and private industry in the areas of electromagnetism, remote sensing from satellites, lasers, fluid dynamics, ballistics, and many other things. I ran my own company for many years, and consulted for the Army, Air Force, Navy and C.I.A., as well as many large and small private corporations.

This gave me the freedom to pursue my own direction of research. It also helped me understand the secret world of government research, and how politics and economics influence defense decisions. I learned that the real motives and goals are often very different from what the public believes. I worked in the suburbs of Washington, D.C. in those days, "inside the beltway," and received a first-hand education in how decisions get made in the capital of the "free world." This was an eye-opening experience in itself, as I shed many naive beliefs. But one day I experienced an even greater awakening. One day I learned something that changed my world-view forever.

My Paradigms Start to Shift

That was the day I came face with face with information that I could not dismiss and could not explain. I was riding in a car with a couple of scientists from Washington, D.C. They were talking about something I had never heard of before. It was called "remote viewing." They told me about a man who could go into a trance in a shielded room, and send his mind out into the world. They mentioned experiments where he could look into locked rooms, peer into locked safes, and read secret documents half way around the world…while never leaving his chair in the shielded room!

The scientists telling me this were people I knew and respected. This was not some rumor they were passing on. It was a project they had direct knowledge of. I could not dismiss this information, and yet it violated everything I had been taught about physics.

The experiments had been conducted in a heavily shielded room, so electromagnetic waves were ruled out as an explanation. Gravity waves have never been seen, and could not explain the data. Nuclear forces are short range and could not reach half way around the world. There was no known force which could explain these experiments.

Even more disturbing was the way it was done. The remote viewer did not simply receive a signal from someone outside. He described the experiment as though he actually left his body and <u>went</u> to the location. He could move around when he was there. He passed through walls of steel like they weren't there. In some cases he described events a half hour <u>before</u> they happened. This was something new. It was a revolution in physics if it were true. It meant a new theory was needed.

I followed this up with further research to verify what I had heard. I discovered that there were published papers on this subject, in fact there was a great deal of confirming research, but I had never known to look for it before. Probably I wouldn't have believed it before. Once I knew that there was something important missing from the "old" physics, I began searching for more information. I tried to keep an open mind while at the same time remaining rigorously objective.

My education, as well as the influence of the media, caused me to be skeptical about all claims involving the paranormal, psychics, and other unconventional phenomena. The media had presented all these topics as being due to hoaxes and hallucinations. But as I investigated more deeply, I was amazed at how many top quality researchers, M.D.s and Ph.D.s from top institutions, had performed research into psychic phenomena. And contrary to what I had always been taught, they found very real effects, solid experimental results that cried out for scientific explanation.

A doctor friend of mine introduced me to my first "energy healer." He was a recent émigré to America from Poland. In that country he had been one of three such healers who were approved to work in medical centers alongside doctors. His name was Mietek Wirkus. I was told that he could both diagnose and cure diseases without ever touching the patient, simply by interacting with mysterious invisible "energy fields" surrounding the patient.

The doctor, a Harvard-trained physician, had been doing experiments with Mietek and had verified that he was accurate. Mietek could even detect bones which had been broken and healed ten years before. He could seemingly "see" inside the body. I had always been taught that, if there was anything to psychic phenomena, it was very unreliable. But Mietek could, seemingly, always do what he did. It was consistent.

I began to get excited. I thought, if he can <u>always</u> do it, then I will get some instruments and make some measurements while he is healing. Then I will learn what the force is that he is using. I discussed this with Mietek and he was willing. But as I talked more with him, I began to realize how much I did not know. He explained the principles he used. He showed me a chart of the human aura and tried to describe "subtle energies" to me. This was all new. I did not know if it was true or not, but I did realize I had a lot to learn.

Then he said, "Stand up, and I will show you!" (This was translated by his wife. Mietek spoke no English at that time.) For the next twenty minutes he walked around me moving his hands and breathing funny. But I began to notice a change. I had come to him very tense, hopped up on too much coffee, and carrying a lot of anxieties. Twenty minutes later my state was euphoric. I felt completely relaxed, healthy, and filled with the most powerful energy I have ever known. I felt wonderful. If I ever felt that I could fly, it was after that session. This was not a psychological effect. My body felt different, better, at all levels. Mietek had said absolutely nothing during the session, but something in my body had changed dramatically.

As my research continued, it extended to many areas of science in which anomalies have been seen. In each area, I knew I had to figure out which phenomena were real and which were not. My only agenda here was finding out the truth. The phenomena that are real need to be included in our scientific theory. Otherwise a theory cannot be correct. It must explain the real universe, as it really is. And this must be done objectively. No matter how much ridicule and propaganda has been heaped on a subject by the media and vested interests, if the evidence supports the phenomenon, then I wanted to thoroughly understand it.

In my quest to figure out what was true, I began to learn all I could about ESP, psychometry (picking up information from objects), psychokinesis or PK (moving things with your mind), prophecy, levitation, energy healing, psychotronics (machines using paranormal forces), reincarnation and many other subjects.

My Research Program
I approached all these subjects with an open, but skeptical mind. If something was real, I wanted to know it. I did not want to exclude a phenomenon just because it was ridiculed in the press. I knew that if I excluded something that was real, my theory could never be correct. Likewise, if I were duped to believe in a phenomenon that was fake, and included it in the theory, this would also make the theory wrong. So I had a lot of incentive to find out the truth: to have neither a closed mind nor a hole in my head.

What has amazed me on this quest is the huge amount of high quality research which is available. I was amazed to discover that some of the greatest scientists of history knew that paranormal phenomena were real, and studied them. Among these are the giants, Newton, Maxwell and Faraday, who gave us our laws of gravity and electromagnetism. Sir William Crookes, who invented the forerunner of the fluorescent light and vacuum tube, spent a lifetime doing experiments with the powerful psychic D. D. Home.

One day it occurred to me that if these phenomena were real, then someone somewhere in this universe must have already figured it out a long time ago. We humans are just beginning to study these phenomena. Our "modern" science is less than one hundred and fifty years old. But on some other world older than ours or with smarter people, they would have reduced these ideas to engineering long ago.

They would have built craft incorporating these technologies. Such craft might be able to levitate and to travel faster than light. And then I thought of UFOs. What if they are somebody else's engineering? If they are, then I can learn about what is possible in the universe from studying them. Again, as with all these subjects, a careful process of separating fact from fiction was a crucial element in the research.

As my research program continued, I quickly discovered an unusual aspect of it. My education in school had not prepared me for this. I discovered that there were powerful vested interests involved in these topics. There are corporations, for example, who have patents on existing technology. They will not be happy if their patents are made obsolete by a revolution in physics. And there are military interests which want to keep scientific breakthroughs secret for their own use.

Because such controversial research is often the target of negative attacks, it has been important for me to get to know the scientists on the front lines of this new research. If they are engaged in fraud, or are just sloppy and unreliable, then I wanted to know about it. I do not want to waste years working on a theory which is based on flawed experiments. I attended dozens of conferences, interviewed many of the scientists, and formed a personal evaluation of their credibility and honesty whenever possible. In the process I have read thousands of books, and an equal number of research journal articles.

But there is one more avenue to be explored in this process. Many of the breakthroughs involve consciousness. The most convincing type of evidence is direct experience, so I investigated some of these topics directly, by trying them out myself. For example, I took a "psychic development" course, which involved several months of meditation and learning to do some of the things a professional psychic does.

One evening, in a group of 15 people, I held a metal object belonging to one of them, not knowing whose it was. I described the images that came to my "imagination". I do not consider myself psychic and had no reason to believe that my imagination is anything more than that. But the images I described, a horse farm, a spotted horse beside a white fence, an old blue pickup truck, a white house with a screened side porch, details of the stairway inside, all related to one specific person in the group, and no other. And it was the person who owned the item. This is called "scrying" or psychometry, and I had seen psychics doing it. But I never imagined that I would be able to do it.

I took several courses in Remote Viewing. Although I don't consider myself especially talented at it, I realized, even after the first session, that the images appearing in my mind often bore a startling resemblance to the actual targets, which were kept secret from us until after the session. Even though my sessions were not perfect, there was a definite sense of being in contact with something, a place, a time, an event. Images came in flashes and fragments as the session proceeded. In a few cases I felt like I was actually there, and it took hours to recover. When experiences like this happen to you, over and over, it is convincing that there is something real here, something important. Science must not continue to ignore these subjects.

I have taken a course in "energy healing" to see what it felt like, and to attempt to understand it better. I have taken part in "ghost hunts" with the latest high-tech electronic equipment. Some of the magnetic readings, photographs and video obtained cannot be explained by conventional physics. I have fire-walked, together with 1,500 people, at an "Unlimited Power" weekend conducted by Tony Robbins. It was another of many experiences in which the power of the mind to affect reality was illustrated in a powerful and unforgettable way. These are just a few of the personal validations that have reinforced the "book learning" and convinced me that the phenomena described here are very real and very important.

Personal Growth and Transformation

So that is how my journey began, more than fifteen years ago. Since then I have met some amazing and wonderful people. I have been helped in my journey by so many. And in the process, something else unexpected happened. I began to realize that these new "laws" I was learning about applied to me directly.

Much of the physics of the paranormal involves consciousness. It involves the human 'soul', if you will. You cannot talk about the paranormal for very long without encountering the human soul. How is it that the remote viewer can send his consciousness half way around the world to read documents in a safe? What actually goes there? It is certainly the center of his awareness, based on how he describes the experience. Is it his soul or some part of it? There is now evidence to suggest that perhaps it is.

In some out-of-body (OBE) and near-death (NDE) cases, as well as in actual death cases, a physical manifestation is seen or measured. A faint glowing orb has been witnessed which may be the physical manifestation of this energy. It has affected electronic sensors, such as strain gauges and optical sensors. It has even been photographed. This seat of consciousness, or soul or some aspect of it, is very real.

When one studies the evidence for reincarnation, again it is surprising how much high quality evidence there is. Thousands of cases have been painstakingly researched by highly qualified academic scientists (Stevenson, 1960, 1975, 1977). The findings are persuasive, even overwhelming. Once more it reinforces the notion that the soul, the identity, continues after death. It makes us realize that we humans are much more than we have been taught.

And when you see enough evidence that the human consciousness does not need a physical body to operate, then it opens up the idea of non-physical intelligences. The new physics will have to account for a "field of consciousness," and it may have to deal with the idea that intelligence and awareness does not require a physical body in the sense we are used to.

There have been important breakthroughs in research on reincarnation, near-death experiences, energy healing, the power of prayer, and non-physical consciousness. Many of these will be reviewed here. It is but a short step from this point to realize that the new science begins to resemble, or at least support, some of the tenets of religion. Not any specific dogmatic religion, but the general principles underlying all religions.

As we stumble our way towards the ultimate "unified field theory," we may find to our surprise that it bridges the gulf between science and religion. As our understanding becomes more profound, the differences between these two belief systems may become smaller.

There is, after all, only one universe. There is only one true description of it at the deepest level. This understanding would heal the rift warned of by the Hopi. It would offer an integrated view of the universe and of man. This would be the ultimate "unified field theory." These books are intended to help us as we journey toward that goal.

Claude Swanson
Colorado Springs
July 4, 2003

CHAPTER 1 - REMOTE VIEWING

"Using the standards applied to any other area of science, it is concluded that psychic functioning has been well established."
   -- Dr. Jessica Utts, member of CIA review panel on Remote Viewing (Utts, 1995)

"I never liked to get into debates with the skeptics, because if you didn't believe that remote viewing was real, you hadn't done your homework."
   -- Major General Edmund R. Thompson, U.S. Army Assistant Chief of Staff for Intelligence, 1977-81, Deputy Director for Management and Operations, Defense Intelligence Agency 1982-84 (Schnabel, 1997)

DEFINITION-REMOTE VIEWING: The ability to see and sense things at a distance or at other times through paranormal means. In the present context, it often involves specific procedures and protocols to assist in the process.

DEFINITION-PRECOGNITION: The act of becoming aware of something before it actually occurs.

DEFINITION-PSI: The abbreviation for all psychical or paranormal phenomena, including extended sensory awareness, ESP and exertion of paranormal forces, which is psychokinesis.

A Remote Viewing Session

I am in a gray cubicle in a room with seven other students, each in his own gray cubicle. The instructor is standing. He speaks clearly and firmly:

"All right, here are your coordinates: eight-zero-two-nine-seven-nine-five-one."

My hand moves quickly on the paper, making a single smooth motion. This is called an ideogram. Its purpose is to allow the subconscious mind to move the pen, tapping into whatever it has received from the numbers. The numbers correspond to a sealed brown envelope somewhere, probably outside the room. They are written on its exterior. Inside the envelope is a description of our target. This is a remote viewing class. I am following a rigid procedure and hoping that I am receiving information from inside that envelope. But my focus is to stay relaxed, keep my mind clear. I say a little meditation mantra and breathe deeply to relax. The numbers are repeated two more times. Each time my pen scribes a quick ideogram. Next, these will be "decoded," by moving the pen over the squiggle, and writing down any descriptions or sense impressions.

I do not consider myself a good remote viewer. I am a scientist. But I want to understand what it feels like. I want to see if I can do it. Dr. Courtney Brown, who is a Professor at Emory University and founded this school, says that we have about 3 seconds after the subconscious mind receives a sense impression, before the conscious mind analyzes and interprets it. Analysis is where errors come in. Remote viewing is based on the idea of keeping the student busy, so the analytical conscious mind never has time to analyze the impressions. Then, all I have to do is quickly record whatever impressions come, stay relaxed, and follow procedure. In this first phase I have picked up the sense of grass, natural, brown and falling. All very vague, which it is supposed to be at this point.

Then we open up to sense impressions. What sounds do I hear? (I hear water) What textures? What is the temperature? Visuals? Tastes? And so forth. It is like word association, in a way. Just write down the first things that come to mind. Don't analyze. Don't think. I pick up the sound of seagulls crying and waves breaking, and the taste of salty.

Next we do an impressionistic sketch. I draw whatever comes to mind, just letting the pen make marks where it wants to. The theory is that, as the session proceeds, the subconscious mind homes in on the target closer and closer, so more and more specific information will become available later in the session. Next we fill out a table which categorizes our impressions in nine columns: "senses", "magnitudes," "physicals," etc. Each impression I get is to be quickly written in the correct column. This keeps my analytical mind busy. I see a big mountain (in my imagination). I write "big" in "magnitudes," and "mountain" in "physicals," It keeps my left brain, my analytical mind, very busy deciding where to place things.

Which is great for me, since, like most Americans, my left brain is in the habit of always jumping in and analyzing information. Having been trained in the sciences, the tendency to analyze is deeply ingrained. So I am happy that the Farsight procedure keeps my left brain distracted with busy work. This goes on for several pages. We are then given a movement exercise, which asks us to view the target from a different perspective. Of course, my conscious mind still has no idea what the target is. But my next drawing is labeled a "Spanish style house with fountain."

More tables to fill in. When a coherent thought is received, I write it down as a sentence or paragraph. I see a "flurry of activity" and pick up "crowd" and "urgency." I think of "Exodus" and the "Red Sea." I deduce "The Destruction of Pompeii." I describe "a scene with many people and much frantic activity, animals, confusion, fear and urgency." In the "feelings" column I write "frantic, urgent, threatened, crowded, fear, determination." Then a full paragraph, which we learned to call a "thought-ball":

Figure 1.1 Final sketch of Remote Viewing session on March 13, 1997, at approximately 9:00 p.m., by Claude Swanson at Farsight Institute. Target: Pompeii-Volcanic Destruction Event.

"Lots of people, wooden beams, crowded, struggling. They're frantic but determined, something is coming and they're trying to prepare for it. Involves protecting themselves-houses, livestock, older time-tunics, sandals, slipping and sliding, hay, straw…Something flowing toward them. Animals squealing." My last drawing for the session is shown in Figure 1.1.

Then we are told the session is over. We are told what the target is: The destruction of Pompeii. Later I realized that the "Spanish-style house" I saw had a clay-tile roof and garden, and looked just like the Roman houses at Pompeii. In my final drawing, above, I wrote "V-F (Viewer Feeling): "It's making me cry." The sketch shows a man at lower right in a Roman soldier's uniform motioning with his hand, and others in frantic activity. In the upper left is written "dark" and upper center is labeled "Danger-Light" and something above the horizon is glowing. The figures seem to be constructing a barricade of some sort as imminent danger approaches. The sketch is shown again below (Figure 1.2) with shading added and the handwritten comments typed in to make it easier to understand.

For an amateur remote viewer like me, this is a pretty good session. Out of the total of 30 or 40 targets I did in three courses at Farsight, maybe 20% were this good. In a good session you really feel like you are there, even if you are not quite sure where "there" is. You pick up emotions, and feelings, and tastes and sounds, and the images are pretty clear. In maybe half of my sessions, my conscious mind was too active, and I seemed to guess and go off the track. Even in those sessions, upon review, I could see information coming through, but being distorted or misinterpreted.

"VF-It's making me cry"

Figure 1.2 The final sketch in the remote viewing session has been shaded here for easier understanding. It is based on the colors as I saw them in my mind's eye. There are Roman-looking soldiers in the foreground working frantically to build a barricade. The distant sky is dark and ominous. There is a bright light in the sky, which must have represented the volcano. There is water on pavement in the foreground making it slippery. "VF" stands for "viewer feeling": The scene was making me cry.

But in some of the sessions, there would be a quick image at some point, or maybe a clip of a movie. My best session, I thought, was the sinking of the Titanic. After floundering around in the session for half an hour or more, I heard a sound like someone banging on a metal locker in the boys' gym. It was the sound of metal reverberating, maybe metal buckling. Then I saw a man sliding sideways on a wet, angled steel deck. Then I was in the water, cold water, at night being pulled out by a man in a lifeboat behind me. I saw the angled end of a huge ship sinking, and knew it was the Titanic.

So even average people like me can learn to remote view. It is simply a matter of paying attention to your imagination, not being judgmental, relaxing, and following the procedure. One thing I learned is that, when you start receiving information from the real target, and not from your analytical mind, it feels different. It is called the "signal line." When you are really tuning in, information starts coming faster and faster. It is a fascinating technique. If you take a course in remote viewing, it will teach you that our awareness is not limited to the signals coming from the five senses. We humans are capable of a great deal more than that. It is to explore these other abilities, and their implications for a new physics, that this book was written.

The Great Remote Viewers

It is one thing for an amateur like me to do remote viewing. It is something else entirely when it is done by an expert. The U.S. intelligence community found that only about 1% are capable of the consistent, high accuracy required for military usefulness. One of the top remote viewers, Joe McMoneagle, stated that of 3,000 potential remote viewers tested by the army, only six were selected. That would be 0.2%. So the best remote viewers are in a very elite league.

For me, during much of the session, there is a feeling of floundering, of floating on a foggy sea of the unknown. Occasionally a thought or image floats by and I grab it. But for the experts, men who served as remote viewers in the secret military program for twenty years, it must be more like sailing the Caribbean on a clear day. You can see a hundred miles. Transcripts from those sessions which have been published show that the viewers lock onto the target quickly, and move around it freely. This made the technique of great interest to the intelligence community.

A variety of different methods are used. The one I was taught, sketched above, is a variation on the method developed by Ingo Swann. Swann is a New York artist who has a great gift for remote viewing. He worked closely with Dr. Harold "Hal" Puthoff and other scientists from the beginning to develop remote viewing protocols. He also wanted to understand the physics behind what he did, so he made himself available to researchers and conducted numerous psychic experiments. The scientific community owes a great debt to pioneers like Swann and Dr. Puthoff, for helping in the birth of this new science.

Different remote viewers use different methods, tailored to their own personality. One of the greatest was Pat Price, a retired businessman who had briefly served as Police Commissioner of Burbank, California. There he became aware of his natural intuitive ability, which he felt had helped him solve some police cases. In the early 1970's he teamed up with physicists Dr. Puthoff and Dr. Russell Targ at the Stanford Research Institute (SRI), who wanted to explore scientifically various aspects of "psi". It was a match made in heaven.

One remarkable example is the following session, which was conducted with Puthoff and Targ as the monitors and Pat Price as the remote viewer in 1973. The target was given to them by the CIA, which was trying to determine if remote viewing would be of use for intelligence gathering. This site was a secret Russian facility about which they knew very little, but wanted to know more. So it was truly a "blind" test, in the sense that no one in America knew what was going on there .

Figure 1.3. Photograph taken in those exciting days (1973) when remote viewing was young. Left to right are shown some of the pioneers, CIA scientist Dr. Richard Kennett, remote viewer Pat Price and Dr. Hal Puthoff (*Courtesy of Dr. Harold Puthoff*).

In Price's session, after he went into a light trance and became very relaxed, he began giving impressions of what he was seeing. The first thing he said was that it reminded him of the old joke of a man who bought a penthouse apartment in New York and looked up to see the girders of the Third Avenue El over his head. What he saw was a steel structure that went up over the top of a building. As he explored this site further, he followed the girders and noticed they actually were supported on the ground by wheels that traveled on a railway. In fact there were two sets of rails, one on each side of this building. The crane-like structure extended over the top. It straddled the building and rolled along carrying large equipment, depositing it in various places in the facility.

As the session proceeded Price went inside the building, in his mind, and saw large, thick steel sections of a sphere. They were twelve to fourteen inches in thickness and appeared to be sections which, when welded together, would form a huge steel sphere about 60 feet in diameter. He described Russian technicians welding the sections of this sphere together into a complete sphere, all done inside the building. They were using special new welding techniques to do this. Figures 1.4 and 1.5 are sketches made of the facility. (Targ, 1996).

When this information was reported back to the CIA monitors, they didn't quite know what to make of it. They didn't know much about this facility themselves. No spy had been able to get into it. The concept of huge steel spheres inside the building, with a large crane outside, was very strange. They weren't quite sure how to evaluate the success of the session. However, after asking around and exploring other information within the intelligence community, they managed to find a photograph of the site, which showed a large steel crane-like structure straddling the building with wheels on both sides. It was virtually identical to the drawing Price had made.

It took four years and a great deal of work by conventional U.S. intelligence to fully understand the site. One by one, each element Price had seen was confirmed, including the huge steel spheres inside the building. When they finally were assembled they measured almost exactly sixty feet in diameter and were 12 to 14 inches thick. It was also true, just as Price had said, that the Russians had developed new welding technology to assemble the spheres.

Years later, this site became the center of a heated controversy. It began in 1977 in an *Aviation Week and Space Technology* article, which claimed the site was part of a Soviet program to develop anti-ballistic missile (ABM) beam weapons. The steel spheres were to contain explosions which created the enormous pulse power for the weapons. This controversy was the beginning of a debate which evolved into Ronald Reagan's "Star Wars" program.

Figure 1.4 Drawing of gantry crane from remote viewing session by Pat   Price (Targ, 1996) *Courtesy of Dr. Russell Targ.*

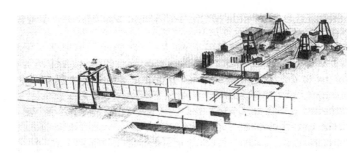

Figure 1.5 Drawing of Semipalatinsk site by a CIA artist (Targ, 1996) *Courtesy of Dr. Russell Targ.*

However, when Pat Price first remote-viewed this target, only a few people inside the CIA even knew it existed. Although it took years to confirm all that Price reported, the data which could be confirmed immediately was very impressive. It was dramatic confirmation of the power of remote viewing.

Another session which the CIA assigned to Price was a country house in West Virginia. And Price actually missed this one. But he discovered in the process that the subconscious mind, when faced with a boring target and a very interesting one next to it, will choose the more interesting one.

When the coordinates were given to Price, he began describing a building that was quite different from the little country house that was supposed to be his target. He described a circular driveway and a road that passed nearby, purposely designed to be secluded and difficult to see from the air. There was a round circular aperture out front, and a flagpole, and there were underground storage facilities and storage containers. Price said lots of records were kept there.

As he continued with his description, it was amazing how much detail he was coming up with. He found, in this underground facility, many classified storage compartments and top secret filing cabinets with code names on them. When Hal Puthoff heard this, he asked Price if he could read some of the code names on the folders in the safes. Price came up with several of them: *Cueball, Flytrap, Minerva*. He also read the name tags on some of the soldiers who were present. It was an extensive description. (Schnabel, 1997)

It was difficult to believe that Price had simply made up all of this information. When the sponsor first heard about it, he decided the session must be a failure. It wasn't the country house. But upon thinking more about it, he drove out to the area to see if anything resembled the site Price described.

Amazingly enough, only a couple of miles away he found a site which was fenced off with "U.S. Government-Keep Out" signs posted around it. Something very mysterious was going on there. He went back to his superiors and began making inquiries. Eventually he learned that it was involved in eavesdropping on Soviet satellites and that much of what Price had said about it was correct, including the code words and personnel names.

In another case involving Price, the interiors of two foreign embassies were chosen as his targets. He was to "visit" them using his remote viewing ability and locate the coderooms inside each embassy. This is the room which handles the highly classified incoming and outgoing encrypted messages. Price successfully located the coderoom in each embassy. In addition, he provided detailed information about their interiors, such as the locations of interior doors and the colors of the marble fireplaces and stairs. Although some of the information was incorrect, a large amount was accurate, and the CIA operations officer concluded: "It is my considered opinion that this technique - whatever it is - offers definite operational possibilities." (Kress, 1977)

The SRI Experiments

The following examples, performed at SRI in the 1970s, illustrate the kind of accuracy which can be achieved by talented remote viewers. On the left is shown the target, which was contained in a sealed envelope in a secure location. The viewer knew nothing about the contents of the envelope. The viewer was kept isolated in a heavily shielded room, and contact was only by intercom controlled from outside. This prevented the remote viewer from receiving electromagnetic signals from the target or the interviewer.

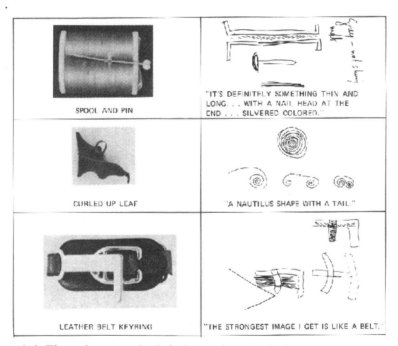

Figure 1.6. The column on the left shows three typical targets. On the right are shown excerpts from the remote viewing session, summarizing impressions obtained by the remote viewer of the target. (Puthoff, 1981) *Courtesy of Dr. Harold Puthoff.*

Subjects were found among Stanford University students, or were occasional psychics who had demonstrated talent at remote viewing. Above, in Figure 1.6, are shown some typical results from some of these experiments. A series of small, roughly cylindrical shaped objects were used as targets. It was found that the viewer could see fine detail in the target smaller than one millimeter. (Puthoff, 1981)

On the right in the figure is a sketch and description by the remote viewer. The first target is a spool of thread and a pin. The viewer sketched a cross-section of a spool and also sketched the pin, which he/she describes as "something thin and long...with a nail head at the end...silver colored."

The viewer was clearly picking up specific information about the target. It included information about shape, texture, color, material, and other qualities. Statistical judging tests were performed afterwards, in which impartial judges attempted to match up the sketches with the original targets. The results were highly successful, far exceeding chance expectations. It was concluded that remote viewing provided significant and unique information about each target

Some History- How the Remote Viewing Program Began

Although most of the documents about the U.S. military remote viewing program are still classified, the outlines of its history are available from declassified documents. The best overall history of the program is a book by James Schnabel, *The Remote Viewers* (Schnabel, 1997). It is highly recommended for the reader who wants to know more.

Some of the earliest government studies of the paranormal date to the early 1950s. These include lectures by the Defense Department in 1952, a 1961 CIA study, and a review article by Stephen Abrams, the Director of the Parapsychological Laboratory, Oxford University under the auspices of Project ULTRA. This review article stated that ESP was demonstrated but was not understood or controllable (Mandelbaum, 2000).

In 1970, the book *Psychic Discoveries Behind the Iron Curtain* by Ostrander and Schroeder was published (Ostrander, 1970). It created a sensation in certain military and intelligence circles. It told of how the Soviet government had conducted successful psychic communication experiments across thousands of miles. It described the successful telepathy experiments conducted by Dr. Leonid Vasiliev, who had been awarded the Lenin Prize. It described how the Soviet Military and the Soviet Secret Police had funded over twenty laboratories in the Soviet Union for the study and development of psychic abilities and psychic phenomena (Ostrander, 1970).

The priority placed on this new science by the Soviets led to the perception that a "psychic gap" was developing. Their book described the work of Dr. Edward Naumov, Chief of Technical Parapsychology at a special laboratory affiliated with the Department of Physics at the State Instrument Engineering College of Moscow. This work was presided over by eminent Soviet physicists who were confident that psychic phenomena were completely real and needed to be understood by modern physics. They told Ostrander and Schroeder:

"We believe ESP is enmeshed with all of everyday life...We believe ESP affects any group situation. Our scientists are trying to study and measure ESP objectively among groups of people...We believe man has a vast, hidden potential. It is vital, we must investigate these untapped resources of human beings in every possible way."(Ostrander, 1970)

This book opened up Western eyes to certain talented individuals in Russia who were able to move objects with the power of their mind. It revealed that others had built strange devices which seemed to respond to thought. There were many revelations in this book, and for government and military thinkers charged with the national defense, the concern naturally arose: What if this capability is developed for military uses? It may have been such concerns which helped pave the way for the military remote viewing program which began in 1972.

The Cold War was still very much on. There were new leaders in the Kremlin, Brezhnev and Kosygin, who were perceived to be hard liners. In the wake of these revelations, there was an awareness that psychic forces were real, and the Soviets were ahead of us in exploiting it.

One report written by the Defense Intelligence Agency (DIA), dated 1972, is titled "Controlled Offensive Behavior-U.S.S.R." (LaMothe, 1972) The unclassified, publicly available document has been heavily censored, but a single quote will indicate that there was serious interest in psychic phenomena behind the doors of secrecy:

" Two things are certain: (1) that parapsychological phenomena are due to the little-known faculties of the subconscious mind; and (2) that the powers of the subconscious mind are vastly superior to those of normal consciousness...The only way we can learn more about these little-understood processes is through intensive study and experimentation. The stakes seem high enough." (LaMothe, 1972)

A later warning about the threat from Soviet psychic research came from the military historian Dr. Roger A. Beaumont in the January 1982 issue of *"Signal: Journal of the Armed Forces Communications and Electronics Association."* (Beaumont, 1982) The science editor of the *Journal of Defense and Diplomacy*, Charles Wallach, published an article in the September 1985 issue entitled "The Science of Psychic Warfare", in which he recommended that a "Psychic Service Corps" be recruited and trained to support the U.S. Military in the these areas. The 1986 edition of *Military Intelligence* which is published by the U.S. Army Intelligence Center at Fort Huachuca, Arizona, published an article by an intelligence officer, Captain Richard Goller, further supporting these initiatives.

In this environment, Dr. Puthoff, at that time a physicist at the Stanford Research Institute (SRI), submitted a proposal to the CIA. He proposed to investigate the capabilities of psychics for "remote viewing," a form of psychic spying where they would sit in an isolated room in a relaxed state or mild trance, and attempt to obtain information of intelligence value.

After several successful preliminary demonstrations, including some of the remarkable sessions of Pat Price, described above, the program was funded. This was the beginning of a top-secret remote viewing program in 1972. This may not be the first or the last of the military psychic spying efforts, but it is one which has been made public. Details of the beginnings of this program have been described by several of the principles, including one of the original CIA scientific officers involved, Dr. Kenneth Kress (Kress, 1977), the scientists Targ and Puthoff (Targ, 1996; Puthoff, 1996), the remote viewers (McMoneagle, 1993; 1998), and a comprehensive history of the program was written by James Schnabel (Schnabel, 1997).

An unclassified article describing some of the early results was published in 1976 in the Journal of the IEEE (Puthoff, 1976). This caught the attention of the Army Intelligence, which provided additional support to the program, and led to subsequent phases under various code names, including GRILLFLAME and STARGATE. An active effort was begun to recruit talented remote viewers from among qualified military personnel (McMoneagle, 1999). Soldiers who had had Near-Death Experiences (see Chapter 11) or other unusual psychic experiences were interviewed. Many of the well-known remote viewers of today, such as Joe McMoneagle, were recruited during this phase.

During its lifetime this program had many dramatic successes. If not, it would never have survived so many years, since it was based on a premise that is antithetical to conventional science and the military mindset. One of the officers in charge of the program was Major General Edmund R. Thompson, Army Assistant Chief of Staff for Intelligence during 1977-81, and Deputy Director for Management and Operations of DIA, 1982-84. Of the science behind it, he said:

> *"We didn't know how to explain it, but we weren't so much interested in explaining it as in determining whether there was any practical use to it." In commenting on its usefulness, he said: "I never liked to get into debates with the skeptics, because if you didn't believe that remote viewing was real, you hadn't done your homework." (Schnabel, 1997)*

The Debunking Effort and the "Official" Evaluation of the CIA Program

Toward the end of the top secret remote viewing program, in the early nineteen nineties, several problems developed. The most serious was that one of its remote viewers, David Morehouse, had decided to go public about the program, even though he was still in uniform. He was working on a book and a movie, and eventually a lawsuit which would have blown the cover off the entire operation. In view of this, the government decided to terminate the program and hired a company, AIR, to conduct an "objective" final assessment.

In such situations it is classic intelligence procedure to discredit the program. Whether this was the motivation or not, an ardent, long-time skeptic of remote viewing, Dr. Ray Hyman, was hired to lead the investigation. On a later *Nightline* television interview with Ted Koppel, he ridiculed the program as having no value, and left millions of viewers with the impression that the government had abandoned remote viewing because it didn't work.

Hyman had taken a public stand against remote viewing more than ten years earlier (Hyman, 1981, 1982), and therefore was hardly an objective reviewer. He was a member of the controversial anti-psi group which calls itself "Committee for the Scientific Investigation of Claims of the Paranormal" or "CSICOP." This group actively lobbies against any research into paranormal and non-traditional scientific subjects. Hyman was most emphatic and blunt in the interview. He left the impression with the public that there was little of value in the program and that it should be dropped. Dr. Hyman stated: "The case for remote viewing is not just very weak, but non-existent."(Schnabel, 1997)

This conclusion was very different from that reached by his colleague at AIR, Professor Jessica Utts, a Statistics Professor at the University of California, Davis, who also participated in the investigation. Hyman's televised statements even differed somewhat from his own written conclusions in his final A.I.R. report. But the public only heard his strident televised remarks, which left the impression that the program was abandoned because it didn't work.

By contrast, Dr. Utts concluded in her evaluation:

> *"Using the standards applied to any other area of science, it is concluded that psychic functioning has been well established. The statistical results of the studies examined are far beyond what is expected by chance...A statistically significant laboratory effect had been demonstrated." (Utts, 1996)*

Even Hyman himself, in his final written evaluation of this work (Hyman, 1995) wrote:

"I agree with Jessica Utts that the effect sizes reported in the SAIC experiments and in the recent ganzfeld studies probably cannot be dismissed as due to chance. Nor do they appear to be accounted for by multiple testing, filedrawer distortions, inappropriate statistical testing or other misuse of statistical inference...So I accept Professor Utts' assertion that the statistical results of the SAIC and other parapsychologists experiments are far beyond what is expected by chance...The SAIC experiments are well-designed and the investigators have taken pains to eliminate the known weaknesses in previous parapsychological research. In addition, I cannot provide suitable candidates for what flaws, if any, might be present..."

By these words, even Hyman seemed to acknowledge the success of remote viewing, beyond what can be explained by chance or coincidence. However, these remarks received no publicity. The public was left with the impression that there was little of value in the remote viewing program.

One may contrast the negative public stance of Dr. Hyman with that of a CIA scientific officer, Dr. Ken Kress, who was closely involved with the program during its operation, and observed the program at close range: "There are observations, such as the original magnetic experiments at Stanford University, the OSI remote viewing, the OTS coderoom experiments, and others done for the Defense Department, that defy explanation." (Kress, 1977)

The later effort by the CIA to debunk Remote Viewing, on *Nightline* and elsewhere, has itself been discredited by the remote viewers who took part in the program. Joe McMoneagle, one of the most consistently accurate viewers and the first active career military remote viewer, stated:

"They [AIR] were supposed to do a full assessment of the intelligence gathering utility from 1977 to the present. There's 121 boxes of operational files, and they were supposed to hire people to review those in detail. They had from June to September of 1995 to do that -- not enough time to go through three of those boxes. So it was intended, I think, from the beginning to fail." (McMoneagle, 1999)

According to McMoneagle, "Only about two boxes of material were reviewed, and that was sanitized beforehand," because the investigators did not have sufficient clearances to see most of the raw operational data. It would appear that the negative outcome of the review was intentionally preordained by the selection of reviewers known to be negative to the program, combined with extensive filtering and limiting of the data they would be allowed to see, and the short amount of time, 3 months, they would be allowed to perform their review.

McMoneagle has also pointed out that there were three committees overseeing the STARGATE project during its 18 year history. Of the 26 people on those committees, none were considered believers in the paranormal, but they continually approved the extension of the project based solely on operational performance. Of those 26 people, the A.I.R. investigators talked to only one. A.I.R. also totally ignored the list of end users of STARGATE, which "reads like a list of Who's Who in Washington." They disregarded the end users to avoid potential political embarrassments.

Reflecting on the termination of STARGATE, McMoneagle says that there were some serious managerial problems toward the end of the program: "Many of the managers were afraid of the paranormal or didn't know anything about it." And perhaps, superseding that were the political sensitivities. Remote viewing violated the conventional world view in so many ways. The weirdness factor was considered bad for one's career: "We were somebody that nobody wanted to be caught dead standing next to." (McMoneagle, 1999)

Statistics and Scientific Confirmation

No matter how many dramatic successes are achieved by remote viewing, the skeptical scientist will, and should, ask: *"OK, was that just coincidence or can you do it again?"* In other words, no matter how dramatic are some of the remote viewing sessions, such as the drawings by Pat Price of a Russian military facility, still the "hard scientist" wants you to do the experiment over and over again, to eliminate the possibility that you just got lucky the first time. This is called statistical analysis. It is the only real, solid way to verify that remote viewing and other psychic abilities are real and not just due to luck and coincidence.

Statistics requires that the experiments be repeated many, many times. You may get lucky the first time, but if you flip a coin and it comes up heads 10 times in row, you may have to consider that something else is going on. Some kind of influence is being exerted to make the coin land a certain way. There is still a small probability that the coin could land heads 10 times in a row by chance. The probability of this is about 1 in a thousand. By flipping even more times, it becomes possible to reduce the odds that the performance can be explained by chance. Then we say that a real effect has been observed, to within a certain probability. This is really the nature of all scientific experiments, although it is seldom stated as such.

In the experiments below, the Princeton PEAR Lab conducted remote viewing sessions using many different viewers against many targets. Their large database of results has enabled them to determine, with rigorous scientific statistics, whether or not remote viewing is real. The remote viewers used were not the highly trained military experts of the STARGATE program, but instead were more or less "average" people. Dozens of such viewers were used in thousands of experiments.

The Princeton Lab varied the remote viewing protocol in several ways. First, it used two viewers for each scene. One would actually go to the scene at some time and catalog the scene according to a set table of characteristics: did it have trees, was there a house, was it urban, was it quiet or noisy, etc. Each category was binary, i.e. it could have a yes or no answer. There were 30 such categories. Therefore each scene would be categorized by a yes or no answer to these 30 criteria, making it easy to "score" the session on a computer.

A second viewer, this one the remote viewer, would "look" at the scene psychically. This could occur simultaneously with the first viewer or at some earlier or later time. The distance between the viewer and the scene was varied, and the times between the viewing of the first and second subject were also varied. This made it possible to determine not only how accurate the remote viewing session was, but whether the accuracy depended on distance or time between the two sessions.

Basic statistics is just like flipping a coin: if it is a random process, one expects to get as many heads as tails. If one flips the coin ten times, and counts a head as 1 point and a tail as zero points, then the typical total score would be expected to be five, since we expect five heads and five tails on average. But some people get four heads and six tails. Others get three tails and seven heads. This should be less likely. If many people flip their coins ten times, and we look at how often each score comes up, we expect a bell-shaped curve, just like they use in school for grading tests.

The average score is at the peak of the curve, and is the most probable. (We are simplifying the discussion here. If you are a statistics whiz you can skip this part.) Scores that depart from the average are found out on the "tails" of the curve, and are less likely.

If the average score on a school test is 50, then you don't expect to find many 100's nor many zero scores. Most scores are expected around the average value.

Figure 1.7 below shows this type of result for the remote viewing tests conducted by the Princeton PEAR Lab. There were 334 separate experiments conducted. The expected curve would be a bell-shaped curve if the scores were completely random. This would occur if the remote viewers were just randomly guessing.

But the Princeton lab found that the scores were NOT random. They found a distinct "hump" on the right side of the curve. When they subtracted out the "random" bell-shaped part of the curve, they were left with something they called the "residue". This "something" is due to the remote viewing sessions which were right more often than would be expected by chance. This little, offset, bell-shaped curve labeled "residue" is due to the remote viewers picking up the real "signal" from the target.

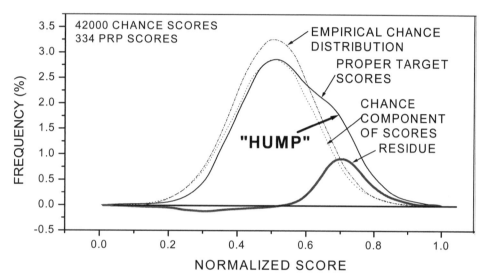

Figure 1.7 Statistical results for large number of ESP and remote viewing sessions, from (Jahn, 1987b) The small gaussian peak labeled "Residue" indicates the results which show deviation from chance, or the actual "signal". The large gaussian curve represents random noise. As in many remote viewing experiments, the noise is large, but the signal is still detectable. *Courtesy of Drs. Robert Jahn and Brenda Dunne.*

The important result is that, given the large number of measurements that were made, this "signal" can only be due to chance with a probability of ONE IN FIFTY-FIVE BILLION. (In the most recent compilation of all data, the cumulative odds exceed a trillion to one.) In other words, the probability that this little "hump" is due to chance is astronomically small. Therefore it is due to a real signal. It proves that remote viewing is real!

Dr. Dean Radin, in his landmark book *The Conscious Universe* (Radin, 1997), notes that these results have been replicated by many laboratories around the world. This underscores the significance of these results. They demonstrate a real and replicable phenomenon, despite articles like a 1995 *Newsweek* cover story on these experiments, which claimed that Jahn's results could not be duplicated by other experimenters. Of this, Radin commented:

> *"If true, this is an important criticism, because it implies that a lone researcher's results might be due to error or fraud. The statement, however, is pure fiction...Jahn's research has been replicated by more than seventy researchers*

worldwide, both before and after Jahn produced the main body of his work."
(Radin, 1997)

The Princeton experiments used remote viewers who were more or less average. They were not selected and trained like the military remote viewers. It is not surprising, then, that the accuracy of trained, professional military remote viewers is reported to be much higher. One of the best known and highly rated military viewers, Joe McMoneagle (McMoneagle, 1999) says that he averaged about 65% accuracy rating on target data. In terms of McMoneagle's accuracy and the general usefulness of the information which he was able to provide, McMoneagle points to the prestigious Legion of Merit ribbon, which he was given in 1984. He said "'I got that for providing over 150 essential elements of information that were of critical value to the defense of the nation' and were unavailable from any other source." (Guthrie, 1995)

Remote Viewing Breaks Time and Space Barriers

Remote viewing breaks many of the rules on which our science is based. One of these is that signals cannot travel faster than light. Another is that signals cannot travel backward in time. According to conventional physics, it is impossible to foresee the future, because that would defy these principles, which are referred to as "causality." The cause is supposed to precede the effect, not vice versa. Remote viewing often breaks both of these rules.

In one of the early remote viewing experiments, conducted at Stanford Research Institute (SRI), Hal Puthoff and Bart Cox drove away from the lab following a protocol in which they would make turns in traffic depending on what the car in front of them did. This guaranteed they had no prior knowledge of where they were going. After a half-hour, they were to stop driving and stare at the location, wherever it happened to be. The remote viewer, back at SRI in a Faraday-shielded room, was to pick up their psychic impressions and try to describe the scene. The remote viewer was Pat Price.

His monitor was Dr. Russell Targ, who stayed with him at the lab. Targ began testing the tape recorder after Puthoff and Cox had been driving for ten minutes. The normal protocol would be to wait another twenty minutes until the "outbound team" had stopped driving before Price would attempt to remote view their destination. But this time Price said "We don't have to wait that long. I can tell you right now where they'll be. What I'm looking at is a little boat jetty or a little boat dock along the bay."

He pointed to one of the walls in the shielded room, indicating the direction in which they could be found. "Yeah, I see the little boats", he continued. "Some motor launches, some little sailing ships, sails all furled, some with their masts stepped, others are up. Little jetty or little dock there…looks like a Chinese or Japanese pagoda effect. It's a definite feeling of Oriental architecture that seems to be fairly adjacent to where they are." (Targ, 1984)

It turned out that Price was absolutely accurate in his description. But the really amazing thing was that he had described the destination a full twenty minutes *before* the team arrived there. At the time Price gave his description, the outbound team was still driving in a random pattern based on their protocol. They had no idea where they would end up. So Price had remote viewed their *future* location when no one else knew what it would be. This early success in remote viewing indicates that looking into the future is definitely possible. In fact, the accuracy can be fairly high.

These results are confirmed by the Princeton PEAR Lab remote viewing experiments. When the accuracy of a session is plotted versus the distance between the remote viewer and the target, the graph shown in Figure 1.8 results. The remarkable aspect of this graph is that the remote viewer accuracy is small but constant with distance.

Note that the largest distance over which these remote viewing experiments were conducted was 6,000 MILES. Yet the PEAR Lab found that the accuracy was the same at these distances. All of the physical forces with which we are familiar, such as electromagnetism and gravity, rapidly become weaker with distance. But the psychic "force," or whatever makes remote viewing possible, does not seem to weaken with distance.

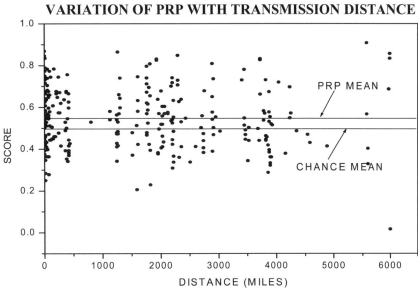

Figure 1.8. Dependence of remote viewing accuracy on distance from the target is plotted. This data is based on a particular remote viewing protocol labeled "PRP." The Princeton PEAR Lab, through thousands of experiments, found that remote viewing and ESP transmission and reception appears to be independent of distance. This makes it very different from electromagnetic or gravitational signals, which weaken with the square of the distance. (Jahn, 1987b)

To quote from Princeton Professor Robert Jahn, former Chairman of the Engineering Department at Princeton University, and director of the PEAR Lab which conducted these experiments:

"...up to intercontinental distances of several thousand miles, there appears to be no discernible advantage for closer targets. Certainly, there is no $1/r^2$ dependence that might be expected for various wave-propagation mechanisms that have been proposed for such phenomena."(Jahn, 1987)

Likewise, the Princeton data were analyzed to see the effect of time. Recall that the "first" viewer actually went to the scene and described it by the 30 binary categories: urban or rural, quiet or noisy, etc. The "second" viewer never went to the scene but only viewed it remotely at a different time. In some cases he remote viewed it BEFORE the "first" viewer went there. In other cases he remote viewed it AFTER the "first" viewer went there. What the Princeton lab found is that the accuracy was the SAME. It did not matter whether the remote viewing took place hours ahead or hours after the first viewer. These results are summarized below in Figure 1.9. The vertical scale is the accuracy of the session. The horizontal axis is the time difference between the two viewers. Although most of the sessions used a small time difference, and are therefore clumped together around "zero hours", yet the average score is found to be positive, and INDEPENDENT of time.

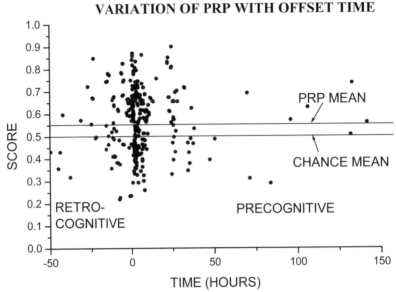

Figure 1.9. Accuracy of Remote Viewing versus time offset. It is found that the remote viewing sessions demonstrated an accuracy that could not be accounted for by chance, and therefore showed a real effect. The accuracy was the same for past, present and future targets, and did not diminish even for sessions in which the target being viewed was many hours in the future or in the past. (Jahn, 1987b)

Again a quote by Professor Jahn sums up this surprising result:

"All forces known to physics, like gravity for example, diminish with distance. And no forces in physics operate freely across time like this. It's as if consciousness is somehow able to direct its influence directly across space and time, an understanding that certainly poses a challenge for science." (Jahn, 1992)

Consequently, the PEAR Lab data leaves modern physics with several anomalies. First, there is a mechanism by which information can be sent directly to a person's mind. This can include visual information, pictures, as well as details about the age, construction and history of the subject being transmitted. Secondly, this "signal" does not seem to weaken with distance. Thirdly, this signal seems to be independent of time. It can be sent in the future and received in the past, or vice versa. It doesn't seem to matter. It works just as well being sent forward in time or backward in time. There are no known physical forces which behave this way. And yet the statistics are so good that there is definitely information being transferred. So this leaves the question: How? What is the force, if it is a force?

These concepts are totally alien to conventional science, and yet the data seems to bear them out. The PEAR Lab experiments show that time and distance don't seem matter when it comes to psychic phenomena.

This same time effect was seen in the military remote viewing program: Joe McMoneagle states that his accuracy was measured in a comprehensive analysis of his sessions. Depending on the criteria and method of scoring, his accuracy was between 65% and 80%, and was the <u>same for past, present and future targets</u>. This means that viewing the future is definitely possible, and the accuracy can be surprisingly high.

This freedom to move about in time, to go forward into the future and backward into the past, is in total violation of conventional physics. According to Quantum Mechanics, the Uncertainty Principle introduces randomness into the system each time someone makes an observation. Since humans are making observations all the time, the future should only evolve in a probabilistic way. The number of possible futures should be uncountably huge. The probability of someone randomly "guessing" a correct future event in detail should be small. Yet apparently some remote viewers are able to look into the future and describe it in detail.

There are some strange aspects to this form of "time travel". Remote viewers sometimes have focused on a location and described in detail buildings which weren't there. Such sessions are graded as mistakes. But Joe McMoneagle has described at least one case where the building he "saw" in his remote viewing session was actually built many years later. It was a shock to Joe as he drove along the freeway past the formerly empty lot, the site of his missed target, to find a shiny new building matching perfectly the description he had given years earlier. (McMoneagle, 1993, 1998)

Just as in the case of the country house in West Virginia, which Pat Price had overlooked in favor of a top secret NSA groundstation nearby, so in this case McMoneagle shifted in <u>time</u> to find a more interesting target than the empty lot. It seems that the consciousness can easily move in space and in time, and this poses a serious challenge to present science.

Mainstream Business, Technological and Medical Applications

Remote viewing has now, rather quietly, entered the mainstream American business world. At least a dozen remote viewing schools have been established, many by former Military remote viewers or their students.

Corporations such as DuPont are said to use remote viewing techniques to help their scientists become more creative. They are guided into a light trance and taught to remote view the future. They attempt to look into some future time, examine a high technology item from that time period, then describe it in sufficient detail to be able to copy it. Then they apply for patents on it.

Dr. Courtney Brown told me of one inventor in the southwestern United States who does this type of thing full time. He conducts remote viewing sessions every day, and has assistants who quickly check whether the new invention has already been patented. He has been very successful in creating new inventions by this process.

This ability of the remote viewer to "travel in time" and bring back technology from the future is reminiscent of the scene in the movie *Star Trek IV*, where Scottie gave the formula for "transparent aluminum" to a twentieth century engineer. When Doctor McCoy asked him if he might be changing the future, Scottie answers "How do we know he didn't invent the thing?" In the same vein, remote viewing is being used today to attempt to circumvent the "natural" time line and bring technology "back from the future."

This method of inventing has become more systematic with remote viewing procedures, but there has probably always been a psychic element to inventing. The physicist Niels Bohr related how he came up with his famous model of the atom, which won him the Nobel Prize in 1922. It began with a dream. He dreamed he was sitting on a sun of burning gas. Planets were rushing past, hissing and spitting, and they all seemed connected to the sun by fine threads. Suddenly, as the gas seemed to solidify, the entire system became motionless. At that moment, he woke up and knew that what he had seen was the model of the atom.

In a similar way, in World War II, the radar-guided anti-aircraft gun system was first seen in a dream by a Bell Telephone engineer. The next morning he woke up and drew a sketch of what he had seen in his dream. Within a year or two, it became a reality (Rheingold, 2000).

Joe McMoneagle has discussed several inventions of this kind (McMoneagle, 1998). He was asked by Dr. Dean Radin, who at that time was Director of the Consciousness Research Laboratory in Las Vegas, to use remote viewing to describe a machine that was not yet in existence. They did not know how far into the future they would have to go to find the machine but they knew it does not exist today.

McMoneagle reports that they have succeeded at bringing back small parts of the machine, which appear to work as envisioned. These new parts open some unusual doors into other areas of technology which were not previously envisioned. He reports that this may result in patents in these new areas. They have not yet been successful in bringing back the entire machine. The project is ongoing.

In medicine, some doctors are being trained to remote view inside their patients, the better to diagnose an illness. In my remote viewing classes there were both doctors and nurses learning to remote view for this purpose. The Chinese government has conducted national surveys to find people who are talented at this. One such person is an 11-year old boy named Xie Zhaohui from Hubei Province (Dong, 1984). In government sponsored experiments he was found to have the ability to look inside the human body and diagnose disease. After this, he was given one year of training to learn anatomy to help him understand what he was seeing.

In tests, he was asked to diagnose 105 patients with various illnesses. He was allowed only to gaze at each patient for a few minutes from several feet away. He then described what he saw. He diagnosed 93 of them correctly and misjudged only 12. The 24 medical staff members who took part in the experiment concluded that this ability is real, and that it improves with training (Dong, 1984).

One can imagine that petroleum engineers and geologists would find this a useful method for discovering mineral and oil deposits. Ingo Swann, one of the developers of Remote Viewing, has described this as a twenty-first century technology which may have been discovered too early. But it is here, and it is beginning to be used.

Remote viewing also has applications in business. A number of professional remote viewers, such as Gerald O'Donnell, use their talents in the stock market (O'Donnell, 2000) and have trained professional traders to remote view as a means of enhancing their insight and profitability.

The September 11 terrorist attacks have made industrial security a timely issue. Companies operating in the U.S. and overseas must anticipate threats. Some of them are resorting to remote viewers to help foresee where and when the next strike might be, so it can be counteracted.

In a story appearing recently in the *Sunday Times* of London, it was reported that "U.S. intelligence agencies are recruiting psychics to help predict future attacks and to find Osama Bin Laden" (Times, 2001). Three professional remote viewers were quoted in the article. Prudence Calabrese, who has set up a team of 14 remote viewers, confirmed that the FBI had asked her company to predict sites of future attacks. Angela Thompson-Smith and Lyn Buchanan, former members of the U.S. military remote viewing program, also confirmed that they had been approached to provide similar information.

Independently of the London *Sunday Times* story, I know two additional highly rated psychics who have also been hired by the CIA and/or FBI to provide information about the likely hideout of Bin Laden and to identify future targets. This suggests that, despite their public posture, the FBI and CIA still consider remote viewing to be a valuable resource.

Military Usefulness

Remote viewers are able to view individuals as well as places. In one remote viewing session described in Schnabel's *Remote Viewers* (Schnabel, 1997), the CIA wanted to check on one of their foreign agents who was due to come in for a polygraph (lie detector) exam in two weeks. This agent worked for a CIA case officer in a foreign country, and had met with him recently. One of the remote viewers, Joe McMoneagle, was tasked to remote view that recent meeting and describe it. Skip Atwater was the monitor for the session. As McMoneagle went down into his "zone" he described the two men at the meeting. One of them, the agent, had a briefcase with him. What was in the briefcase, McMoneagle was asked. A large amount of cash, came McMoneagle's answer. He detected certain irregularities with the agent's finances. Something was not right with his financial dealings.

The results of the session were shown to the CIA's polygrapher before the agent was brought in for the exam. The agent was asked about his finances. Were there any problems with money, any payoffs or other improper transactions he wanted to tell them about? No, the agent resolutely answered. Nothing irregular. "What about all the money you had in that briefcase last week?" he was asked. The agent nearly fell out of his chair when he heard the question. "How could you have known about that?" was his reply.

In 1979 certain members of Congress were allowed access to some of the results of the remote viewing program. One of these was Charles Rose, the Chairman of the House Sub-Committee on Intelligence Evaluation and Oversight. When interviewed later about his evaluation of the SRI long-distance remote viewing sessions he stated:

"All I can say is that if the results were faked, our security system doesn't work. What these persons 'saw' was confirmed by aerial photography. There's no way it could have been faked...Some of the intelligence people I've talked to know that remote viewing works, although they still block further research on it, since they claim it is not yet as good as satellite photography. But it seems to me that it would be a hell of a cheap radar system. And if the Russians have it and we don't, we are in serious trouble." --Congressman Charles Rose. (Targ, 1984)

As President Carter said about the location of a lost Russian Tu-22 bomber which the U.S. Air Force and CIA located using remote viewers: "She went into a trance, and while she was in a trance she gave some latitude and longitude figures. We focused our satellite cameras on that point and the plane was there." This event occurred while Carter was President. His description is a simplified account. There were two remote viewers involved, and several sessions were needed to match up their drawings with high resolution photographic and map imagery. However the end result was that they did locate the downed Russian plane, which had crashed in heavy jungle in Africa. It was then recovered by the U.S. for intelligence analysis (Schnabel, 1997).

Given this history of usefulness, there are many remote viewers who believe that secret government programs continue in this area. Nevertheless, the great value for the larger society may well be the far-reaching and profound lessons we have begun to learn from remote viewing.

Summary

The remote viewing program teaches us several important lessons about the laws of our universe and our true abilities as human beings. These new lessons pose a challenge to contemporary science and to our stereotypes of what a human being is:

(1) Remote viewing teaches us that we are more than our physical bodies. We have a "consciousness" that is not limited by our physical body, and can move seemingly anywhere in space and time and bring back information.

(2) When we are in that state and "go there" it feels like the events we see are happening "right now," even if the event occurred thousands of years ago.

(3) This suggests that our ideas of linear time are wrong. If events in the past and even in the future can be visited at will, then there is a connectedness of the universe in time which is very different from the present scientific ideas about "cause" preceding "effect."

(4) Our present physics cannot explain remote viewing results. There seems to be some new "force" involved which is left out of present models.

(5) The force or effect is weak, in the sense that the information is often noisy. Errors occur along with good data. For some very gifted individuals, the accuracies can be high. Extensive statistical studies have demonstrated that even for the average person, remote viewing is a real phenomenon.

(6) The "force" responsible for remote viewing does not weaken with distance, making it unlike other known forces.

(7) This force seems to defy the conventional rules of cause and effect and of the direction of time, which are central to our existing physics.

(8) This force passes easily through walls and barriers which stop the known forces of electricity and magnetism.

Remote viewing teaches us that there is far more to humans than the physical body. If Pat Price can leave his body in a chair at Stanford, while his consciousness zips halfway around the world to read documents in a locked safe, then it would seem there is a lot more to us than science understands. These new aspects of human abilities and consciousness will lead to a revolution in science, and an expanded view of both science and ourselves.

Remote viewing is but one method of acquiring psychic information about the world. It is based on specific procedures and protocols. However, we have all experienced momentary flashes of intuition, or had that "gut feeling" about someone or some event. We usually brush it off. We have been taught by our educational system to ignore such impulses. But research is teaching us that these impulses are often valid, and psychic ability may be a universal, but untapped, ability.

This ability often goes by the name of ESP or extrasensory perception. We will see in the next chapter, from the extensive research of Dr. Robert Jahn at the Princeton PEAR Lab and many other researchers, that even "ordinary" people have ESP. We will see from the work of Dr. Rupert Sheldrake that even our pets have it. Laboratory research has been carried out in the last thirty years by many scientists which proves, rigorously and scientifically, that ESP exists and is real, and is a far more widespread and common ability than we would have guessed. Rather than being "extra-sensory," it is more accurate to describe it as a sixth sense which we all have and are just beginning to understand.

CHAPTER 2 -EXTRA-SENSORY PERCEPTION, OR ESP

"Extrasensory Perception is not a matter of belief. There is a great deal of serious scientific work being done in it, and it has been established over the last thirty years that it is a matter of probability, and the probabilities have been established beyond chance. I think it is important work. I happen to be curious about it, and thus have been pursuing it for many years. This happened to be an opportunity (Apollo 14 Lunar Mission) to do another little step - a piece in the scientific puzzle of what man's all about."
-Apollo 14 Astronaut Captain Edgar Mitchell (Mitchell, 1971)

"Telepathy was affecting the bioplasmic energy of the subject's bodies! It seems telepathy is picked up by the bioplasmic energy. The ancient cannons of acupuncture had led them to a new method of charting telepathy."
-- Ostrander and Schroeder (Ostrander, 1970)

DEFINITION-ESP: Extrasensory Perception refers to the ability to receive information by means of telepathy, precognition, or clairvoyance.

The NASA ESP Experiments

The sky outside was deep black. The stars were bright and seemed much nearer than they had on earth. They do not flicker in the vacuum of space. Outside the window of the tiny space craft it was cold and empty and black. Without a pressure suit a man would die in seconds. The earth hung in the sky 200,000 miles away as the craft hurtled toward it. The mission to the moon was complete. Now all they had to do was get home safely.

Crowded into the tiny vessel known as Apollo 14 were three NASA astronauts: Mission Commander Alan Shepard, the first American to ever go into space back in 1961, Command Module pilot Stuart Roosa and Lunar Module Pilot Dr. Edgar Mitchell. All three men were the best of the best, the cream of Air Force and Navy test pilots and fighter pilots.

Dr. Mitchell was an engineering graduate of Carnegie Institute of Technology and the Naval Postgraduate School, with a Ph.D. from M.I.T. in aeronautics and astronautics. He had flown fighter jets off aircraft carriers in the nineteen fifties, and had served as a research pilot for the Air Development Squadron. He had graduated first in his class from the Air Force Research Pilot School, and had been an instructor there afterwards.

Figure 2.1. Photograph of Capt. Edgar Mitchell, Ph.D., NASA Astronaut and sixth man in history to walk on the moon.

He had been Chief of Project Management for the NASA Manned Orbiting Laboratory project. This time his job was piloting the "LEM," the Lunar Module, when it landed on the moon. In doing so he became the sixth man ever to walk on the moon's surface (Mitchell, 1996).

The mission so far had been successful, but not without tense moments. The worst was when they attempted to re-dock the LEM with the Command Module, and the latches did not take hold. Some debris picked up during the lunar landing had probably jammed the clasps. But on the sixth attempt they closed at higher speed than normal, and the latches caught. A sigh of relief went up from Houston as well as in the space craft.

There were memorable moments too. Mitchell and Shepard had become the third NASA team ever to walk on the moon. Alan Shepard showed it was possible to play golf there in its reduced gravity. Calling it a huge sand trap, he used the wedge of a six-iron attached to the handle of his sample collector to drive a ball over 100 yards with a one-handed swing. They spent 33 ½ hours up there, collected priceless geological samples, conducted seismic tests, and took hundreds of photographs to document the geology and the terrain.

As they settled in for the long trip home, Mitchell began a secret experiment he had not mentioned before to the others. He pulled out a piece of paper containing images of a deck of cards, a somewhat unusual deck. They all had strange designs on them. The images were chosen in random order. One by one, he began concentrating on the card images, visualizing each card as intensely as he could. He had arranged for several psychic "receivers" back on the earth to tell which card he picked.

He repeated the experiment many times during the long ride home. He was conducting the longest distance ESP test ever done. He was testing whether it was possible to send a psychic message across the vacuum of space, across 200,000 empty miles to human receivers on earth. When he got back, he compared his cards to the choices made by his psychics on the ground.

The test was not perfect because, due to the rigors of his schedule aboard the spacecraft, he had not been able to perform all the tests, nor perform them at a regular time. Nevertheless, there were over 200 cards selected in sequence and transmitted during the test, and the accuracy rate was well above chance. Two of the four subjects correctly guessed 51 sequences, "far exceeding anything expected." The odds of these results being due to chance alone were 1 in 3,000. Therefore it was considered a significant and successful demonstration. Subsequent papers were published in a scientific journal, the June 1971 *Journal of Parapsychology* (Mitchell, 1971).

Of this experiment Mitchell later said:

> *"To me the paranormal event now has been sufficiently well established, using classical techniques, to prove to anyone who desires to study a little bit that these events are real. I'm trying to get the world of science to awaken itself to the world of consciousness...If you have a mule and you want him to do something, the first thing you have to do is get his attention – and that usually takes a two-by-four between the ears. In my opinion, forcing the scientific community to look at the so-called paranormal or psychic event in its reality is a two-by-four between the ears."(News, 1971)*

Government Interest in ESP

These statements by Apollo astronaut Mitchell acknowledge some of the long distance ESP experiments conducted during the U.S. space program. Adrian Clark, a NASA rocket scientist involved in Skylab and Apollo 5, among other programs, confirms that Mitchell did indeed participate in successful ESP transmission experiments when aboard Apollo 14 (Clark, 1973). One of the key telepathic receivers on the ground was the well-known psychic Olof Jonsson (Jonsson, 1971), who had participated in numerous scientific studies of his psychic ability. (A photograph of Jonnson is shown in Chapter 8, in which he is exhibiting his psychokinetic ability.)

36

Astronaut Mitchell became so impressed by the positive results of these experiments that, after retiring from the space program, he established a national organization to study psychic phenomena. It is called the Institute for Noetic Sciences. Of his continuing effort in ESP research, Mitchell said:

"I'm one of those guys that if I happen to get a glimmer…that there's something in it for real, even though we may not know the answer, I'm a bulldog. And I'm bound and determined to get good solid evidence, and good theory, and good fact. And hang onto the wheat and throw away the chaff. But I don't mind wading in and looking at it. And I've done that for 30 years, because I knew I was onto something."

Another NASA astronaut, Dr. Brian O'Leary, a physicist, also conducted numerous ESP experiments, and wrote the book *Exploring Inner and Outer Space - A Scientist's Perspective on Personal and Planetary Transformation* (O'Leary, 1989), in which he described some of his experiences. One of them is described in Chapter 4.

The Russian, or formerly the Soviet, space program has also conducted long-range ESP experiments in space. To quote an excerpt from a 1972 Defense Intelligence Agency (DIA) report:

"In 1967, the <u>Soviet Maritime News</u> reported, "Cosmonauts, when in orbit, seem to be able to communicate telepathically more easily with each other than with people on earth. A psi (short for psychic faculty) training system has been incorporated in the cosmonaut training program," but the <u>News</u> provided no further details. Some informal reports related to Ostrander and Schroeder indicate that the Soviets are working on psi systems for space use, involving not just telepathy, but also precognition." (LaMothe, 1972)

The U.S. Army became interested in ESP when they analyzed field data from Vietnam which suggested that certain soldiers may be able to psychically sense the presence of the enemy, thereby avoiding ambush. According to Dr. Ken Kress, a CIA officer who oversaw the early remote viewing program research:

"The Army Material Command learned of CIA interest in the paranormal. We discovered the Army interest was generated by data which emerged from Vietnam. Apparently certain individuals called point men, who led patrols into hostile territory, had far fewer casualties from booby traps and ambushes than the average. These point men, needless to say, had a following of loyal men and, in general, greatly helped the morale of their troops under a brutal, stressful situation. The army gave extensive physical and psychological tests to a group of unusually successful point men and came to no conclusion other than perhaps that paranormal capabilities may be the explanation!" (Kress, 1977)

As mentioned in the previous chapter, one of the truly unusual and unexplainable aspects of psychic awareness is that it does not seem to weaken with distance. Conventional signals such as radio waves or sound waves die off as the square of the distance, so the signals become four times weaker if one goes twice as far away. But ESP does not conform to this. This makes it potentially an ideal system for long-distance communication. As indicated in the above quote from a DIA report, it also seems to work better in space than on the earth's surface. This may be due to less interference from man-made electromagnetic fields, since ESP experiments also show that putting the receiving person in a shielded room actually IMPROVES his accuracy. It also makes it of great interest to the space program.

Laboratory Evidence for ESP

Extrasensory Perception (ESP) has undergone extensive scientific testing since the 1930's. Contrary to what the public is often told, ESP has been thoroughly demonstrated in the lab. It has been subjected to rigorous statistical tests and proven as a scientific fact. The experiments have been conducted carefully by many laboratories over a seventy-year period. The statistics are valid, the results are replicable. All that is missing is that mainstream science still resists looking at the data or allowing it to be published in the "hard science" journals, such as physics and biology journals.

During a seventy-year period ending in the 1940's there were 142 published articles describing 3.6 million trials using 4,600 separate participants (Rosenthal, 1978; Radin, 1997). Dr. Dean Radin has reviewed and evaluated this large body of experimental data, and focused especially on subsets of these data which can be compared to one another. These were of the "card-guessing type" in which a subject will attempt to use his psychic ability to guess or "read" a concealed card. These were well-controlled tests conducted between 1936 and 1939 by two dozen independent researchers, using the standard five ESP cards. The combined number of trials for all of these experiments was 907,000.

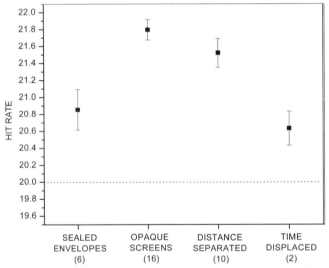

Figure 2.2. Accuracy rate for several types of card-guessing experiments involving the five standard ESP cards. Because there are five cards, random guessing would expect to have a hit rate of 20%. In the first type of test, using sealed envelopes, 130,000 trials were made, with an average hit rate of about 20.85%. This is much higher than chance for such a large data base. In the second set of experiments, the cards were also placed behind an opaque barrier. Here the hit rate soared to 21.8%. There were 497,000 trials of this type. In the third type, separating the subject and the cards by distance, there were 164,000 trials, and in the time displacement experiments there were 115,000 trials. *Graph courtesy of Dr. Dean Radin (Radin. 1997)*

Radin (Radin, 1997) summarized the combined results of all their experiments. This is plotted above in Figure 2.2. There were four distinct types of card-guessing experiments. The results for each are plotted. The first involved cards hidden inside sealed envelopes, while the second set further concealed them behind opaque screens. The third type of card guessing involved a spatial separation, or distance, between the subject and the cards. The fourth type had the subject "guess" cards which were randomly selected at a later time. Therefore this latter set involved precognitive "guesses" of the future cards, or a "time displacement."

For each category of experiment, the expected hit rate based on chance alone is 20%, since there are five distinct ESP cards. However, we see from the data that, for each type of card guessing experiment, the actual hit rate was WELL ABOVE 20%. There were a total of 907,000 trials for all four types of experiments, and an average score or hit rate of well over 21%. To a scientist, these are highly significant results. Although the ESP accuracy was only one or two percent above the average, the large number of experiments make this an extremely important result. In scientific terms, the results are "statistically highly significant." The odds that these results are due to chance are less than one in a billion trillion. This strongly indicates that ESP is a real effect (Pratt, 1966; Radin, 1997).

Dr. Radin concludes:

One might think that the body of evidence summarized in [Figure 2.2], reflecting only the high-security studies reported by nearly two dozen investigators from 1934 to 1939, and 907,000 trials, would have been sufficient to settle the question about the existence of psi perception. And in fact, these experiments did cause many scientists to take psi phenomena seriously. (Radin, 1997)

And Professor H. J. Eysenck, Chairman of the Psychology Department at the University of London, wrote in 1957:

Unless there is a gigantic conspiracy involving some thirty University departments all over the world, and several hundred highly respected scientists in various fields, many of them originally hostile to the claims of the psychical researchers, the only conclusion the unbiased observer can come to must be that there does exist a small number of people who obtain knowledge existing either in other people's minds, or in the outer world, by means as yet unknown to science. (Eysenck, 1957)

Radin concludes his analysis by considering the "file drawer effect" and other possible errors which might somehow explain away these powerful results. The "file-drawer effect" involves the idea that a researcher, when he conducts a study with a null result, i.e. no psychic effect is observed, might tend to store away such a result in his file drawer and never publish it. On the other hand, if he gets a positive result on an ESP experiment, he might be more likely to publish it because that is more exciting. The "file drawer effect" is an example of the type of bias which might enhance the hit rate in Figure 2.2 if the negative experiments had been filed away and never published.

It is difficult to prove or disprove such an idea. But, by using statistics, it is possible to calculate how much data would have to be hidden to be able to account for these positive results, if they are due purely to chance. According to Radin, this would require the assumption that more than 3,300 unpublished, unsuccessful reports have been filed away for every successful report that has been published. This is a ludicrously large number, and "again demonstrates that chance reporting and selective reporting cannot reasonably explain these results."(Radin, 1997)

The results of seventy-eight studies on ESP and clairvoyance were analyzed and summarized by British psychologist Julie Milton (Milton, 1993). These studies were conducted by thirty-five different investigators, and involved 1,158 different ESP subjects. These studies were similar in that the subjects were in the normal, fully awake state of consciousness. They were unselected volunteers, which means they volunteered for the experiment but were not chosen for any known psychic ability. As far as the investigators could tell, they were ordinary people.

Results were categorized by the type of ESP test being used, and are plotted in Figure 2.3 below. The results for the different types of tests were converted to a percentage "hit rate." (Radin, 1997) This makes it possible to directly compare the results from different kinds of ESP tests. These results and many more are recounted in the landmark book *The Conscious Universe*, by Dr. Radin. This book is a fascinating and highly readable survey of this field, by one of its leading experts.

The error bars in Figure 2.3 represent 95% tolerance for each type of measurement. The overall accuracy for all of the different tests was greater than 54%, when 50% would be expected based on chance alone. The total number of ESP trials represented by this graph is more than five million. The odds against chance for these results are <u>greater than ten million to one</u>. As in the previous meta-study, it is demonstrated with overwhelming odds that psychic functioning is real.

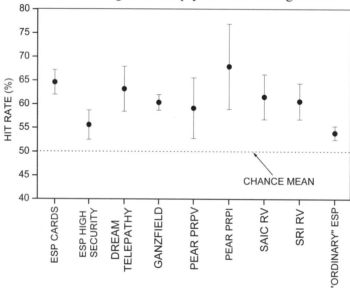

Figure 2.3. This graph summarizes the meta-study of Milton (Milton, 1993) who analyzed and compared the results of 78 independent clairvoyant studies. Several involve remote viewing and others were obtained from remote viewing experiments. All are seen to show accuracy well above chance. The data were converted and replotted for convenient comparison by Radin (Radin, 1997). *Courtesy of Dr. Dean Radin*

A modern variation on the ESP experiment was conducted by the Czech scientist, Dr. Milan Ryzl, who developed an error correction code which he used successfully with psychic Pavel Stepanek to transmit and receive a 50 bit random sequence of numbers with <u>100% accuracy</u>. The procedure required that Stepanek go over the sequence again and again, each time "guessing" or attempting to receive, the numbers in the sequence. These guesses were combined using a majority-vote, error-correcting protocol, a technique often used in signal processing to pull weak signals out of noise. Combining the results from 20,000 readings taken over several days, the complete sequence of 50 numbers was recovered with 100% accuracy.

This experiment is important because it demonstrates that paranormal functioning can be 100% accurate if one has the patience to collect enough data and process it to reduce the noise. Such procedures are commonplace in modern communications, where there is always noise along with the signal. Sophisticated methods have been developed to pull weak signals out of noisy backgrounds. Ryzl's experiments show that the same methods can be used with psychic communication. It suggests that in many cases, the inaccuracies in psychic data can be removed with additional sessions and mathematical processing.

Chinese Government Demonstrations of ESP

The Chinese government in Beijing has become interested in paranormal abilities. It has conducted nationwide searches for talented young people, in whom these abilities are usually strongest. They term the ability "Exceptional Human Functioning" or EHF, and do not treat these abilities as strange or fraudulent. Instead, the attitude seems to be one of encouragement, in which unusual abilities are identified and studied.

Writer Paul Dong reports (Dong, 1984) that, between 1979 and 1981, in a well-organized program to locate psychically gifted children, the Chinese government located 30 who qualified as "EHF" children. A few of them, along with their unusual psychic abilities, are listed below:

"Tong Yu (male, 13; functions: reading and color perception by ear)...

Zhang Lei (female, 13; functions: sensing another individual's thoughts, moving objects by thought, remote viewing)...

Sun Liping (female, 12; functions: clairvoyant vision, moving objects and breaking twigs by power of thought) She was the one who 'flew' flower from the garden into a covered teacup...

Shao Hongyan (female, 12; functions: clairvoyant vision, moving objects and breaking twigs by power of thought, adjusting watches from a distance..."

Dong notes that several hundred additional children were identified as having less conspicuous, but still exceptional, abilities, and these will also be trained to enhance their abilities while they are being studied scientifically.

One such highly talented individual is a young girl named Yu Rui Hua. In an experiment conducted by the government, she sat at the front of the room and was asked to look out into the audience consisting of seven security men, a group of reporters and some scientists. She was told that one of them was armed, and was asked to identify the person. She immediately narrowed it down to two individuals. When asked to be more specific, she asked that the lights be turned down. Within less than one minute, as she sat on the stage, she was able to say which person had the gun and exactly where on his body he was carrying it.

She was tested by a number of national laboratories in China, including the High Energy Physics Institute, Atomic Energy Institute, Chemical Engineering Institute, Biological Physics Institute of the Chinese Academy of Sciences, the Military Medical College, the Science and Technology Association, and several major universities. In one demonstration of her abilities, sponsored by the Atomic Energy Institute, she was handed a sealed lead tank weighing 20 kilograms (44 pounds). This tank is normally used for transporting radioactive materials. Inside the tank was a piece of paper which she was asked to try to remote view.

After eighteen minutes of concentration, she shouted "I've got it." She described a drawing of a little man with his arms outstretched and a pair of legs with his feet raised high. She described his head as colored red and his body as blue, and a small circle by his feet. When the container was unsealed, she was found to be correct in every aspect of her description. The circle at the man's feet was an apple.

In another case in China, a young boy named Wei Ruoyang, eleven years old, was found to be so proficient at remote viewing that he could look into the ground and find buried pipelines. He performed this feat on many occasions with an engineer checking his results against blueprints. He was able to describe the pipeline configuration in minute detail, as if the ground itself were transparent to him (Dong, 1984).

Demonstration of ESP in Pets

Dr. Rupert Sheldrake (1999, 2000) has called attention to the psychic ability of our pets. In his book, *Dogs That Know When Their Owners Are Coming Home,* (Sheldrake, 1999) he recounts hundreds of cases of psychic functioning by animals. One of the most common of these is the ability of dogs to know the exact moment when their owner decides to come home. In simultaneous video studies of the dog waiting at home and the owner at work, it was confirmed that dogs become excited and go the door in anticipation at virtually the same moment that their owner decides to come home. The owner is many miles away, and the times of return vary greatly, so no other external cues are available to the dog. It appears that the behavior is truly an example of ESP.

To make this observation more scientific, Sheldrake recorded fifty videotaped sessions with a dog named Jaytee whose owner is Pam (Sheldrake, 1997, 1998, 1999, 2000). The results of some of these experiments are shown in Figures 2.4 and 2.5. Jaytee's movements and activities were recorded on videotape at various times of day. The number of seconds Jaytee spent waiting at the window was recorded for each ten-minute time period.

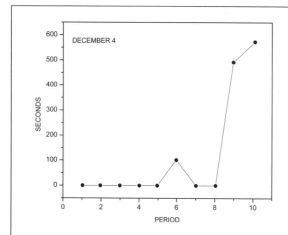 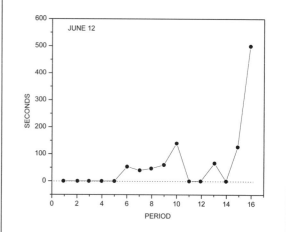

Figure 2.4. Time spent waiting by the door during a ten minute (600 second) time period. Average of six short sessions. Note that during the last two periods, as the owner is coming home, the dog spends almost the entire time by the door. (Sheldrake, 1999)

Figure 2.5. Time spent waiting by the door, based on an average of eleven long sessions. Note that during the last session, as the owner is coming home, the time shoots up to nearly 100% of the period. (Sheldrake, 1999)

The last period shown on each graph represents the first ten minutes that Pam was on her way home. The length of time Pam was gone and her time of return varied in a random manner in each experiment. In the left graph, the results of six short-duration experiments are averaged together. In the right hand graph, 11 long duration experiments are averaged together. It was found that only when Pam started for home did Jaytee go to the window and exhibit anticipatory behavior. This is shown by the last one or two points on each graph, which are much higher than the others.

The results with Jaytee and Pam illustrate that ESP in pets is a real phenomenon, and not just the imagination of the owner. Sheldrake's book contains countless testimonials from pet owners which further buttress the case for animal ESP. One story will provide the flavor of these observations. The wife of a Coast Guard captain, whose ship was stationed at a port 20 miles away, described the behavior of their dog, Jackson:

"[My husband] would arrive home at odd hours. When the ship had come into port, Jackson would get excited, go to the door, and want out. Most of the time he would go and sit at the end of the sidewalk, stationing himself to look in the direction he knew the car would travel. He got so good at this, I couldn't help but notice, and sometimes would use Jackson's warning to freshen my hair and makeup before my husband arrived! If I was cooking dinner and was at the point of deciding how many portions to cook or places to set for the meal, I would use his prediction and add accordingly." (Sheldrake, 1999)

Such behavior in pets has been observed by many people. It highlights the widespread, almost commonplace, nature of ESP. We see its effects every day, but we don't call it ESP. We may call it a "gut" feeling, or "intuition" or a "hunch". It may be an idea that springs into our head instantly from "nowhere". It may be that we find ourselves thinking of someone we haven't seen for a long time, and then, within a few hours, they call. We brush aside these everyday occurrences, calling them "coincidence." But in many cases they are legitimate examples of a deep, universal form of communication, which although ubiquitous, has been until very recently overlooked by science.

ESP in Police Work
ESP and psychic ability are sometimes used in police work in cases when conventional methods have failed or there is little tangible evidence. Police departments often resist calling in psychics, or admitting they use them, because it may invite ridicule or be considered an admission that conventional methods have failed. Nevertheless, psychics are often brought in anyway, as a last resort, and have been instrumental in cracking difficult cases. In the book *The Blue Sense*, by Lyons and Truzzi (Lyons, 1991), some of these cases are recounted.

One case involved the murder of a young woman. She had gone on a date with her boyfriend and had not been seen since. Her boyfriend had been arrested for the crime, but since the police were unable to find her body after six months of searching, the case was shaky. They called in a well-known psychic, Greta Alexander of Delavan, Illinois. Alexander moved her hand over a map and pointed to the area where the body would be found. She also provided them with other crucial information which allowed them to find the body in three days.

Detective William Fitzgerald cited twenty-two "hits" Alexander had made concerning finding of the body. For example, she predicted that the foot would be separated from the body, and the man who found the body would have a "bad hand". The Officer who found the body did indeed have a deformed left hand, which had been injured in an accident, and the foot of the girl was indeed missing. Fitzgerald stated afterwards: "I was skeptical to begin with, but I guess I'm going to be a believer now."

Lyons and Truzzi describe numerous cases in which police departments use psychics to help solve crimes. Psychics are typically only brought in for the most difficult cases, when conventional police methods have been unsuccessful. A 1979 survey conducted by the California Department of Justice found that, of eleven police agencies reported by newspapers to use psychics, eight reported that the psychics had provided them with otherwise unknown information that they considered helpful. In three of these cases, missing bodies were found in areas described by the psychics. The survey report concluded:

> *"a talented psychic can assist you by helping to locate a geographic area of a missing person, narrow the number of leads to be concentrated upon, highlight information that has been overlooked, or provide information previously unknown to the investigator." (Lyons, 1991)*

Iverson (1992) provides further evidence supporting the usefulness of psychics in police work. He recounts the deeds of such famous psychics as Gerard Croiset, Peter Hurkos and Alex Tanous. In Miami in 1958 Hurkos was called in to solve a murder which was committed in a taxi. Hurkos sat in the taxi for a few minutes, and received the following impressions: the killer was tall and thin, had a tattoo on his right arm, and walked like a sailor. Hurkos said the killer had been in trouble with police in Havana and Detroit, and was known as "Smitty". Hurkos said this same man had committed another murder a few hours earlier on the same night. Following these leads, the police quickly found a man satisfying every part of the description: his name was Charles Smith, known as "Smitty," and he matched the physical description perfectly. He had bragged to a waitress that he had killed two men in one night, but she did not believe him. "Smitty" was subsequently convicted of the crime, and Hurkos received a great deal of the credit for solving the case.

Methods of Enhancing ESP

Several techniques have been discovered which enhance ESP accuracy. One of these is hypnosis. Researchers have found that, when the subject is placed in an altered state by hypnosis, his accuracy as an ESP receiver improves. Dean Radin, in his book *The Conscious Universe*, reviewed several studies of this effect. He described the comparative study carried out by Stanford and Stein (Stanford, 1994) in which twenty-nine research studies were compared to determine the effect of hypnosis on ESP. These studies were carried out by eleven different investigators over a 37 year period.

Although the protocols differed somewhat , they all involved ESP subjects in both hypnotized and "normal" states, and it was possible to make an overall analysis of their relative accuracy. These were ordinary individuals, selected at random, who had no demonstrated psychic ability. The researchers found that, in the case of subjects in normal consciousness, who were not hypnotized, the ESP accuracy was about 50.6% over many tests, where 50% represented pure chance. This was slightly higher than average but not considered statistically significant.

However, when the same individuals were hypnotized, the accuracy rose to 52.3%. Although this may seem like a small increase, it involved a huge number of experiments. Because of this, even small shifts away from average are highly unlikely. When they occur, it is highly significant and suggests that a real effect is present. In this case, the difference in results between the unhypnotized and the hypnotized cases would only occur ONE TIME IN 2,700 if it were due to chance. Even though the percentage increase in accuracy may seem small, it is a very real and important increase and cannot reasonably be explained by chance or other factors. Therefore, it is a statistically rigorous conclusion to say that telepathy is more accurate with hypnotized subjects. Hypnosis improves the ability of subjects to receive ESP messages.

Hypnosis quiets the conscious mind, and this may be the reason ESP scores were higher under hypnosis. As we shall see in the next section, even when the conscious mind is unaware of an ESP message, the subconscious mind and the autonomic systems of the body "know" when such a signal has been received. The reactions have been measured.

Other methods of quieting the mind involve filtering out external disturbances, such as sound and electrical signals. In addition, certain frequencies of sound, called *hemisync*, can be fed stereophonically into the ears inducing brain wave patterns which are known to enhance relaxation and psychic sensitivity.

At the Monroe Institute in Faber, Virginia, for example, there is a cubical room which is virtually perfect as an environment for ESP reception, although that is not its primary purpose. It is mounted on shock-absorbers, with multi-layer thick walls, having both electromagnetic and sound isolation (see Figure 2.6). Inside this room, the subject lies on a waterbed. The walls are covered with thick, acoustically absorbing black foam. The subject is completely isolated from the outside world except for an intercom. During experiments, he is physiologically monitored to determine when he is in the deepest state of relaxation.

Figure 2.6. Special isolation room at the Monroe Institute, designed to assist in reaching deeply relaxed altered states. *Photograph Courtesy of Carol Sabick and Skip Atwater, The Monroe Institute.*

Research has established that certain changes in skin resistance and voltage measured on the body are clear signals that the subject has entered a deep state of relaxation. By following a procedure of this kind, it is possible to put an individual into an optimum state for ESP reception, and to monitor him to make sure he remains in that state.

During a session the physiological state of the subject, including skin resistance, EEG and other parameters, is measured and monitored by a staff member outside the chamber in the control room. As the relaxation of the subject becomes deeper, the hemi-sync signals being piped into the headphones of the subject can be varied to control the "ascent" and "descent" of the subject during the session.

Physical Reactions to ESP

Remote viewers and psychics learn to quiet the "left brain," the analytical side of the brain. This talkative, conscious part of the mind, so highly developed by Western education, actually seems to interfere with psi functioning. It is believed that the subconscious mind picks up the ESP signal. This is why meditation and hypnosis can be helpful in improving psychic accuracy: these techniques quiet the chattering, analytical part of the brain and allow information from the non-verbal, subconscious mind to filter through.

If this notion is correct, then various subconscious systems of the body, such as brain waves and heart rate, may reveal when ESP messages are received. By measuring these automatic (autonomic) functions which are beyond normal control, several methods have been discovered that can detect the moment when a psychic signal is received. It causes measurable physiological changes in the autonomic systems of the body.

Dr. Douglas Dean, working at the Newark College of Engineering, showed that, when a person is receiving an ESP message, his blood volume increases. This can be measured by a plethysmograph, which measures blood volume in the thumb. The person receiving the ESP message may not be consciously aware of it, but the pressure indicated by the plethysmograph indicates when an ESP message is being received (Dean, 1962, 1966).

At Rosary Hill College in Buffalo, NY, Dr. Justa Smith found, by using very sophisticated tests, that certain chemicals in the body such as enzymes are affected by psi (Smith, 1969). Changes in EEG (electroencephalogram, or brain wave pattern) are also affected when telepathic messages are being received (Pavlova, 1967; Lloyd, 1973). Dr. Lutsia Pavlova, a Russian scientist, conducted a long series of tests with the famed Russian psychic Karl Nikolaiev. Nikolaiev was famous for his abilities as a psychic receiver, and had demonstrated remarkable accuracy in receiving ESP signals over a distance of 6,000 miles. Pavlova discovered that when Nikolaiev began receiving a psychic message, his brain showed unusual electrical activation which was visible on an EEG.

Another way to detect reception of an ESP message involves monitoring the voltages between acupuncture points. A device called a CCAP (Conductivity of the Channels of Acupuncture Points) measures the pattern of conductivity of the acupoint system. It shows distinct changes during telepathy. Dr. Viktor Adamenko conducted a series of experiments in Moscow using two groups of volunteers, both attached to the CCAP machine. One group was the control group. The second group was hypnotized. A doctor in a distant room at the institute attempted to send telepathic messages to specific volunteers. The scientists watched the output of the CCAP. As the doctor transmitted thoughts to various people and with varying intensity, the scientists were amazed at the accuracy of the CCAP response.

Brain waves also change when an ESP message is being received, whether the receiver is aware of it or not. In a carefully conducted set of experiments by Lloyd (Lloyd, 1973), a telepathic sender and receiver were set up in separate, isolated and shielded rooms. The receiver was instrumented with EEG electrodes attached to his scalp. These measured small changes in the electrical activity of his brain. The receiver knew he would be sent various telepathic messages, but did not know when or what the content would be.

His brain response to normal stimulation was tested by turning on an audible beep, a sound tone at a set frequency, for a half-second, and recording his brain wave response. This is shown in the upper curve in Figure 2.7. Thus, when he heard a beep, his brain responded with that brain wave signal. This curve is called an Average Evoked Response (AER) since it averages the brain signals over many trials.

The interesting part came next. The telepathic sender, on a command, attempted to send a psychic message to the receiver. The brain wave response of the receiver is plotted in the lower curve.

The response of the brain is almost identical for the two forms of stimulation. <u>An audible beep and a quiet undetectable psychic message caused similar changes in the brain waves of the receiver.</u>

Therefore the receiver's brain is receiving the telepathic message. It "knows" on some subconscious level that it is being sent a message. Its evoked response is almost identical to when it receives an audible, conventional message. However, based on questioning after the test, the receiver had no conscious knowledge that a telepathic message was being sent or received.

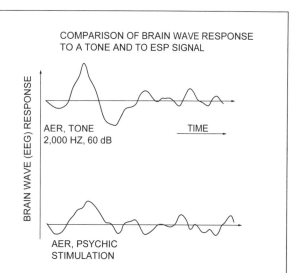

Figure 2.7. Comparison of EEG brain wave response to hearing a 2000 Hz tone (top curve), and to receiving a telepathic message of "cup of coffee" (lower curve). These graphs are based on the average response over 60 trials, called the Average Evoked Response (AER) (Lloyd, 1973)

This observation is the key to several forms of psychic training and enhancement. It shows that the subconscious mind, or the "lower level" autonomic functions of the body, often receives psychic information of which it is unaware at the conscious level. Hypnosis, meditation and biofeedback training are three methods which can train the conscious part to be quiet, and which therefore improve the ability of the receiver to be aware of the psychic messages.

Dr. William Braud has summarized the results of a continuous thirteen-year long study of psychic communication and influence (Braud, 1991). In these experiments, human operators were isolated from their "targets," the animals or people they were trying to affect. They and their targets were placed in isolated, non-adjacent rooms in the laboratory. A wide variety of different experiments were conducted. In some cases the operator attempted to affect the blood pressure, skin resistance, muscle tremor (steadiness of hand), or "ideomotor response" (the involuntary movements of a pendulum held by the target individual).

In other cases, animals were the target. In one set of experiments, the operators attempted to influence the orientation of a knife fish (*Gymnotus carapo*). In other tests, the goal was to control the activity of gerbils on a treadmill. In some tests, the targets were human red blood cells. They were placed in saline solutions of various strengths, and the goal was to affect how long they would survive in these solutions.

In all the experiments, great care was taken to remove spurious influences which might lead to errors. The activity of each target type was monitored and measured whether the operator was or was not trying to influence it. In this way, the normal statistical variations of each target type were established. This made it easier to determine when the target was responding unusually. All of the data were analyzed by standard statistical methods. Figure 2.8 summarizes the results of all the experiments. It can be seen that for every type of test, except the induction of tremors, the operators were successful well beyond chance in affecting the target in the desired way. Several of these "targets" were subconscious autonomic human functions, such as blood pressure and skin resistance. Once more we see that these subconscious parameters respond well to psychic messages, even when the conscious mind is oblivious.

These results suggest that ESP reception ability is widespread, but the problem lies in poor communication and awareness between the subconscious and the conscious mind. This is the reason that meditation, relaxation and hypnosis protocols are often useful in improving ESP scores.

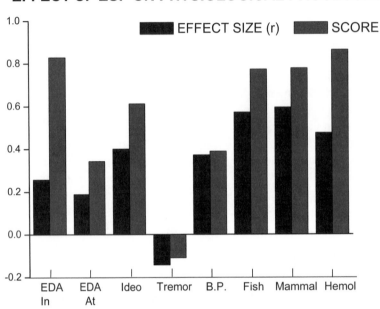

Figure 2.8. Effect of ESP on subconscious physiological properties. This graph summarizes the results from a wide variety of different physiological measurements, such as skin resistance and blood volume. The bars above the graph indicate that there is consistent physiological response when ESP messages are being sent to the subject. In many of these cases the subject was not consciously aware of the messages, but his bodily functions responded anyway (Braud, 1991).

The polygraph, or lie detector, has also been used successfully to monitor ESP signals. The work of Cleve Backster, owner of the Backster School of Lie Detection and a recognized expert polygrapher, found that a polygraph machine connected to plants was capable of measuring their reaction to various external phenomena. The changing signal on the polygraph machine registered changes in plant conductivity, and these were affected by the emotions and intentions of other living beings.

According to Backster, this response indicates some sort of primary perception channel or a "consciousness" in every living cell. This could explain why human physiology responds to psychic messages at the subconscious level. This may be the same level at which plants respond and cells communicate. It may be our cells which are picking up the psychic messages, which are then relayed with difficulty up to the higher organs. Backster's discoveries are described in greater detail in Chapter 4.

These are merely hints of what may one day turn out to be the components of a model of ESP. So far, they are question marks and tantalizing clues.

ESP Among Ancient and Traditional Cultures

Douchan Gersi is a Czechoslovakian-born explorer and writer who spent time among many remote, traditional cultures. In his fascinating book *Faces in the Smoke* (Gersi, 1991) he describes how many tribes use a form of ESP in communicating across great distances. While living with the Tuareg people of the Sahara desert, he observed this on numerous occasions. One day when he was staying in the camp of a man named Oizek, he was informed that part of the tribe would be returning in a couple of days from a long trading mission. Since they had been gone for more than three months, and these nomadic journeys are highly unpredictable in their duration, Gersi asked how Oizek knew so accurately when they would be returning.

Oizek replied that one of the women was in telepathic contact with her husband, who was part of the returning party. "The *taleb* [shaman] said that she is able to communicate with her husband mentally." Gersi sought the woman out and asked her more specifically when her husband was returning. She replied "Tonight!" Skeptically, Gersi scoured the horizon with powerful binoculars but could see no sign of anyone. He jumped into his Land Rover and drove for two hours out into the desert, looking for any signs she might have seen that would provide clues to her husband's return. But he found nothing. At 5:00 in the morning he was awakened to be informed that her husband had just returned to camp from his journey. So her prediction came true. (Gersi, 1991)

In another example from the Tuareg, Gersi had been driving across the desert when he encountered a single Tuareg nomad sitting by his camel. From the tracks, Gersi could tell he had been sitting at that spot for several days. He stopped and shared tea and water with the man, and inquired why he was waiting at this desolate, seemingly unmarked spot in the middle of the desert. The nomad explained that he was waiting for a friend. He explained, under Gersi's questioning, that seven months earlier, in the town of Gao, in Mali, six hundred miles away, he had made a date to meet his friend at this spot. Each of them was on a journey across the desert of several hundred miles, in different directions. This was the closest spot at which they could meet. So he was waiting.

Gersi was somewhat dubious: "I looked around us and saw only rocky hills, sand and stones. 'How do you know that this is the meeting place?' I asked. 'Can't miss the place,' he said describing and giving names to everything that surrounded us." However, the nomad's water was running low, and he said he would have to move on if his friend did not arrive in the next three days. The next morning he announced that he had communicated with his friend during the night, and he would be arriving in two more days. The Tuareg's friend had explained to him about a detour he had made to fill up his water bags. Again Gersi questioned the nomad:

"How did he tell you that? Did you dream about him?"

"No, I didn't dream about him. He just told me where he was."

"But how did he tell you that?"

"He told me that in my mind. And in the same way I answered him that I will be waiting for him."

Out of curiosity, Gersi waited with his car for two more days to see if the Tuareg's psychic information was correct. Sure enough, on the second day, as predicted, the Tuareg's friend arrived.

The Effect of Time and Position on ESP

Scientists have discovered that there are certain times of day when ESP and remote viewing are much more accurate. In fact, they are so accurate that the successes during this time period seem to explain almost all of the positive results from psi experiments. This is a remarkable discovery. It means that by timing the psychic experiments correctly, accuracy can be greatly improved.

This discovery was recently announced by Dr. James Spottiswood, a physicist at the Cognitive Sciences Laboratory in Palo Alto, California. In the *Journal of Scientific Exploration* he reported (Spottiswood, 1997) an analysis of 1,468 published trials in which ESP and other types of paranormal functioning were measured. Subsequently, he analyzed an additional 1,015 trials. He found that the success rate, that is <u>the accuracy of the paranormal functioning, depended on the position of the ESP subject on the earth relative to the fixed stars in the sky at the time of the experiment!</u> This is called the "sidereal time" of the experiment, which is very familiar to astronomers.

Spottiswood found that the best results were obtained when the constellation Virgo is overhead in the sky above the ESP receiver. This region of the sky, at 13.5 hours sidereal, is known as the "Great Attractor" because it is a huge concentration of "dark matter." It is a region toward which the galaxies in the local group, including our own galaxy, are being pulled. Since there are no large, visible concentrations of matter in this region, and yet it has a strong gravitational pull, astronomers have concluded that this region has a high concentration of "dark matter."

A theory for this effect is described in Volume II of this series, in Chapter 7 of *Life Force, The Scientific Basis* (Swanson, 2009). It is based on the observation by Russian scientists that "left handed" torsion is correlated both with "dark matter" and with increased ESP. This connection is explained in detail in that book.

Joe McMoneagle, the well-known and highly rated former U.S. military remote viewer, has also commented on these results: "We took all the remote viewings from 31 studies and put them across a sidereal time scale. We found a huge peak of accuracy for remote viewing at 13.5 hours sidereal" (McMoneagle, 1999).

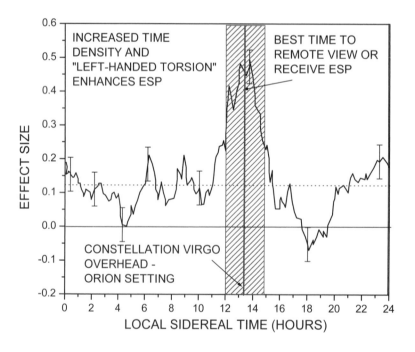

Figure 2.9. Mean effect size versus local sidereal time, from a comprehensive study of many remove viewing and ESP experiments. Reception is four times more accurate when Virgo is overhead and Orion is setting, corresponding to 13.5 hours sidereal (Spottiswood, 1997). *Courtesy of Dr. James Spottiswood*

The results from Spottiswood's comprehensive survey are shown in Figure 2.9. The graph combines data from 21 separate studies of ESP and Remote Viewing, and consists of a total of 1,468 separate experiments or "trials". The horizontal dashed line shows the average success rate. On the horizontal axis of the graph is "Local Sidereal Time", which can be translated loosely into which stars were directly overhead of an observer when an ESP or remote viewing experiment was conducted. The vertical axis measures the success rate of the experiment.

It can be seen from the graph that the success rate is <u>greater than average by a factor of four</u> for trials conducted at a time corresponding to 13.5 hours sidereal. This is a remarkable and powerful result. It means that remote viewing and psychic reception experiments should always be conducted at this sidereal time, regardless of whether it is day or night. It shouldl improve the psychic accuracy fourfold.

Spottiswood conducted a rigorous statistical study of the data to determine the likelihood that such a peak could occur by pure chance. He found it to be less than one in a thousand. Moreover, the peak was found first in one combined data set, and then confirmed in a second large set of independent data.

This sidereal time occurs when the constellation Orion and the star Sirius have just set on the western horizon, and the last bright star on Orion's shoulder (Betelgeuse) is about to go below the horizon as well. At this moment the handle of the Big Dipper (Ursa Major) is overhead in the Northern hemisphere and the last star at the tip of the handle will be at its highest point in the sky.

On May 1 this corresponds to about 11:20 pm local standard time. If it is summer, then the time must be corrected for daylight time in many areas, by adding one hour, making it 12:20 AM daylight time, just after midnight. On June 1, the optimum time when the stars have this configuration will be 9:20 PM standard time, or 10:20 PM daylight savings time. On August 1, this occurs at about 5:20 PM standard, or 6:20 PM daylight time. On October 1, the center of the window is about 1:20 PM standard time; on December 1 the optimum time moves to about 9:15 AM, and on February 1 the best time is about 5:10 AM. On April 1 the center of the window occurs at about 1:15 AM, standard time. These times are all local times and therefore apply for any time zone. They denote the center of a "time window," so psychic reception should be best one hour before and one hour after this time.

Summary

Results such as Spottiswood's can be useful in enhancing the accuracy of ESP and Remote Viewing. According to his findings:

> "...it may be possible to increase effect size [accuracy] in AC [anomalous cognition] experiments by as much as four-fold by timing them near 13.5 h." (Spottiswood, 1997)

In other words, by properly choosing the local time of the experiment as described above, ESP and remote viewing accuracy can be INCREASED BY A FACTOR OF FOUR. This is very exciting and important.

There are also other means by which ESP can be enhanced. As we noted above, hypnosis is one method. Another is meditation. Both of these quiet the "left brain" logical mind and make it easier to sense the messages from the subconscious. The optimum state of the receiver can also be enhanced by hemi-sync audiotapes and acupuncture, both of which help create the optimum brain wave state. ESP experiments are also more accurate when the receiver is in a low noise electromagnetic environment, such as a shielded room, or during times of low geomagnetic activity. Distraction can be very damaging to good ESP reception, so it is also best to minimize disturbances due to sound, light, and low frequency vibration.

To summarize, ESP accuracy should be greatly enhanced by combining all the factors which are known to improve ESP accuracy:

(1) Conduct experiment around the Local Sidereal Time of 13.5 hours. This refers to the location of the receiver, and occurs approximately when the constellation Virgo is overhead and Orion has just set.
(2) Place receiver in electromagnetically shielded room, including magnetic shielding.
(3) Isolate from all vibrations, acoustic noise, and visual distractions
(4) Place receiver under hypnosis and optimize relaxed, meditative, trance-like state.
(5) Devices such as hemi-sync tapes may help entrain the brain waves to optimal, relaxed brain wave state (deep alpha to theta)
(6) Monitor physiological condition.
(7) Stimulate key acupuncture points
(8) Weight the data according to physiological condition. Data would be most strongly weighted when the subject is in the optimum state, with brain waves in deep alpha or theta, and when the acupoint system, EEG and blood volume changes (plethysmograph) confirm ESP reception.

The evidence in this chapter is powerful support for the existence of psychic ability. Together with the research on remote viewing discussed in the previous chapter, it is clear that the human mind can acquire knowledge by means that defy our present understanding. Neither space nor time are barriers. Consciousness seems to involve a new force which enables us to acquire information from virtually anywhere in the universe. Science has barely begun to address this. It has far-reaching implications.

In the next chapter, another important aspect of psychic ability is explored. It is one thing to acquire knowledge about a remote place or event. It is quite another to actually AFFECT or CHANGE a remote event. The ability to reach out with the mind and psychically affect an event is called psychokinesis or PK.

We see in the next chapter that, just as consciousness can bring back information from remote places and times, it can also AFFECT those events. In the Princeton PEAR Lab experiments it has been found that a housewife in San Antonio can, by focusing her mind, affect the behavior of a mechanical device in Princeton, New Jersey. From millions of experiments with many dozens of participants, this effect has been proven with rigorous scientific statistics. And even more challenging to our world-view, this influence can be exerted a week BEFORE or a week AFTER the data is actually taken. There is an enormous body of scientific data which proves that this happens.

The ability to use the mind to use intention, prayer, and visualization to bring about change in the physical world is not a new idea. It is as old as the Bible. What is new is the scientific evidence that it actually works, that "thoughts are things" and that the intentions, hopes, and dreams of the mind, if held with persistence and intensity, can change the world. The experiments which prove this are presented next.

CHAPTER 3 – PSYCHOKINESIS: MIND OVER MATTER

"Geller has bent my ring in the palm of my hand without ever touching it. Personally, I have no scientific explanation for the phenomenon."
-- Dr. Werner Von Braun, Director, Marshall Space Flight Center
Directed development of German V-2 and American Redstone and Saturn V rockets

"I think Uri is a magician, but I don't particularly believe that he is using trickery. I believe there are psychic abilities. They don't accord with any science we have at the moment, but maybe some future science will back them up with theories."
-- Brian Josephson,
Professor of Physics, University of Cambridge
Winner of the Nobel Prize for Physics, 1973

"Uri's ability to perform amazing feats of mental wizardry is known the world over...Uri is not a magician. He is using capabilities that we all have and can develop with exercise and practice."
-- Dr. Edgar Mitchell
Apollo 14 Astronaut and sixth man to walk on the moon

"Uri bent a spoon for me. The first time he did, I thought there must be a trick. The second time I was stunned - completely, completely stunned and amazed. It just bent in my hand. I've never seen anything like it. It takes a lot to impress me. Uri Geller is for real and anyone who doesn't recognize that is either deluding himself, or he is a very sad person."
-- David Blaine, Professional Magician

DEFINITION-Psychokinesis or PK: The ability to move or effect objects or living beings at a distance without touching them, involving only mental and psychic interaction.

The Stanford PK Experiments

Ingo Swann is an artist who lives in New York. He is also a gifted psychic who has demonstrated his ability in numerous scientific experiments. Some of these were described in Chapter 1. One day in 1972, he was visiting the laboratory of two physicists, Dr. Harold (Hal) Puthoff and Dr. Russell Targ, at the Stanford Research Institute (SRI) in Menlo Park, California. They were discussing what experiments they could do when Puthoff, on the spur of the moment, thought of the superconducting magnetometer under the building. It was heavily shielded against every conceivable disturbance. "Let's let Ingo try to affect that!" suggested Puthoff (Puthoff, 1974).

A magnetometer is a device which measures magnetic field. However, this device was specially designed to search for a particular type of elementary particle, the quark, which is believed to be one of the fundamental building blocks of all matter. The device was heavily shielded against all normal outside influences. It was located in a well under the building and was covered by heavy magnetic (mu-metal) shielding on all sides. It was further encased in an aluminum container, surrounded by copper shielding, and most important of all, a shield of supercooled, superconducting niobium, which should exclude all traces of electromagnetic field. In fact, as Puthoff and Targ state: "In previous tests, no signals had been induced in the shielded magnetometer from outside." (Puthoff, 1974)

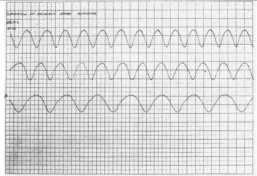

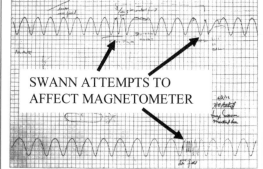

SWANN ATTEMPTS TO AFFECT MAGNETOMETER

| Figure 3.1. The output trace of the magnetometer during slow decay of initial magnetic field, under normal conditions. *Graph courtesy of Dr. Harold Puthoff.* | Figure 3.2. The output trace of the magnetometer during slow decay of initial magnetic field. Note anomalies when Swann focused his attention on the magnetometer. *Graph courtesy of Dr. Harold Puthoff.* |

The detector inside all of this shielding is a superconducting device, called a SQUID, which measures magnetic fields. The experiment starts out with an initial magnetic field inside the container which decays over time. The strength of this field is measured by the wavelength of the waves on the chart (see Fig. 3.1). As the field decays, the wavelength of the waves gradually becomes longer and longer, indicating that the field inside is weakening. The chart on the left, in Figure 3.1, shows the normal behavior of the device.

The device was explained to Swann, who was then asked to attempt to influence the magnetic readings. Swann said he would attempt to "place his attention" inside the device. At the moment he did this, the frequency of the output waves doubled. This can be seen in the right hand chart, Figure 3.2 above. Two very quick, short-period cycles occurred at the point where Swann attempted to focus his attention inside the device. This behavior indicates a momentary doubling of the magnetic field inside the device. The heavy shielding should make the device impervious to any outside influences. Such a glitch had never occurred before.

A short time later, Swann attempted to affect it again, and again was successful. On several more occasions, as shown on the graph, each time Swann was asked to think about the insides of the device, the chart output showed highly unusual behavior. Swann told the physicists that, as he looked with his mind at different parts of the device, it seemed to cause different effects. The high-frequency disturbance shown in the lower trace in Figure 3.2 occurred when Swann said he was focusing on the Niobium ball in the device.

This observation is even more interesting, because it seems that these disturbances were caused as Swann was "looking inside" the device with his mind, or remote viewing it. The device itself was not visible to normal sight, being underground and wrapped in multiple layers of shielding and instrumentation.

The only conventional way to understand these data is if Swann were able to go inside the device himself, to penetrate through the shielding and actually be inside, carrying a magnetic field with him. In Chapter 10 we shall see evidence that the "astral body," the part of our consciousness which travels around during an out-of-body experience or some types of remote viewing, is able to go through walls and often brings with it (or causes) electromagnetic disturbances (Mitchell, 1987). More evidence for this will be presented in later chapters.

Therefore, one way of understanding these data is to assume that Swann's "astral body" went inside the device when he said he was "focusing his attention" on it and "looking at it" from inside. As outlandish as this explanation may sound to some, there is no conventional explanation for these effects. Data like these force us to reconsider the present physics paradigm.

Spoon-bending and Demonstrations of Uri Geller

The average Westerner who was alive during the nineteen-seventies has heard of Uri Geller. For a time he was famous. He had an audience with President Carter and dinner with Rosalyn Carter and Secretary of State Henry Kissenger. He was personal friends with the President of Mexico, and starred on a national television special in England. But people also say "Oh, yeah. Didn't they show he was a fraud, that he used tricks?" And this is what the average person remembers.

There was a powerful effort made to debunk and discredit Uri Geller. A stage magician named "The Amazing Randi" went around claiming that Geller used tricks. Randi even showed how to bend a spoon by using slight of hand to exchange a good spoon for one that was already broken. Randi's attacks on Geller were well publicized, and Geller's refutations of Randi were not. So there is the lingering vague impression that Geller wasn't very special. Or even, as Randi would like to have people believe, that Geller was a fraud.

But to those who met him in person or saw some of his more unusual deeds, there was no doubt that he was genuine and exhibited very unusual abilities. The quotes at the beginning of this chapter indicate the quality, intelligence and integrity of those who vouch for Geller. These include a Nobel Prize winner in Physics and the man most often credited with the success of the U.S. missile program, Dr. Werner Von Braun. The reader must decide for himself whose testimony he trusts more.

Figure 3.3. Photograph of (left to right) Dr. Henry Kissenger, Uri Geller, and First Lady Rosalynn Carter. Mrs. Carter is holding a spoon which Geller has just bent by gently touching it (Geller, 1986). *Photo courtesy of Uri Geller*

At a dinner party hosted by the wife of the President of Mexico, Lopez Portillo, President Jimmy Carter's wife Rosalynn shared the table with Secretary of State Henry

Kissenger, and Uri Geller (see Figure 3.3). At the same table was the American Ambassador to Mexico and the son of President Ford.

During the dinner, Mrs. Carter wanted to see a demonstration of spoon bending. Geller had Mrs. Carter hold the spoon while he lightly stroked it with one finger. It soon began to curl upwards in the usual way, and Mrs. Carter was delighted. Then Geller took his hand away completely, and the guests watched in astonishment as the spoon continued to bend until there was a right angle bend in it. "Oh, my!" said Mrs. Carter. "I wish my friends could see this. I must show it to Jimmy."

Kissenger observed this, and in addition benefited from a first hand ESP experiment he did with Uri at the table. Uri asked Kissenger to draw something on his napkin in secret, and then, keeping it hidden, face Geller and stare into his eyes. As he did, Geller described the drawing perfectly. Kissenger recoiled in alarm and ordered Geller not try to read his mind for any secrets (Geller, 1986).

The most convincing aspect of Geller's spoon bending talent is that it did not require Geller at all. People soon discovered that spoon bending was a teachable skill and that many people could do it. They just followed Geller's instructions, relaxed and sent "energy" into some part of the spoon. Then they were to visualize the spoon bending. At a certain moment a "softening" of the spoon would occur and it could be easily bent. Some spoons were twisted up like pretzels in this condition, when under normal conditions it might require all one's might to make a simple bend.

Sometimes the spoon bent on its own, and Geller was nowhere around. One very well-witnessed event occurred in 1983 at a "spoon-bending" party held by some highly respected military officers who were familiar with the U.S remote viewing program. Among these were Major General Albert Stubblebine, the U.S. Army Commander of INSCOM, and Major General Edmund Thompson, Deputy Director for Management and Operations, Defense Intelligence Agency (DIAO). Also present was Deputy Director of the CIA John McMahon:

"General Thompson watched as his own spoon began to curve down at the point he was holding it, down and around as if it were melting in his hands. John McMahon's spoon bent, too. By the time all the psychokinesis had stopped, the deputy director's spoon looked vaguely like a corkscrew. He went into the CIA headquarters the next day and told some of his friends and aides about it." (Schnabel, 1997)

Literally thousands of ordinary people found they could bend spoons at parties such as this. Some gifted individuals, such as aerospace engineer Dr. Jack Houck, have led hundreds of such spoon-bending parties across the country, removing any doubt from such experiencers that spoon bending is something very real. It is not due to trickery. It tells us something important about the true human potential, and it tells us that there are some things our present science cannot explain.

I have been to one such spoon-bending party, and even though I could not get my spoon to bend, I watched with envy as a ten-year-old boy next to me twisted his into a pretzel. The process was fascinating. All the spoons start out quite stiff and ordinary. Each person is given instructions on gently stroking the spoon and visualizing it getting soft. I think there were some instructions about "sending energy" down my arm into the spoon. Being the skeptical and analytical scientist, I often have trouble with this. But the ten-year old next to me must not have known it was impossible. After maybe twenty minutes in a room full of one hundred people, some people began getting excited, shouting that their spoons were getting soft and bending. Then a sort of emotional chain reaction set off, and in a few minutes more than half the people in the room got their spoons to bend.

Figure 3.4. The sterling silver sculpture is in Longleat, the home of the Marquess of Bath. The sword below the horse's tail was bent by Uri Geller and the silver spoon was bent to the breaking point without touching it, while being filmed by BBC television (Geller, 1986). *Photo courtesy of Uri Geller*

Now I was very careful to watch this process closely. Obviously, by brute strength Arnold Swartzenegger can bend a spoon, and so can I. But the spoon resists and shows a strength, a normal stiffness. But at the moment that "bending" began in the audience, the spoons became as soft as putty. My ten-year-old friend easily twisted his spoon into a corkscrew with two fingers. The normal stiffness of the metal went away.

On another occasion I watched as a friend bent a spoon for me as a souvenir. This was a heavy stainless steel spoon which I could not have bent without a lot of leverage and huffing and puffing. She was a slight fragile thing, but after a few minutes "sending it energy" she twisted it up with ease. I was inches away, trying to understand.

There was no trickery. A restaurant in Bimini is missing a soup spoon as a result, but I have a souvenir to remind me of the limitations of our present understanding.

On a website http://www.tcom.co.uk/hpnet/houck1.htm, Dr. Houck provides an in-depth description of some of the measurements he has made during his spoon-bending workshops. He offers a "graduate school" spoon-bending party for individuals who have attended a number of spoon-bending parties. He gives them two long tine dinner forks, and has them hold one in each hand at the bottom of the handle. They are not allowed to touch the fork with the other hand. Then they command the forks to bend. He finds that on the average 11% of the people experience spontaneous fork bending under these conditions. Sometimes both forks bend. Houck points out that these people are not trained magicians (Houck, 1993).

A Stanford Professor in the Materials Science Department, Dr. William Tiller, performed materials analysis on some of the spoons which Geller had bent. He analyzed the bent and broken spoons under an electron microscope, which is capable of very great magnification. He found that in the region where the bend had occurred, the metal had an appearance that was different from any material he had ever seen (Tiller, 1992).

It was suffused with many tiny regions, each about one thousandth of a millimeter in diameter, which appeared to have been the centers for some kind of local melting of the metal. It had just flowed around these tiny regions in what Tiller called "plastic flow". But there was no evidence that the rest of the metal had been heated at all. It was only in these small regions, like tiny bubbles, where the metal seemed to have melted. It was as though energy had been sent into the spot on the spoon which was to bend, but only placed there in these tiny, microscopic hot spots and nowhere else. This phenomenon is unknown in materials science. Neither Tiller nor anyone else knows how to replicate this effect. It points out that spoon-bending is a very real phenomenon and that it is based on a mechanism which is unknown to present-day science.

For those die-hard skeptics out there, we present a photograph in Figure 3.4 of a sterling silver centerpiece on display at Longleat, the home of the Marquess of Bath in England. On one occasion, which was filmed for BBC television, Geller caused a Georgian spoon to break and caused the silver sword directly below the horse's tail on the Landsdown Centerpiece to bend without touching it. This monument to Geller's ability is preserved on permanent display at the Longleat estate.

A new book on Geller by Jonathan Margolis (Margolis, 1999) sheds more light on the Geller controversy. Margolis began his research as a skeptic, but became a convert as he learned more and more about Geller. A reviewer for the Jewish Chronicle said of Margolis' book: "I came to this book a rationalist and a skeptic. Yet, open-mindedness requires me to report that Jonathan Margolis' carefully researched, scrupulously detailed and even-handed exploration of Uri Geller's paranormal capacities suggests some of our current scientific understandings will need radical revision in the next century."

Princeton PEAR Lab Experiments

The remarkable demonstrations of Ingo Swann and Uri Geller tell us that certain rare individuals have abilities which defy present-day science. But what are the laws of this strange force? And how widespread are these abilities? The most convincing, scientifically rigorous large-scale study of these questions has been conducted by the Princeton Engineering Anomalies Research Laboratory (PEAR Lab), headed by Princeton Professor Emeritus Robert Jahn and laboratory director Dr. Brenda Dunne. They have supervised many hundreds of thousands of experiments with "ordinary" people to answer these questions.

In these experiments, the subjects are often called the "operators." They are asked to attempt to affect or influence some electronic or mechanical device. The results are recorded in a computer database to measure how their abilities vary with distance from the device, time of day, time offset, and many other factors. The device being "influenced" is one which normally gives random results.

One type of device is the "random mechanical cascade" shown in Figure 3.5. It is a distant cousin of the pinball machine. A metal ball is dropped in at the top and hits an array of metal pegs as it falls downward. These cause the ball to bounce and careen in a random pattern before it lands in one of the bins at the bottom. When many such balls are dropped into the machine, they tend to distribute at the bottom in the familiar bell-shaped curve characteristic of a random process.

However, in the PEAR Lab experiment, the operator was asked to attempt to influence the falling of the balls, using PK, to cause them to land more on the right side or more on the left side. The scores and distributions of balls were added up for thousands of such experiments and compared to what the operator was trying to do. If psychokinesis does not exist, then the distribution of balls would remain random, and not be affected by what the operator was trying to achieve.

Several other devices are also used to generate random results. One is electronic and uses the random noise from an electronic diode. A second type of device uses the decay of a radioactive material, detected by a Geiger counter, as the source of random signal. All of these devices generically are called "random event generators" or REGs. Since they output random numbers, they are sometimes called "random number generators." The two terms are interchangeable.

In each case, the device generates an average number of blips or pulses per second. The actual number varies around the average in a random way. The operator is sometimes asked to attempt to make the number of pulses higher than the average. At other times he may be asked to try to make them lower than average.

The physics of each type of REG is somewhat different. The radioactive decay device is governed by the physics of the atomic nucleus. But in our present day science we are taught that the decay rate of radioactive materials is a constant value. It is not supposed to be affected by the desires or will of the human mind. Likewise, the noise from the electronic diode is based on the quantum mechanics of electrons in semiconductors. This too, should not be affected by the attention of a human operator. And of course, the mechanical collisions of a steel ball as it careens against metal pegs should not be affected by mental intention either.

The Princeton Lab has conducted hundreds of thousands of experimental trials using several dozen different operators, asking them to attempt to influence the operation of these REGs with their minds. In some cases they are asked to make the random numbers trend higher than average. In other cases they are asked to make them trend lower. In some cases, the operator can decide what he feels like he wants to do that day. But he must log his intention at that time and call it in to the lab. These are called "volitional" sessions.

One important aspect of these experiments is that the operator is not hovering over the machine. In many cases he or she is thousands of miles away. Most operators are typical Americans who have lives and homes in other parts of the country. At certain times of day, by agreement, they will turn their mental attention to the REG, which is back in the Princeton Lab, and put in a session. Over a twenty-year period, the PEAR Lab has accumulated hundreds of thousands of sessions in this way.

Another interesting twist is that the operator may be asked to affect the machine not in the PRESENT, but at some time in the PAST or in the FUTURE. In other words, hypothetical operator John Doe, operator #200 let's say, may receive a call from the PEAR Lab asking him to do a session at 10:00 am this morning. They may ask him to affect the REG results for the hour around noon of the PREVIOUS DAY. They may ask him to go high, to make the numbers larger than average.

So at 10:00 AM John Doe spends a session focusing on making the numbers around noon of the <u>previous</u> day larger than average. This is what he is trying to do. He is not told what his results are. But the PEAR Lab computer tallies his results against his intention and logs these results in their database.

Of course the whole idea of using intention to affect a radioactive random process, or electronic noise, or the random falling of a metal ball, flies in the face of all known physics. And the idea of doing it two thousand miles away is even more of an insult to current physics. But to top it all off, the PEAR Lab often asks the operator today to make YESTERDAY's results different.

And worst of all, for those who want to maintain the present scientific paradigm, they are getting positive results. They are finding that, even under these strange and unlikely circumstances, mental intention does affect the random process.

Figure 3.5. (from Jahn, 1987) Mechanical random event generator used by PEAR Lab. *Photo courtesy of Dr. Robert Jahn, Princeton PEAR Lab.*

Figure 3.6 below summarizes the results for all of their PK experiments over a 12 year period (Jahn, 1987; Dunne, 1995). It represents more than 800,000 trials, each trial consisting of 200 separate pulses, the equivalent of 200 binary pulses from the REG, which is like 200 coin flips. Each coin flip is a "bit", having a value of either +1 or –1.

The graph is based on the idea of a "random walk". Suppose you flip a penny many times, and each time it comes up heads you move up vertically one space on the graph, and each time it comes us tails you move down one space. Now, on the average, over any given number of flips, if there are more heads than tails you will move up vertically. Likewise, if there are more tails, you will move downward. On the average you would expect the heads and tails to be in balance, so the net position would be near the middle of the graph, the zero position or the "base line". The vertical position shows the net difference between heads and tails on the REG.

Three sets of data are shown on the graph. The top set of points corresponds to the cases when the operator was trying to get heads, that is make the REG "go high" by making more pluses than minuses. This line is marked "PK+" in the graph. Since it is rising with increasing number of trials, it is apparently working.

The lower curve corresponds to the trials when the operator was told to make the REG "go low." It is marked "PK". Apparently this works too. As the number of trials increases, the total value of these runs has more minuses than pluses. That is why it is trending downward, going negative. The middle line is the "baseline," when the operator was not trying to influence the device. We see that this curve does indeed hover near zero.

Because of the random nature of the pluses and minuses, all three curves are expected to wander away from the centerline from time to time. One must look at how far these lines wander from the central baseline (labeled BL in the figure), and compare it to how far they would wander due to purely random variations. It is this important statistical analysis which determines if the results are scientifically significant. Can they be explained by random chance, or do they reveal the presence of a systematic force affecting the results?

The smooth curved lines in the graph, labeled "0.05", correspond to 5% probability. Data on these lines have a 5% chance of being due to random variations. This means roughly that when the data is on this line, the odds are 20 to 1 that they are significant, i.e. due to a real, physical phenomenon.

The graph shows that, when the operators were trying to make the results come out high, on the average they did. At the end of all the runs, the total score for the high runs has less than 0.0004 probability of being due to chance, or 4 parts in 10,000. When the operator was trying to make the random event generator go positive, it did indeed go positive, on the average. There was a real effect.

Likewise, the lower data curve corresponds to the times when the operator wanted the REG to go negative. The total of these scores does indeed trend in the negative direction. For the final total of over 800,000 trials, each one involving 200 bits of data, this curve continues to go negative. There is less than 1% probability that this result is due to chance. Combining the two, the overall probability that these results can be explained by chance is <u>less than 8 in a million</u>. In other words, PK is real.

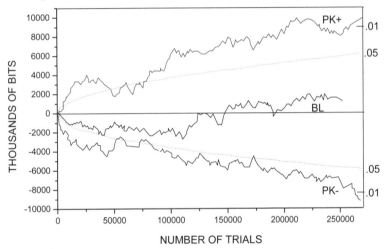

Figure 3.6. Total cumulative data for all PEAR Lab PK experiments, for 33 operators over 7 years on two different machines. The probability of the overall result occurring due to chance is 1 part in 5,000. (from Jahn, 1987b) *Courtesy of Dr. Robert Jahn*

We note that, based on the graph, the overall effects are weak. The total number of bits deviation between the high and the low curves is a little more than 30,000 out of a total of 160 million. Yet the PEAR lab, by running the experiment many times with different operators and conditions, has established that a very real effect is present. It is reasonable to conclude that psychokinesis, PK, the ability to affect and move objects at a distance without the use of known physical forces, has been proven.

Very little has been done to optimize these results. The operators were chosen at random, or self-selected, and did not have reputations as psychics. No effort was made to optimize the time of day, the weather conditions, or any other effects which are known to affect psychic phenomenon. Therefore, these results provide a <u>lower bound</u> to what might be expected. The important conclusion is that the data prove that PK is real. That is an important beginning.

As we have seen earlier, some people are more proficient than others at psychokinesis. Let's look at the charts of several people who are quite talented. The first data set, from PEAR Operator #10, is shown in Figure 3.7. In 120,000 trials, the high and the low curves are more cleanly separated than for the group as a whole. The probability that the "high" curve is due to chance is 0.000002, and for the "low" curve, the probability that it is due to chance is 0.0005. The combined probability that both these curves are caused by chance is <u>ONE PART IN A BILLION</u>. We may say that, for operator 10, there is no question that PK is real and he/she is able to manifest it.

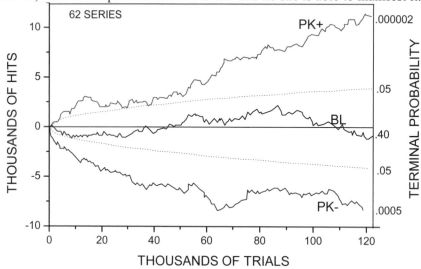

Figure 3.7. PK results for PEAR Lab Operator #10 (Dunne, 1995). *Courtesy of Drs. Robert Jahn and Brenda Dunne.*

Figure 3.8 is a similar chart showing data taken by different researchers during one of the pioneering experiments in this form of PK research. It was conducted by Dr. Helmut Schmidt (Schmidt, 1971). It shows the results from two operators, KG and RR. KG was described as an extroverted woman. She was consistently successful at getting the REG to move in the direction she wanted it to move. Her data are shown as the upper curve in the figure.

The operators were asked to attempt to influence the apparent movement of a circle of blinking lights which were controlled by the output of a random event generator (REG). By affecting whether the output of the device went "high" (more ones than zeros) or "low," they could alter the behavior of the lights.

Operator RR was described as introverted and quiet, but gifted at energy healing. His data are plotted in the lower graph in the figure. When he looked at the lights and tried to control the direction of their apparent motion, they consistently moved in the <u>opposite</u> direction. A "trial" consisted of staring at the circle and trying to control the movement of the lights as they changed direction 128 times.

KG managed to make the lights move in the direction she wanted, an average of 52.5 percent of the time in 6,400 trials. RR consistently made the lights move in the opposite direction 52.25 percent of the time. The odds of obtaining these results by chance alone, due to random variations of the random event generator, is more that 10 million to one. Experiments such as this have been conducted by numerous experimenters. The results consistently confirm that humans, by using the power of their minds, are able to influence the output of a random event generator. There is, without question, a phenomenon here, a "force", which modern science does not understand.

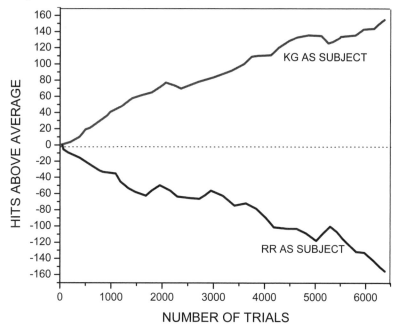

Figure 3.8 REG results for two gifted subjects, one making the numbers "go high" (KG) and the other making the numbers "go low" (RR). The odds of such results occurring by pure chance are 10 million to one. (Schmidt, 1971)

.

In another experiment using a different kind of random event generator, these results were further substantiated. In one case, the random numbers were generated at the rate of 30 per second, and the subjects were able to influence the outcome with odds of 7 billion to one. That means the odds are <u>SEVEN BILLION TO ONE</u> against explaining these results by chance alone. Such huge odds are just the statistician's way of saying there is a real effect here. The human operators did indeed affect the device, and there is a real phenomenon which defies known physics.

The dependence of PK on distance and time offset is shown in the following two graphs, Figures 3.9 and 3.10. These graphs are derived from the PEAR Lab PK data (Dunne, 1992). They are based on all the Princeton data collected up to that time on humans interacting psychically with machines. These were experiments in which volunteers attempted to influence REGs some distance away. The distance varied from less than a mile up to 9,000 miles. In many cases they attempted to affect the device in the past or in the future. The devices being influenced were of various designs. Some were based on the "random event cascade" (the pinball machine of Figure 3.5 above.) Some were electronic REGs. Other devices were also used.

The first graph shows how the PK scores vary with distance, up to 6,000 miles. Although the data are noisy, there is a definite effect. The average of all the events shows that the operators were successful at affecting the behavior of the machines using their mental intention. But the trend does not weaken with distance. The data definitively ruled out any inverse distance squared dependence (or any faster decay), which is the rule by which electricity and magnetism and gravity weaken with distance. The known nuclear forces weaken even faster with distance and are ruled out as well. The force responsible for this psychic influence does not appear to weaken with distance and is therefore different from the other forces known to science.

The second graph, Figure 3.10, shows the PK scores versus time-offset between the operator session and the measurement. These occurred when the operator attempted to influence the machine in the past or in the future. Again, to within the accuracy of the data, the PK scores are positive and have the same magnitude for all time offsets. Therefore the PK effect seems to be independent of time offset.

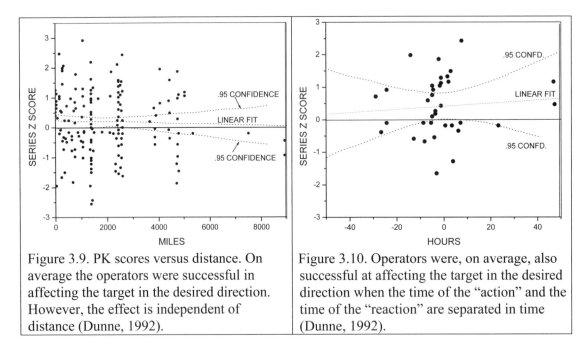

Figure 3.9. PK scores versus distance. On average the operators were successful in affecting the target in the desired direction. However, the effect is independent of distance (Dunne, 1992).

Figure 3.10. Operators were, on average, also successful at affecting the target in the desired direction when the time of the "action" and the time of the "reaction" are separated in time (Dunne, 1992).

Using the language of statistics, Drs. Dunne and Jahn concluded:

> *"The only significant term in a standard regression analysis is a constant displacement from chance value, which lies well within the 95% confidence intervals for the linear slope. In other words, none of the higher order terms statistically support attenuation of the effect with increasing distance…The high-intention off-time data can be similarly arrayed as a function of the time difference between machine operation and operator effort. The positive numbers on the x-axis indicate efforts up to 73 hours prior to machine operation, and the negative numbers efforts up to 336 hours after the schedules sessions. Again there is no significant correlation between time of effort and size of effect, over the range studied." (Dunne, 1992)*

These results, together with the other powerful results above, establish once and for all that PK, or psychokinetic ability, is completely real. It has some very unusual characteristics, since it seems to be independent of spatial distance and time offset. Now it is up to our science to try to understand this new and strange force.

Psychokinesis in Baby Chickens

As the Princeton PEAR Lab experiments show, random event generators (REGs) can be affected by mental intention, or PK. One fascinating application of this was developed by a French researcher, Dr. Rene Peoc'h. He built a small, moving robot which moves and turns based on the output of an REG (Peoc'h, 1988, 1995). Then he introduced this little robot to hatching chicks and goslings. When baby birds are first hatched, if their mother is not present, they tend to bond to whatever or whomever is present (Lorenz, 1978). In this case, Peoc'h arranged that the first moving object they saw was his little mobile robot. Consequently, the chicks formed a bond with it.

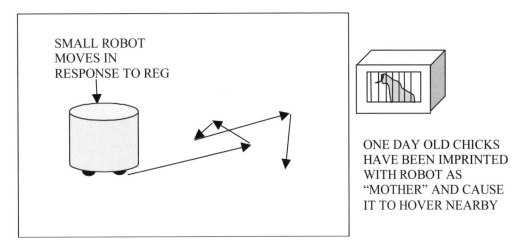

Figure 3.11. Psychokinesis demonstrated by baby chicks (Peoc'h, 1988, 1995).

In the experiments shown below, in Figure 3.12, the movement of the robot within a small rectangular room is tracked (view from above). The zig-zagged lines show the movement of the robot around the room. The small cage on the right in the figure shows the location of the baby chicks, who could see the robot. In the top figure, labeled A, there are no chicks in the cage. As can be seen, the robot simply wanders randomly around the rectangular room. This is the expected behavior of the robot.

In the lower diagram in Figure 3.12, the experiment is repeated, but this time baby chicks are placed in the cage. These chicks are only one-day old and have formed a maternal bond with the robot. They think the robot is their mother. Astonishingly, the robot no longer moves randomly. It hovers near the cage where the baby chicks are!

Such behavior should be impossible based on what we know about modern science. The random event generator on board the robot is apparently no longer producing random numbers, but rather numbers which cause the robot to stay near the chicks! The most reasonable explanation is that the chicks are influencing the random event generator via psychokinesis, to cause the robotic "mother" to stay nearby. This is a dramatic demonstration of the powers of the mind, and a confirmation that psychokinetic ability is not limited to humans. Quite the contrary, it may be that animals are far better at it than we are (Peoc'h, 1988a, b, c; Sheldrake, 1999).

Nina Kulagina

As Uri Geller was famous for PK in America at one time, so was Nina Kulagina in the former Soviet Union. She was discovered by Soviet scientists in the 1960's during her stay in a hospital where she was being treated for exhaustion. She spent a lot of time sewing. The doctors noticed that she could pick any color thread she wanted out of her sewing basket without looking at it. This is a form of eyeless sight or touch color perception which has received much research in Russia and China.

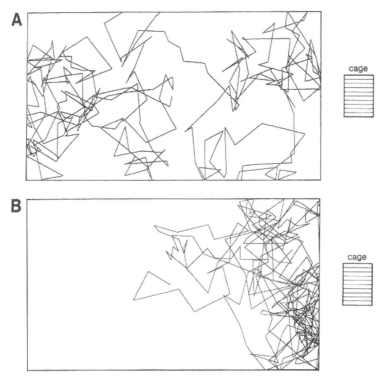

Figure 3.12. Psychokinesis experiments conducted by Rene Peoc'h on young chicks interacting with a robot controlled by random event generator (Peoc'h, 1988, 1995). Figure A shows behavior of the robot when the cage was empty. Figure B shows the motion of the robot when one-day-old chicks which have been bonded with the robot are present in the cage (Sheldrake, 1999). *Courtesy of Dr. Rene Peoc'h.*

The doctors notified local scientists, who began testing her. They found she had extraordinary healing powers. She was often able to diagnose illness with only a glance at the patient. Holding her hands over a wound was found to speed up healing enormously. But she became most famous for her ability to move objects with her mind, without touching them.

Numerous photographs and newspaper articles from the time, as well as a movie made in 1978, document her feats. Dr. Gennady Sergeyev, one of the scientists studying Kulagina, found that enormous energy was emitted from her head during these experiments (Sergeyev, 1972a-d). He found that she was able to project energy onto photographic film, causing it to develop as if it had been exposed to light or some form of radiation.

Dr. Sergeyev summarized: "In experiments in Leningrad, we placed underdeveloped photo film in a black envelope. By looking at the envelope, she was capable of exposing the film inside!" There were several irregularly shaped white dots all over the photographs. "She never touched the envelope, just looked at it." In other experiments, Dr. Sergeyev found that Kulagina was able to create simple patterns such as crosses on the film by staring at it while she moved her eyes in the desired pattern. This ability to project energy which exposes photographic film in certain patterns is reminiscent of the "thought photography" of Ted Serios, discussed later in this Chapter (Ostrander, 1970, 1974, 1976; LaMothe, 1972).

During a PK experiment, while Kulagina was concentrating on moving a ping-pong ball remotely, Sergeyev held up unexposed film near her head. He found that the brightest exposures occurred on film held near the back of her head. This even occurred when he used multiple layers of film, each sealed in black, light-tight envelopes. It demonstrated that some unknown form of energy was being generated during these experiments. Sergeyev stated that, in these experiments Kulagina had succeeded on occasion in moving objects as heavy as one pound (Gris, 1978).

Figure 3.13 Nina Kulagina (known to the Russian public by a pseudonym, Nelya Mikhailova, to protect her privacy at the time) demonstrated psychokinesis in numerous laboratory tests in Russia. (Sketch by H. Shapero)

Kulagina's abilities were studied and verified by some of the most famous scientists in the Soviet Union, including the Chairman of Theoretical Physics at Moscow University and holder of the Laureate of the State Prize, Dr. Ya. Terletsky, and Academician and Hero of Socialist Labor, Professor A. Mikhulin. Both of these men made public acknowledgments of the reality and importance of her abilities.

Experiments with her included careful searches for hidden magnets and any other tricks and often involved tests in which she moved objects protected under bell-jars and out of reach, in specially instrumented rooms. The objects which moved were often non-magnetic, gold, paper, wood, plastic, etc. It would have been impossible for her to move such objects with magnets or any known tricks.

She was often asked to change position during the experiments, and the target objects were often supplied by the experimenters themselves, which included some of the most eminent scientists in Russia. Many of the experiments were done in specially designed laboratories which measured her physiological functions, brain waves and other electrical activity while she worked. It was found that when the phenomenon occurred, her body generated unusual electrical pulses which were actually stronger some distance away from her body, which makes them very unusual.

On occasion she moved a single match stick in a line of match sticks, and on one occasion caused the smoke in a bowl to be split down the middle, so a gap persisted in the smoke hovering in the bowl. These are not experiments which can be accomplished by "cheating" while being physiologically monitored and filmed under close observation by scientists (Rejdak, 1968; Kolodny, 1968; Kurz, 1968; Sergeyev, 1967, 1968).

There was a brief time, in 1968, when the Soviet leaders allowed Western scientists and journalists to have relatively free access to the Russian and Czech scientists working on psychic phenomena, including those studying Kulagina. This was the time during which Western journalists Ostrander and Schroeder conducted candid interviews with many Iron Curtain scientists, and compiled their monumental book, *Psychic Discoveries Behind the Iron Curtain*. It was known as the "Prague Spring," and represented a short-lived thaw in the Cold War as Russia's new leaders, Breznev and Kosygin, established their new regime.

However, it was quickly followed by harsh repression. Movements toward freedom in Czechoslavakia were suppressed by Soviet tanks. By the early nineteen seventies, free exchange of information on psychic phenomena was punished by imprisonment. A Soviet propaganda campaign began to disparage all psychic abilities, and even Kulagina was imprisoned for a short time. A Soviet propagandist, Vladimir Lvov, began claiming that Kulagina performed her feats by using hidden magnets, and similar rumors were spread in the West by Dr. Milan Ryzl, a defecting Russian scientist who had never worked with Kulagina (Ostrander, 1970). Thus, despite the wealth of scientific papers that were published on her abilities in the nineteen sixties by eminent scientists, in the West today there is still controversy about her abilities in some circles.

In summarizing experiments on Kulagina, a Defense Intelligence Agency Report (Maire, 1975) noted that she could cause objects to move toward her or away from her, and she caused no change in the shape of soft objects. Her optimum range for controlling objects was about 1.5 feet, and her maximum range a little over 3 feet. An electrical field was detected in the vicinity of the object she was trying to move, but very significantly, NO FIELD was measured in the intervening space between her and the object. Also significant is the fact that she could not move objects in a vacuum. However, electrostatic screening did not stop this force. On the other hand, during thunderstorms she was unable to manifest these forces.

It is particularly significant that electrostatic screening did not stop the force, but a vacuum did. This suggests that the medium of the force somehow involves matter, but neither electrons nor photons. Her ability to cause a high electric field at the object, up to 10,000 volts per centimeter (Ullman, 1973), but not in the intervening space makes this force very different from static electricity. It appears more likely that the observed charge on the target object was a consequence of some other kind of force or particle emitted by Kulagina. The descriptions do not correspond to any known physical force or phenomenon.

The synchronization of the various fields and biological systems of the body may be a key to understanding PK. In the last twenty years there have been breakthroughs in biology, primarily in Germany, which focus on the synchronized electrical activity which occurs in living systems. Eminent scientists such as Dr. Herbert Frohlich (Frohlich, 1983) and Dr. E. A. Popp of the Max Planck Institute (e.g. Kroy, 1989; Popp, 1979; Popp, 1989) have shown that coherent, synchronized, time-varying electromagnetic signals play a key role in many biological processes. This may help explain how Kulagina and other PK mediums are able to generate synchronized forms of radiation, and large voltages, during PK.

Electrical Measurements During PK

In order to better understand psychokinesis, Dr. Elmer Green of the Menninger Clinic constructed a laboratory in which talented PK subjects were electrically isolated from the walls and floor. The lab, sketched in Figure 3.14 below, was instrumented so any emissions of electrical charge or voltage would be trapped by metal plates and measured (Green, 1993).

Green was curious about the mechanism that is involved in PK. Does it consist of charges of electricity or some other form of energy? And how much voltage or charge can be produced during PK events? At the very least, these experiments disprove the claims of skeptics that it is all slight of hand. Green found that people capable of PK are able to generate very large voltages in their body, and to project beams of "charge" several feet away.

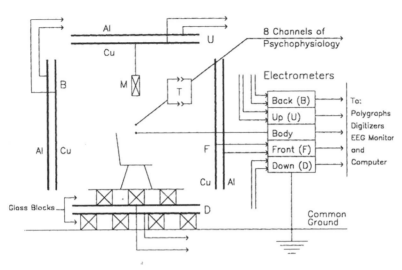

Figure 3.14. Laboratory for observing psychokinetic (PK) activity (Green, 1993; Tiller, 1997). *Courtesy of Dr. William Tiller.*

The subjects chosen for study came from a group of people who were either "energy healers" or Qigong masters, and therefore were believed to have an ability to "project" energy. In previous measurements, an electrode attached to the earlobe of such subjects revealed anomalously high voltages when they were attempting to project energy. Instead of 0.010 volts to 0.015 volts, which would be the typical range for normal adults, the earlobe voltage was measured as high as 30 volts up to 300 volts. This is 10,000 times higher than the normal value (Green, 1993).

As can be seen in Figure3.14 above, a special chamber was constructed to measure the voltage both at the healer and on the walls of the chamber. The healer, or PK subject, sat in the chair inside the chamber. The chair rested on an insulated platform surrounded by metallic, conducting walls on all sides. Sensitive electrometers outside the chamber measured the buildup of electric charge on each wall and the ceiling. The body of the PK subject was also instrumented to measure body voltage and other parameters.

Figure 3.15 below shows typical voltage measurements for such a test (Green, 1993; Tiller, 1997). In a single 30 minute healing session, a healer produced 15 large voltage pulses, each greater than 30 volts in magnitude. The vertical voltage scale on the right applies to the voltage on the body of the healer. The scale on the left applies to the voltage generated at the walls. Therefore we see voltage pulses at the healer of 30 to 50 volts, and voltage changes at the wall of a fraction of a volt. Vb is the voltage at the healer, measured from an electrode attached to his body. The lines labeled VU, VB, VD, and VF measure the voltages on the four walls.

Measurements revealed that the majority of the pulses, 13 out of 15, originated at the second chakra of the subject. This is called the "dan tien," in the vicinity of the navel. This is the location where Qigong masters are taught to build up and store their "energy" before they project it. The voltage pulses defy conventional explanations, but they are remarkably consistent with the explanations given by Oriental Qigong masters and oriental healers. It was postulated that these large voltage changes are due to "subtle energy." This work is discussed further in Volume II of this series.

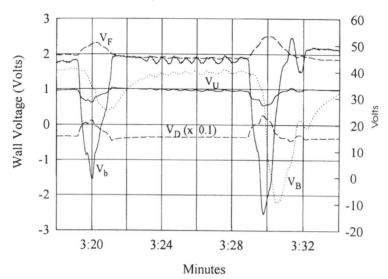

Figure 3.15. Voltage pulses created by a healer, measured at the body, and measured response voltage at the walls of the instrumented chamber (Green, 1993). VF is the voltage of the front plate, VU the upper plate, VB the back plate, VD the bottom plate, and V_b the voltage at the healer. *Courtesy of Dr. Elmer Green.*

Thought Photography

Another form of psychokinesis which is very unusual is called "thought photography" or thought projection. It is the rare ability to project an image from one's mind directly onto a photographic film. The American Ted Serios became famous for his ability to do this. He was investigated thoroughly over several years by Jule Eisenbud, M.D. The feats accomplished by Serios are described in detail in Eisenbud's book *The World of Ted Serios* (Eisenbud, 1967) and in journal articles (Eisenbud, 1981). As Eisenbud relates in his description of the experiments, Serios' ability was of the sort that made you a believer if you were there, but if you were not there and only heard about it second hand, few would believe.

In a typical Serios session, various experimenters would bring their own cameras, loaded with their own film. In turn, each would hold his camera up and allow Serios to stare into it. Polaroid Land cameras were preferred because the film could be developed on the spot, to reduce tampering and the possibility of fraud.

Serios would usually hold a small plastic cylinder, which he called his "gizmo" up in front of the lens. This simple device had a blackened film of plastic attached to one end to block light out of the camera, and the other end was covered with clear plastic. This simple device never failed to arouse suspicion, and was examined closely by scientists on several occasions. It was adjudged to be exactly what it appeared to be, a cover for the lens and a crutch that gave Serios confidence.

From two feet away he would stare into the camera. His blood pressure and pulse would rise, his veins would bulge, and he would attempt to make an image appear on the film when the camera shutter was snapped. Usually one of the investigating scientists would request a particular subject or image, and Serios tried to comply. As Eisenbud relates in his book, the success was far from perfect. Many photographs came out black. Many others were not of the precise subject requested. However, there was often a relationship between the requested image and the one obtained. On one occasion a photograph of the Declaration of Independence was requested, but Serios produced a picture of three Revolutionary War soldiers. Even when the correct subject appeared on the film it was often blurry, but recognizable.

Eisenbud wondered why Serios' ability had not received publicity, since he had been demonstrating this capability for ten years. A professor at a local university who had witnessed some of Serios' earlier deeds was contacted. He was asked why he had not pursued research into the mechanism of this unusual ability. The professor replied that when Serios was asked to produce a photograph of a particular building, he had generated on the film an image of the <u>wrong</u> building. So he was of no use to them. Eisenbud likens this to the proverbial story of the talking horse. People are told to pay it no attention because the horse is a proverbial liar!

Typical success rates, based on Eisenbud's descriptions, appear to be between one in three and one in ten photographs which showed some sort of psychic photographic effect. This is a high success rate for a psychic experiment. Eisenbud arranged for dozens of expert scientific observers to take part in the tests on various occasions, and to sign affidavits verifying what they had witnessed. He conducted experiments with Serios in a shielded nuclear facility and a magnetically shielded industrial lab, where Serios could be monitored for the emission of various types of radiation.

Serios projected his thought photographs through multiple sheets of lead glass, which would stop X-rays, and generated thought photographs while in an electromagnetically shielded Faraday cage. In some cases <u>Serios was as far as 66 feet away from the film which received the image</u>. A light meter placed between Serios and the camera registered no light emission from Serios. It was concluded that, whatever type of energy Serios used to produce the photographs, it could not be measured using conventional electromagnetic means.

One clue to the physical mechanism was noted by Dr. Eisenbud, who carried out most of the research on Serios. He noted that images could be produced through strong magnetic fields (greater than 1200 gauss), but never through a rubber lens cap. Also, in an occasional photograph, something suggestive of light rays can be seen proceeding from Serios' eyes.

The significance of the rubber lens cap will be seen later, in Volume II on subtle energy. A scientist in Russia, Dr. Nikolai Kozyrev, has isolated a new form of energy which may be the key to psychokinetic effects. It may be the long sought-after "chi" or "prana" of Eastern traditions. He discovered that it can propagate like light, and reflects off mirrors. But certain kinds of plastic and rubber, even thin sheets, can stop it. This is related to the twist direction of the molecules in the material.

The famous physicist Leo Szilard, who worked on the Manhattan atomic bomb project, participated in some of the experiments with Serios. He suggested that the camera be used without a lens. Numerous successful photographs were generated in this configuration. Since the camera lens was apparently superfluous, we must conclude that the energy creating these pictures does not follow the normal laws of optics.

An example of the photographs produced by Serios is shown in Figure 3.16, below. As in many of the photographs, the angle of the image could not be controlled. The requested target was a "medieval town." In this case, Serios seems to have been fairly successful at generating the requested image.

In Volume II we will present evidence that 'subtle energy' and other paranormal phenomena sometimes have the effect of bending light, even to extreme angles. This defies contemporary science, and yet there is independent evidence from several researchers which indicates this can occur. We have found, for example, that in the presence of a haunted house, displaced and distorted images often occur.

Numerous photographs are known in which the images of windows, lamps, red LED lights, and other objects are displaced over many feet, and even around corners. In one case a red LED light which was on in a adjacent room is seen to appear as it moves or displaces its image across the photograph. In other photos, the images of lighted windows smear and displace over distances exceeding thirty feet.

Figure 3.16. This image was projected onto film by Ted Serios (Eisenbud, 1967) when the target was a "medieval town." The Roman archway and stone construction seem completely consistent with this. Note the odd angular placement of the image.

Dr. William Tiller of Stanford has demonstrated that paranormal forces can cause distortions and double images in photographs (Tiller, 1973, 1997). This seems to confirm the hypothesis that paranormal phenomena are able to displace images over a distance.

Therefore the question arises, could Ted Serios be making use of a similar phenomenon when he produces his images on film? Instead of creating an image purely from his mind, might he be causing an image from elsewhere to be displaced and projected through the camera lens upon the film? In some cases, Serios produced images which were very similar to those in magazines and photographs. This strengthens this hypothesis. Possible mechanisms will be discussed more in later volumes.

The "P-K Man"

Another individual with seemingly remarkable powers has been described by respected parapsychologist Dr. Jeffrey Mishlove. Mishlove used to host the PBS television program *Thinking Allowed* in which leading thinkers in various fields were interviewed. In the mid-1970's, Mishlove was a graduate student in California studying parapsychology. He knew Drs. Hal Puthoff and Russell Targ, who began the Remote Viewing program at SRI discussed in Chapter 1. Through them he became acquainted with a remarkable individual named Ted Owens.

Owens claimed to be able to affect the weather on a large and dramatic scale. He claimed to be able to cause lightning to strike where and when he wanted it to. He also maintained he was in contact with extraterrestrials who gave him his powers. He had all the earmarks of a kook, so outlandish were his claims. Except that, as Mishlove began investigating him with the encouragement of Targ and Puthoff, he found that Owens was able to deliver on his promises and prove many of his predictions!

This is an uncomfortable subject for parapsychologists. They have become used to thinking of paranormal effects as "small". They conduct experiments in flipping coins, for example. This may involve flipping the coins thousands or millions of times, as in the PEAR Lab experiments. They often do this electronically with REGs instead of real coins. If the behavior of the flips departs from chance by a small amount, this is considered a great success.

But in the case of Owens, he claimed to be able to stop a drought, to make it snow out of season on command, and to control lightning strikes. In Mishlove's fascinating book *P-K Man* (Mishlove, 2000), he documents Owens' demonstrations, including controlled experiments which Mishlove conducted with him. He describes the instructions, the claims, and the results which followed.

The figure below documents just one example from Mishlove's book. It is an affidavit from an attorney, Sidney Margulies, who was watching a rainstorm with Ted Owens on the night of May 10, 1967. He pointed to a specific spot of his own choosing, and asked Owens to cause lightning to strike there. And, a few moments later, it did. In Mishlove's book he also documents the ending of a California drought by a freak snowstorm, exactly as predicted by Owens. Numerous other feats were also described which suggest that psychokinesis may potentially be a more powerful and far-reaching force than is currently understood even among parapsychologists.

I certify this to be a true and correct statement:

On the night of May 8, 1967, while watching a rainstorm in the company of H. Owens (Ted) from the top of a tall building in downtown Philadelphia...Mr. Owens offered to make lightning strike in any area that I might point out, as a demonstration of a new weather principle he had discovered. So I took him up on it, and pointed to an area squarely in front of our window...the bridge leading to Camden.
In a few moments after Mr. Owens concentrated on making lightning strike the aforementioned bridge...a lightning bolt did in fact strike that area, just to the right of the bridge.
Since we were standing at the top of a tall building, our field of view was very wide and expansive. Therefore the lighting bolt striking the pinpointed area which I had designated, was interesting.

SIDNEY MARGULIES, ESQ.
May 10, 1967

Figure 3.17. Affidavit by an attorney, Sidney Margulies, who witnessed Ted Owens produce "macro-PK" events. He pointed out a spot where he wanted lightning to strike, and Owens was able to make it strike there within a few seconds. *Courtesy of Dr. Jeffrey Mishlove.*

The Fire Walk

I remember the night of my firewalk. It was the first night of one of Tony Robbins' "Unlimited Power Weekends." I wondered why he wanted the firewalk on the first night. I wanted three nights to prepare for it. In fact, I wanted to put it off as long as possible. I had researched the phenomenon and knew that my mental state had a lot to do with avoiding injury.

But I also knew that, as a scientist, I had difficulty maintaining an altered state, and that my intellectual curiosity might awaken midway across the fire pit. The worst thing you can do, I was told, is to try to feel the fire, because if you do, you will surely be burned.

Robbins' uses Neuro-Linguistic Programming (NLP) to create a series of very high energy, positive "anchors" which help one to obtain the right mental state during a firewalk. When the time came to walk the coals, I stepped up to the beginning of the pit. Robbins evaluated me and said "More energy!" So I visualized every positive thing I could think of and just got myself more excited. This was repeated two or three more times until I was vibrating with a sense of ecstatic energy.

Figure 3.18. Firewalk participant crosses the flames, *courtesy of Ilmar Saar* , http://www.mastery.net/ firewalk/ gallery.htm,.

Then he said "GO!" and tapped me on the left shoulder, which supposedly released the NLP anchor. I strode resolutely across the twelve foot long firepit, saying in my mind "cool moss, cool moss." The embers did feel soft because they had burned down some. And the words helped convince me they were cool, not hot.

Experiments have shown that these embers range between 600 degrees and 2,000 degrees Fahrenheit, so they really are hot. But I was amazed as I strode across the pit that to my feet, they didn't feel hot. I believe this was due to the preparation. But my scientific, conscious mind was noticing this as I walked, so I started to wonder, "Are the coals really hot?" So in the last two steps I dug my feet down into the coal bed several inches. I could see numerous red hot embers flying through the air when I did this.

Of course I had been taught never to try to feel the coals. And I really didn't want to feel them. But I did want to know if they were hot. My feet felt almost anesthetized as they dug into the red hot coals.

As I stepped off the coal bed I realized that my feet felt funny. They felt a little numb and tingly on the bottom. I wondered if I had burned them with my little stunt. Within an hour, one small blister appeared on the bottom of one foot. By the next day it was gone.

The real question is "How hot is the firepit?" and can the firewalk be explained by conventional physics? Can a thin layer of ash on the coals, or normal moisture on the bottom of the feet, explain the phenomenon? Jack Houck, an aerospace engineer who has conducted a great deal of research into the paranormal, was allowed to make measurements at some of Tony Robbins' firewalks (Houck, 1993, 1986). He took infrared photographs of the firewalkers and made temperature measurements of the red hot coal bed.

He built an apparatus which he attached to one foot of some of the firewalkers. It held one and five mil (thousandth of an inch) thick thermocouples. These were connected by cable to a computer, which recorded the temperature 75 times per second. When the thermocouple was at least 2 millimeters from the bottom of the foot, he found temperatures exceeded 1400 degrees Fahrenheit on the first step onto the coals. The subsequent steps recorded somewhat lower temperatures of 600-800 degrees Fahrenheit. This demonstrates that the coals were plenty hot to damage the feet almost instantly. However, the thermocouple right on the bottom of the foot amazingly showed no temperature rise.

The temperature should be highest when in direct contact with the coals, so the thermocouple on the bottom of the foot should have shown the highest temperature. But instead it seemed to be protected from the heat. Whatever the nature of the "force field" or influence at the bottom of the foot which protects it during the firewalk must also protect this bottom thermocouple. Could it just be a thin layer of ash, combined with the short contact time of the feet, which enables the firewalker to emerge unharmed? For the amateur firewalker such as me, it is hard to be sure. But there are extreme cases which are very difficult to explain by conventional science.

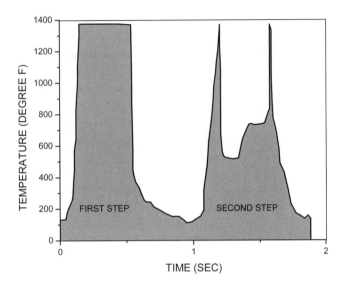

Figure 3.19 Temperature measured by thermocouple near bottom of foot during firewalk (Houck, 1986, 1988). *Courtesy of Dr. Jack Houck.*

Douchan Gersi (Gersi, 1991) describes watching firewalkers in many places, including Sri Lanka, Africa, Asia and islands in the Indian Ocean, lie down on live coals without getting burned and without having their clothes catch on fire. He became convinced after investigating that there was no trickery involved.

The famous medium D. D. Home demonstrated an even more extreme version of invulnerability to fire. He was observed closely by the eminent scientist Sir William Crookes who described the following feat:

"Home removed from the grate a red-hot piece nearly as big as an orange, and putting it on his right hand, covered it with his left hand so as to almost completely enclose it, and then blew...until the lump of charcoal was nearly white-hot, and then drew my attention to the lambent flame which was flickering over the coal and licking round his fingers..." (Picknett, 1987)

A similar ability was demonstrated in the 1970's by the medium Jack Schwartz, who has been the subject of extensive scientific experiments (Green, 1977). With many witnesses at a scientific meeting:

"He put his two hands into a brazier of burning coals held by two medical students with asbestos gloves, picked up a double handful of fire, and carried it around, showing the coals to the doctors; then he put the coals on a newspaper, which burst into flames. Dr. Fantl said that Jack's hands appeared afterward to be normal, not even hot, and with no indication of having been subjected to high temperature." (Green, 1977)

Colin Wilson (Wilson, 1975) describes scientific experiments with firewalkers conducted as early as 1935. A young Indian yogi named Kuda Bux was tested by a group of scientists from the University of London Council for Psychical Investigation. He walked barefoot in an 11-foot-long trench filled with red-hot embers measured at 806 degrees surface temperature. His feet were examined before and after the firewalk, and there was no sign of injury.

An untrained Englishman attempted to duplicate the walk and received very serious blisters on his feet. These experiments confirm the findings of Houck and others that the state of mind does, in some way, prevent the damage to the feet that would otherwise be inevitable. The conventional law of heat transfer would suggest that the tissue of the feet would be unavoidably damaged. Yet this does not happen when the firewalker performs the firewalk in the correct state of mind. Experiences like this suggest that the human mind is capable of influencing matter and forces in ways that Western science is just beginning to take seriously.

Summary

We have seen in this chapter that human beings are able, with their minds, to affect mechanical and electrical systems at a distance. They are able to move objects without touching them. They are able to alter electrical circuits in a desired way, causing real, measurable effects. They are able to alter the output of random event generators to make them go higher or lower than average. This has been done at will, and even from thousands of miles away. This has been demonstrated in millions of scientific trials conducted by many researchers. And the influence of consciousness can affect the past, present, or future as desired.

The experiments of Peo'ch with the baby chicks show that this ability is not confined to humans. When we combine these results with the ESP experiments of Sheldrake, we see that animals, too, have psychic abilities. This means of communication is shared by our feathered and furry friends, which is perhaps why we like having them as companions. This should lead us to greater respect and sensitivity for the lives of other species.

Other physical phenomena, such as heat, also can be controlled, as the firewalk shows. The strength of metals has been altered by literally thousands of people who have attended "spoon bending" parties and workshops. The pioneering work of Uri Geller, who first showed this was possible, has been vindicated and validated by the many "ordinary" people who have learned how to do it. They have countered the criticism and ridicule of the skeptics by showing that these abilities are widespread. In addition to this, magnetic fields, chemical processes, and even the growth of plants, have been affected and altered in scientifically controlled studies.

How can science explain these phenomena? One clue is found among the simplest organisms on the planet. Cleve Backster is an expert at operating the polygraph, also known as the "lie-detector." One day he connected it to a house plant. To his shock and amazement, he found that the house plant reacted to his thoughts. If he decided to cut a leaf from the plant, the lie detector registered what looked like fear on the part of the plant. And even more amazing, it registered when Backster *thought* of the deed, before he made any move to carry it out.

Backster discovered that even plants are psychic, and respond to our thoughts and intentions. He calls it "primary perception," because it is so basic and universal. He even discovered that single cells have this ability. This has provided valuable clues in tracking down the mechanisms which make psychic ability possible. These experiments are described next.

CHAPTER 4 - THE BACKSTER EFFECT: CELL TO CELL COMMUNICATION

"Plants talk...yes, they scream. It only seems that they accept their misfortunes submissively and silently bear pain."
--Pravda, quoted in Tompkins, *The Secret Life of Plants* (Tompkins, 1972).

"This one experiment proved to me as a skeptical scientist that we could measure force fields of communication in consciousness that defy the known laws of physics."
--Dr. Brian O'Leary, physicist and NASA Astronaut

DEFINITION-Backster Effect: The ability of simpler life forms, such as plants and single cells, to respond to the thoughts, intentions and actions of humans, as evidenced by electrical response and other objective measurements.

The Backster Effect: Cell-to-Cell Communication

Cleve Backster is an expert polygraph, or lie-detector, examiner. In the early nineteen fifties he was involved in creating the standards and procedures by which the CIA began using polygraphs to investigate their personnel for security clearances. Since that time he has directed a school in which he instructs police officers and security officers from all over the world in the art of using the polygraph for lie detection. In 1966 he had been up late one night running his school when, on an impulse, he connected his machine to a house plant in the office to see what it would do.

A polygraph generates a very weak electrical current which passes through the body of the subject. It measures a voltage which indicates the skin resistance. As the emotional state of the subject changes, this voltage changes. Polygraph examiners are trained to monitor this signal. Abrupt changes indicate a strong emotional reaction.

As Backster considered his office plant, a *dracaena*, he wondered what might cause it to have an emotional reaction which would register on his machine. He connected electrical contacts from the polygraph to the leaf of the plant just as he would to the fingers of a human subject. Then he left the plant undisturbed for a while to develop a "baseline" on his chart. Then he gave it a drink of water by pouring water into its pot.

Backster expected the increased water would cause an increase in the plant's conductivity, which would cause the needle on his machine to rise. But instead, it fell with a series of sawtooth motions. This resembled a human response corresponding to an emotional stimulation of short duration. He wondered if the plant could possibly be showing emotion.

Polygraph examiners are experts at inducing emotions in their subjects. They are taught to put the subject under stress of various sorts in order to monitor their emotional response on the polygraph. It was probably Backster's training which led him to conceive of the next test. He would burn one of the plant's leaves with a match, and see how it responded to that.

But the moment he thought of the idea, the plant's trace on the polygraph went wild. He had not moved nor done anything to provoke such a response. He had only formed the thought in his mind of harming the plant. It seemed as though the plant was reading his mind!

In subsequent experiments he found that the plant would respond differently if he actually intended harm, as opposed to just pretending. It seemed that the plant could distinguish true intent from mere pretense. The plant really could read his mind!

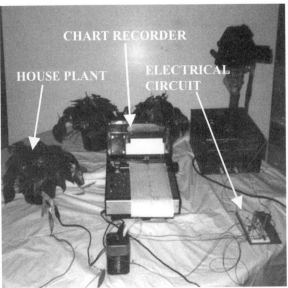

Figure 4.1. The Backster experiment is easy to repeat. This is the layout my son used to replicate the Backster experiment for a high school science fair. The plant on the left has electrodes attached to both sides of a leaf. It is wired up to a simple electrical circuit on the right which measures the plant's resistance. The chart recorder in the center makes a record of the variations of leaf resistance over time. When my son, who was ten feet away, accidentally burned his finger, the plant gave a sharp sudden pulse, in apparent empathic response. *Courtesy of William Swanson*

These experiments have been duplicated thousands of times by Backster and others since this effect was first discovered. Many different plant varieties have been tested. The ability of plants to detect emotion and respond to it electrically is now well established.

In the former Soviet Union, Professor Ivan Gunar and his colleagues at the Department of Plant Physiology of the Tamiryazev Academy of Agricultural Sciences have also confirmed experiments of this type hundreds of times. In an article in Pravda describing this work, he said "Plants talk…yes, they scream. It only seems that they accept their misfortunes submissively and silently bear pain." (Tompkins, 1972).

Backster devoted the next several years to research on this topic. He enlarged his office into a modern scientific laboratory to better carry out systematic experiments. He discovered that it was not necessary to have an intact plant to see the effect. He found that a leaf that was still alive could produce good results. Eventually he learned that small pieces of the leaf could be chopped up and placed between the electrodes of the polygraph, and it would still behave in the same way.

This became the first portable "biological emotion detector." Cellular material could be attached to the electrodes, and it could be carried and used anywhere. As Backster's research proceeded, he realized that the fundamental detection occurs at the cellular level. The individual cells of the plant are responsible for sending and receiving the psychic and emotional information. This is a very important discovery.

A number of plants that he cultivated in his laboratory were kept instrumented all the time. Data from these plants were recorded continuously. Through these studies,

Backster learned that plants develop an affinity for the person who takes care of them. They will exhibit responses which depend on the emotional state of the caretaker. He found when he cut his finger and put iodine on it, his instrumented plants showed a strong response.

Backster extended his research to determine how this communication was affected by distance. Did it weaken when he was far away from the plants? When he went on business trips, he recorded the time of each significant event. When he later returned to the lab, he compared these events to the strong responses of his plants recorded on the polygraph. He found that every time he experienced a stressful or dangerous event, the plants in the lab responded at the same moment. And the moment he decided to return to the lab, they gave a different response which resembled enthusiasm or anticipation.

In Chapter 2 we learned from Rupert Sheldrake's research that dogs and cats know psychically when their master starts heading home. They get excited and wait by the door. But Backster discovered that the phenomenon is much more general. Even his houseplants got excited when he began heading home!

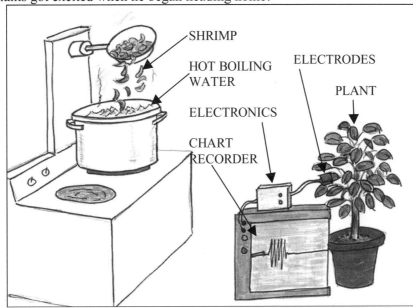

Figure 4.2. Backster experiment in which live shrimp are dropped into boiling water. The instrumented plant reacts sharply to the death of the shrimp, in apparent empathic response. This experiment was automated to remove the human from the loop. The sketch illustrates schematically the experiment. An automated device drops the shrimp into the boiling water. The electronics and chart recorder measure the response of the houseplant.

In another experiment, Backster measured the empathy of plants to the suffering of other species. He devised an automated experiment in which instrumented plants would "witness" the death of brine shrimp by boiling (see Figure 4.2). Each time the shrimp were dumped into boiling water, the plants gave a strong reaction on the polygraph. Backster found that plants respond very strongly to the death of these tiny animals (Backster, 1968).

He noticed a similar effect one day when he was feeding his dog. He decided to add a fresh egg to the dog's food. The moment he made the decision, he noticed out of the corner of his eye motion in the polygraph machine that he had hooked up to an African violet house plant. The machine generated wild movements when he made the decision to break the egg. The graph below (Figure 4.3) shows Backster's data for this African violet. He found that the effect was repeatable. Plants behave as though they are empathic as well as telepathic! (Backster, 2002)

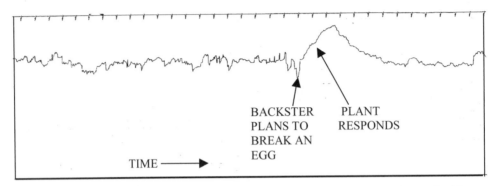

Figure 4.3. Polygraph response of an African violet when Cleve Backster decides to break a fresh egg, which causes a strong response in the plant (Backster, 2002). *Courtesy of Cleve Backster.*

In demonstrations performed at Yale University, Backster showed that an instrumented plant in a room with a spider responded an instant <u>before</u> the spider began to run away from a threatening human. It seemed as though the plant picked up the decision of the spider to make a run for it.

This feature of the Backster effect, that it can respond to emotions or intentions even before an action has occurred, has found application in experimental helmets for fighter pilots. One type of detector uses a paste formed from ground-up leaves or biological substances. Just as in the Backster experiments, this device responds to human thought and emotions. The hope is that, as in the case of the spider, the device will respond the moment an enemy decides to launch a missile at the airplane, even before the missile is fired. It may act as an early warning system that alerts the pilot before his foe attacks him.

Experiments have shown that the subconscious mind can respond much faster to danger than the conscious mind. In fact, it may even have precognitive awareness of the threat. If a missile is fired at the aircraft, the subconscious mind of the pilot may sense the danger long before he can see the missile and respond conventionally. The detector can pick up signals from the pilot's subconscious mind and warn of danger or initiate defensive action before the pilot is consciously aware of the threat. Thus Backster's experiments with the lowly house plant are leading to space-age applications that sound like science fiction.

In another series of remarkable experiments, Backster demonstrated that <u>our cells communicate with one another, even when outside the body and separated by many miles</u>. This experiment has been repeated many hundreds of times, and even visitors to Backster's lab can participate in verifying it for themselves: An individual is given sterile saline solution (salt water) which he sloshes in his mouth and then discharges into several test tubes. This washes loose cells from the lining of the mouth (oral leukocytes) into the solution in the test tubes. They are then centrifuged, which concentrates the cells at the bottom of the test tubes.

After the saline solution is removed, two gold electrodes are placed into the cells at the bottom of the test tube. The electrodes are attached to a sensitive voltmeter which amplifies the weak signal from the leukocytes. No electrical current is passed through the electrodes. Only the voltage spontaneously produced by the leukocytes is recorded. The experimental arrangement is sketched in Figure 4.4.

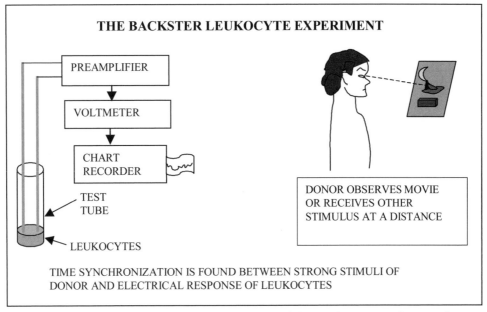

Figure 4.4. Schematic arrangement of one form of the Backster experiment. The subject on the right looks at a movie, reads a book, or engages in other activity which occasionally evokes a strong emotional response. Some of the cells (leukocytes) from his saliva are in the test tube on the left. The voltage across them is amplified and recorded. When the subject experiences a strong emotional response, his cells exhibit a strong electrical response as seen on the chart recorder.

While the leukocytes are wired up, so their response can be monitored, the donor is taken some distance away from the laboratory, typically many miles. In fact, this experiment has been repeated with intervening distances of hundreds and even thousands of miles, and still the effect occurs. When the donor experiences a strong emotion or physical stimulus, <u>his donated cells back in the laboratory respond by generating a large voltage</u>. Backster has replicated this experiment for many subjects, and the response is the same, amazing though it may be.

Figure 4.5 shows one of Backster's typical results for this experiment. The donor of the leukocytes had been in the U. S. Navy stationed at Pearl Harbor during the Japanese attack. He served as a gunner during his naval wartime service. He watched a film entitled *The World at War*. During the only facial close-up of a naval gunner in action against enemy aircraft, his leukocytes responded with a strong voltage pulse. This was the only scene in the movie which related closely to his direct wartime experience. Upon later questioning, the subject confirmed that this one scene had a powerful effect upon him because he, too, had been a Naval gunner in that war (Backster and White, 1985).

Backster's work has been confirmed by other scientists, including Dr. Marcel Vogel, a senior research chemist at the IBM Advanced Systems Development Division Laboratory. Vogel recommended several experimental improvements to Backster's method (Vogel, 1976), including quieting the mind before the experiment. However, the most important element in these experiments was to establish a personal link to the plant being measured. This could involve touching it and spending time with it. Vogel describes this as "'charging' the plant to be receptive to thoughts and emotions from the experimenter.

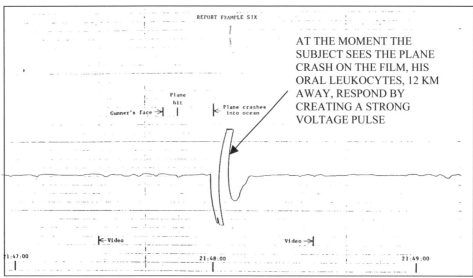

Figure 4.5. Graph of the response of oral leukocytes to emotional stimulation of subject, 12 kilometers away (Backster, 2002). *Courtesy of Cleve Backster*

Backster had noticed a similar effect. He commented that a "relationship" must be established by proximity to the plant for hours or days before the experiment. According to Vogel, this may be a key which enables the plant to tune into the thoughts of the experimenter and to tune out thoughts of all others. Using these methods, Vogel demonstrated high-quality transmissions between a human in Prague, Czechoslovakia and a plant in San Jose, California. This is a distance of almost 7,000 miles (Vogel, 1976).

These experiments demonstrate conclusively that cells from an individual can communicate with one another. This communication works over large distances. The ability of individual cells to filter out all the noise in the environment, as well as all the emotional signals from the other 6 billion people on the planet, not to mention other life forms, and to detect the emotional response of the donor, has profound implications.

The DNA molecule would be an obvious candidate for such a mechanism because it is unique to the individual and is known to be capable of sending and receiving electromagnetic signals. But the power levels and distances involved in these experiments appear to preclude conventional electromagnetic signals as the possible mechanism. Another candidate for the mechanism involves what is called "subtle energy." Dr. Vogel has proposed that the connection with the cells before the experiment is created by charging the plant cells with the "prana" or subtle energy of the experimenter. This occurs naturally when one touches the plant or spends time with it.

Backster has now moved to San Diego and makes these experiments available to visitors to his laboratory. The astronaut Dr. Brian O'Leary described in his book, *The Quest for Reality* (O'Leary, 1989), a typical experience in which a female visitor to the lab had contributed some oral leukocytes for a similar experiment. They were processed and attached to electrodes just as described above. Then, all during the night, as she periodically made passionate love to her boyfriend in a hotel five miles away from Backster's laboratory, her cells in the test tube in the lab recorded the same frenzied emotions and activity.

Dr. O'Leary described other experiments in which he donated his own cells and continued to collect data as he traveled hundreds of miles away from the cells. There was still a high correlation between strong emotions and response of his distant cells. O'Leary concluded that distance did not seem to matter:

"This one experiment proved to me as a skeptical scientist that we could measure force fields of communication in consciousness that defy the known laws of physics."

Organ Transplant Patients

Proof that cells communicate with one another has far-reaching implications for medicine. From Backster's work it is apparent that not only do cells communicate with one another, but they are able to recognize their own kind. In the Backster experiments a person's cells are able to receive emotional information from other cells in the person's body many miles away. This requires them to FILTER OUT all the emotional information from all the other millions of people in the vicinity, not to mention the trillions of other cells from animals and plants.

This raises the question of what happens when a person receives a transplanted organ from another person. Immune suppressant drugs are given to a recipient so the transplanted organ can live in the body and not be rejected. But this transplanted organ has cells with different DNA, unique to its donor. Will the cells from the donor be able to communicate with the host? If so, what kinds of information will be conveyed? What effects will be seen when the transplant recipient integrates the foreign organ into his body?

A large and growing body evidence suggests that donor cells do indeed communicate with the recipient. In many cases the recipient has developed sudden new habits, tastes and characteristics which he never had before. In some cases it has resulted in an emotional awareness, almost a psychic connection, between the recipient and the donor, even when the donor is unknown to the recipient or when the donor has passed away.

The book *The Heart's Code* by Dr. Paul Pearsall (Pearsall, 1998) documents a number of these cases. Dr. Pearsall is a psychoneuroimmunologist, a licensed psychologist who studies the relationship between the brain, immune system, and our experiences of the outside world. With more than thirty years of training in Western medicine, Pearsall was founder and director of a large psychiatric clinic that treated hundreds of seriously ill patients, many of whom received organ transplants. He was director of behavioral medicine in a cardiac rehabilitation program for heart attack victims, and in these roles he collected numerous case histories of patients recovering from major transplant surgery.

On one occasion he was lecturing to an international group of psychiatrists, psychologists, and social workers in Houston, Texas. Following his description of some of his findings, a psychiatrist came to the microphone and told of an experience she had with one of her patients. This was a little girl, eight years old, who had received the heart of a murdered ten-year old girl.

The identity and other information about the donor were completely unknown to the family. However, soon after the transplant, the little girl began waking up at night with terrible nightmares. She was screaming about a man she saw in her dreams who had murdered her donor. The dreams were recurrent and of such intensity that the mother brought the little girl to a psychiatrist. The girl was able to describe the murderer in detail, including the time of the murder, the weapon, the clothes he wore, and what the little girl had said to him. The psychiatrist contacted the police, who, using her information, were able to locate and convict the killer. Everything the girl had reported about the crime turned out to be completely accurate (Pearsall, 1998).

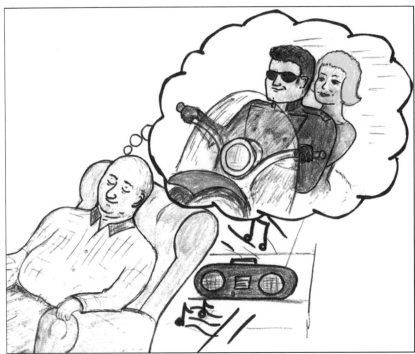

Figure 4.6. A middle-aged man received the transplanted heart of a teenager who was killed in a motorcycle accident. After that, his personality changed: "I loved quiet classical music before my new heart. Now, I put on ear phones, crank up the stereo, and play loud rock-and-roll music. I love my wife, but I keep fantasizing about teenage girls. My daughter says I have regressed since my new heart, and that I act like a sixteen-year-old." (Pearsall, 1998)

A fifty-two-year-old man interviewed by Dr. Pearsall underwent dramatic changes in musical taste after receiving the transplanted heart of a seventeen year old boy killed by a hit and run driver. "…I could never understand it. I loved quiet classical music before my new heart. Now, I put on ear phones, crank up the stereo, and play loud rock-and-roll music. I love my wife, but I keep fantasizing about teenage girls. My daughter says I have regressed since my new heart, and that I act like a sixteen-year-old." (see Figure 4.6) His daughter confirms his observations: "It's really embarrassing sometimes. When my friends come over they ask if my dad is going through his second childhood. He's addicted to loud music and my mom says the little boy in him is finally coming out." (Pearsall, 1998)

In another transplant case, a thirty-five-year-old woman received the heart of a twenty-four-year-old prostitute killed in a stabbing. The woman immediately noticed a big change in how she felt about sex: "I never was really all than interested in sex. I never really thought about it much. Don't get me wrong, my husband and I had a sex life, but it was not a big part of our life. Now, I tire my husband out. I want sex every night and I masturbate two or three times a day sometimes. I used to hate X-rated videos, but now I love them. I feel like a slut sometimes and I even do a strip for my husband when I'm in the mood. I would never have done that before my surgery."

Her husband completely confirms her dramatic behavioral changes: "Not that I'm complaining, mind you, but what I have now is a sex kitten. It's not that we do it more, but she wants to talk about sex more and wants to see sexually explicit tapes which I could never talk her into before…Our worst argument came a few months after her transplant and well before she knew who the donor was. I was joking and at a passionate moment said that she must have gotten the heart of a whore. We didn't talk for weeks." (Pearsall, 1998)

Since the recipients often experience the connection with the donor at a deeply instinctive or subconscious level, it surfaces in dreams and urges, rather than in normal conscious awareness. This communication is similar to psychic messages, which are also typically received at a subconscious level.

According to the Backster experiments, the memory system which is being activated is probably one which plants and animals have in common, such as the limbic system, or what the Russian scientists call the "vegetative nervous system." We have far too little data at this point to develop a physiological theory of how this works, but its existence seems to be well established, and its general characteristics are becoming clear from studies such as those of Pearsall and Backster.

It is encouraging that the Backster effect, or cell-to-cell communication, does not seem to weaken with distance, and is not stopped by electromagnetic shielding. In these ways it is similar to ESP, as we saw in Chapter 2. It also resembles ESP in the way the messages occur at a deep subconscious level. Can these be hints that it is the same mechanism, the same physics, at work?

The challenge for science is that, until recently, there has been a denial that cells have any sort of independent awareness or ability to communicate. This view has been changing as researchers in Germany and Russia (Popp, 1977, 1989; Kaznacheyev, 1969, 1979, 1982) have discovered that cells do exchange weak electromagnetic signals with one another. These are called biophotons. However, this type of communication does not, by itself, explain communication over great distances, or through shielding, or between the living and the dead as in some of the Pearsall cases. Due to the similarity between the characteristics of cell-to-cell communication and psychic phenomena, there is probably a common underlying physical mechanism. This link will be explored further in Chapter 13 and in Volume II.

Connection Between Identical Twins

If cells communicate, and if they communicate best with cells having the same DNA, then would we not expect that identical twins would also communicate in this way? Identical twins, after all, have identical DNA. If there is cellular communication, and if it is selective and tunable based on the uniqueness of DNA, then there should be evidence that some form of subconscious or psychic communication occurs between twins.

This appears to be the case. In a long-term study, the Menninger Institute in Minnesota studied twins who were separated at birth or shortly afterward, and who grew up in separate homes far apart. In most cases, the twins did not know anything about the other twin. Yet in case after case, when the twins were reunited, remarkable similarities in habits and traits were found. It was also found in ESP tests that the twins had an unusually high ability to communicate psychically with each other.

One case involved the identical twins Jim Springer and Jim Lewis, who were reunited at age thirty-nine after being separated at birth and placed in different homes in Ohio (Jackson, 1980). Table 4.1 shows Dr. Pearsall's description of the findings of the case, summarized in chart form (Pearsall, 1988).

Pearsall also notes that research has now shown that <u>twins raised apart are more identical than twins raised together</u>. This is probably because of the struggle of each twin to establish his individuality when living together (Holden, 1980).

TABLE 4.1 - IDENTICAL TWINS RAISED APART

Name given by adoptive parents:	James	James
Number of times married:	2	2
Name of first wife:	Linda	Linda
Name of second wife:	Betty	Betty
Name of one son:	James Alan	James Alan
Name of dog:	Toy	Toy
Beer preference:	Miller Lite	Miller Lite
Smoking habit:	Chain smoked	Chain smoked
Preferred cigarette brand:	Salem	Salem
Make of car:	Chevrolet	Chevrolet
Hobby:	Carpentry	Carpentry
Location of Hobby:	Basement workshop	Basement workshop
Sports dislikes:	Baseball	Baseball
Sports likes:	Stock car racing	Stock car racing
Community Service	Deputy sheriff	Deputy sheriff
Bad habits	Severely chewed fingernails	Severely chewed fingernails
Relations with wife	Affectionate, demonstrative, leaves notes around house	Affectionate, demonstrative, leaves notes around house
Political voting over last twelve years	Voting identical	Voting identical
Past, present or future oriented?	Present	Present
Vacations:	Trips to identical beach in Florida	Trips to identical beach in Florida
Blood pressure	Identical	Identical
Weight	Identical	Identical
Pulse	Identical	Identical
Sleep pattern	Identical	Identical
Health issues (1)	hemorrhoids	hemorrhoids
Health issues (2)	Gained 10 pounds	Gained 10 pounds
Health issues (3)	vasectomy	vasectomy
Health issues (4)	Migraines since age 18	Migraines since age 18
Health issues (5)	EEG identical	EEG identical

Rupert Sheldrake and the "Morphogenic Field"

Dr. Rupert Sheldrake is a respected Cambridge-trained research biologist and former Fellow of the Royal Society. He is interested in the subject of biological morphogenesis, which can be defined as how living organisms take on their specific biological forms and characteristics. As living cells grow from a fertilized egg, for example, they seem to know exactly how to specialize in space and time, so some cells transform into skin cells, others form intestines, bone or liver, all using the same DNA information. Thus the molecular information is somehow transformed into detailed spatial and shape information.

He has proposed that there is some method of information transfer between living cells which carries this information, and which science has overlooked. This is called the "morphogenic field" (Sheldrake, 1995). A similar idea was proposed earlier by Weiss in Germany (Weiss, 1930).

Sheldrake points out that there are forms of knowledge transfer which baffle today's science. He presents the graph below, Figure 4.7, in which the maze-learning skills of rats were measured over many generations within a laboratory rat population. Using the most rigid and conservative experimental controls to separate generations and prevent the possibility of contact or communication between the older and younger rats, the experiments found that the later generations of rats learned the maze much FASTER!

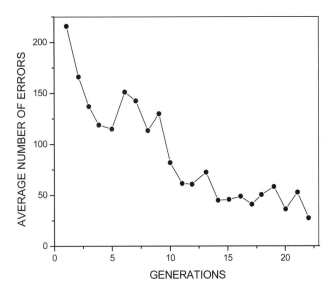

Figure 4.7. Sheldrake's experiment in the learning skills of rats. The graph plots the number of maze-learning errors made by rats of succeeding generations. Later generations learned faster, despite having no contact with earlier generations. (Sheldrake, 1995)

Every conceivable variable was controlled. For example, rats of each generation were always tested when they were the same age, so age was not a factor. Careful controls were placed on the experiment to ensure that the higher aptitude rats did not affect the results. In fact, in some experiments, only the slower, less capable, rats were allowed to breed to provide later generations. Even in these cases the same result was found: later generations learned the maze much faster than their ancestors.

The experiments suggest that it is possible to pass ACQUIRED knowledge down through succeeding generations by some biological or biochemical means. This is in complete contradiction to the present Darwinian model, which says that aptitudes can be inherited but not actual knowledge or memory.

Sheldrake proposes a theory to explain this result. He calls it "morphic resonance." It can be observed at work in a growing fetus, as the multiplying cells create a pattern which serves as a guide for the growth and specialization of later cells.

The nature of this so-called morphogenetic field is not well understood by science, and is still rather controversial in mainstream science. As Dr. Robert Becker and the Yale researcher Harold Saxon Burr discovered, this field has some electromagnetic aspects, but these may not explain everything (Becker, 1985; Burr, 1972). This field may be related to the aura seen around the body seen by psychic healers, and captured on Kirlian photographs. Kulin has related it to the electrostatic field around the body, as well (Kulin, 1980). Such a field has a "shape" as well as a frequency, and may be effective at transmitting information between biological entities. This idea will be discussed in much greater detail in Volume II.

In the meantime, we simply note that such inter-generational learning has no known explanation in modern science. However, it may be possible that the Backster effect is involved. After all, the multiple generations of rats are related genetically to one another, and therefore have similarities in their DNA. Perhaps this enables the cells within the later generations of rats to receive information from the cells of their ancestors.

In the case of transplant patients, we saw that the cells are able to convey information even when the original host has passed away. So perhaps, by sharing some of the DNA with their parents and grandparents, the later rat populations are able to tap into a primary cell-to-cell communication channel, i.e. the Backster effect. Since the DNA is not identical, one would expect the channel to be imperfect. But it is an hypothesis worth considering.

Based on the data, there seems to be either some physical, biochemical means to transmit knowledge about mazes from parent to child, or there is some psychic link between the generations which accomplishes the same effect. Either phenomenon poses a challenge to current science.

Summary

Whatever the physics behind it, there must exist within the heart of each living cell some of the basic machinery of psychic communication. Plants, and even individual cells of plants and animals, demonstrate this form of communication. They respond to the strong emotions of their owner, even at great distance, by producing electrical signals which can be measured.

We do not yet know whether it is the mitochondria, or the DNA, or some other part of the cells which is the primary receptor of psychic information. However, it is probably a cell component which is unique to each individual, and therefore is related to the identity of the individual. The cells from John Doe do not respond to the emotions of Jane Doe, but they do respond to the emotions of John Doe himself, even at a distance of hundreds of miles.

Something about the communication channel enables the cells to be selective about whose emotions they respond to and whose they ignore. This seems to be connected to their biological identity. And we know that DNA in the cell nucleus and in the mitrochondria are unique for each person, based on genetic inheritance. This suggests that these molecular structures may play an important role in sending and receiving psychic information.

When a patient receives an organ from a donor, he takes on some of his cells of the donor, which have the donor's DNA and mitochondria. And amazingly enough, the recipient often develops some of the habits, tastes, and cravings of the donor, even when he has no knowledge of the person. He may even have dreams and memories which belong to the donor.

We have seen examples in which the last memories of a murdered child were somehow transmitted to the transplant recipient. These memories were so vivid that in some cases they have been used to solve the crime. This is a powerful clue that DNA or some other unique part of the cell serves as an antenna and a filter, enabling cells to recognize and communicate with their own kind.

Just as an individual is made up of trillions of cells, and his psychic ability can exceed that of a single cell by coordinating the actions of many cells, in the next chapter we examine what happens when millions of minds act in unison. If one person can exert more psychic ability than a cell by coordinating the actions of all his cells, then it stands to reason that many minds, when coordinated, can achieve more power than a single mind.

We shall see that this is indeed true. When many minds focus on the same subject, it actually alters the physical characteristics of the environment. It can affect radioactive decay rates and other measurable physical properties. And when those minds focus on a common goal, the effects can be even more powerful. Scientific studies have now been completed on a number of global prayer and meditation initiatives. We will see that the effects are not only measurable and provable, but are dramatic. They may point the way to the next step in human evolution, as we begin to realize the enormous potential for good which can result from constructively harnessing the human consciousness.

CHAPTER 5 -COLLECTIVE EFFECTS AND GROUP CONSCIOUSNESS

"No one can flatter himself that he is immune to the spirit of his own epoch, or even that he possesses a full understanding of it. Irrespective of our conscious convictions, each one of us, without exception, being a particle of the general mass, is somewhere attached to, colored by, or even undermined by the spirit which goes through the mass. Freedom stretches only as far as the limits of our consciousness."
-- Carl Jung (Jung, 1942)

"...We do have strong evidence of anomalous structure in what should be random data, and clear correlations of these unexplained departures from expectation with well-defined events that are of special importance to people."
-- Dr. Roger Nelson, Director, Global Consciousness Project (Nelson, 2001)

DEFINITION-Group Consciousness: The state in which many people focus mentally on a single thought or object. It is hypothesized that this may tend to bring coherence to the physiological rhythms of the members of the group, and that the consciousness of the group may be more powerful than the consciousness of a single individual.

The Power of Group Consciousness

We have seen in previous chapters that the human mind, or human consciousness, is able to directly affect external events. What happens when many minds focus on the same thought? Is there a multiplier effect when a billion people simultaneously think the same thing?

This is called a collective effect. When many minds act collectively, in unison, it does indeed affect space, time and physics in a surprising and remarkable way. This effect has been demonstrated in the work of Dr. Dean Radin of the Noetic Society (Radin, 1996), Dr. Roger Nelson of Princeton University (Nelson, 1996), and Prof. Bierman of the University of Amsterdam (Bierman, 1996).

Figure 5.1. Buddhist monks chanting. Religions all over the world have a tradition of praying in the form of synchronized chanting. The scientific results of this chapter suggest that, by focusing many minds on the same thought, the probability of achieving it may be enhanced.

These researchers have discovered that when many minds focus on the same thought, the quantum randomness of the universe is reduced. Devices which depend upon quantum effects show an <u>altered behavior</u>. This means the laws of physics have been modified locally, since this randomness is supposed to be a universal constant built into the foundations of physics.

The devices used to measure this quantum randomness are the same random event generators or REGs we encountered in Chapter 3. They are sometimes called EGGs, which conveys the surprising idea that they respond to life and consciousness. They are devices which produce a stream of purely random numbers. The level of randomness is related to the deepest principles of physics, and should be a constant. However, when many minds concentrate upon a single thought, it has unexpected and unexplained effects upon such supposedly random processes.

The Academy Awards Experiment, 1995

The Academy Awards is one of the most watched programs on television. A TV audience of tens of millions of people focus their attention on this event every year. They watch the Hollywood stars to see what they will wear and what they will say, and most of all, who will win in the various categories. And amazingly, as viewers collectively focus on this event, it has been found that they alter quantum physics at the deepest level.

During the time of the program, minute by minute, the audience varies in size as viewers take breaks for commercials or flock to their TV sets for the most important awards. The Nielsen ratings measure this fluctuation. Thousands of "Nielsen families" have boxes on their TVs which measure their viewing minute by minute. And as their attention waxes and wanes, a corresponding effect occurs on the random event generators, the REGs.

Figure 5.2. When millions of people focus their attention on a single thought, it reduces quantum noise and affects REGs (random event generators) around the world. One such documented case was during the Academy Awards in 1995 (Radin, 1996).

The following results demonstrated this effect in scientifically controlled tests (Radin, 1996). These experiments tested the idea that, when a group of people focus their attention on a single thought, REGs act with less randomness. They begin acting as though a channel had been created which causes them to become linked together.

Normally, the numbers produced by two REGs are independent. You can think of an REG as a person continually flipping coins and recording what he gets. His odds of getting heads or tails should be the same. If he gets a head on one toss, this tells him nothing about the next toss. Likewise, his coin toss should have no effect on a second person tossing a different coin. The results of coin tosses by the two individuals have no effect upon one another. We say their tosses are uncorrelated.

This should also be true for the REGs. The random numbers from one REG should have no relationship to the output of another one. Except that we find, when millions of people are focusing their consciousness on a single event, like the Academy Awards, suddenly my coin toss begins to affect yours. It makes it more likely that, if I toss heads then yours will come up heads, also. The two coin tosses become coupled together, or "correlated." There is some kind of connection between them. This should not happen according to known physics, but it does happen to the REGs when many minds focus on the same event.

Figure 5.3 shows the correlation between two such REGs, located 12 miles apart, as a national TV audience watched the Academy Awards (Radin, 1996). The vertical axis for the graph is a measure of the correlation of the outputs of the two REGs. The horizontal axis is the Nielsen rating for the show. It measures how many people are watching the show. The upward slope of the line shows that, when the Nielsen rating was high, meaning many people were watching the show, the correlation between the two REGs was also high.

To check that this is a real effect, the graph in Figure 5.4 was produced. It uses the same data, but measures the Nielsen ratings 90 minutes later, and compares them with the recorded REG outputs during the Academy Awards. In this case there is no correlation. The trend line is approximately horizontal, as we would expect.

This proves that the correlation found for the Academy Awards is not due to chance but is a real effect. It provides hard scientific evidence that group consciousness does affect events and that the more people involved in the group, the more powerful is the effect.

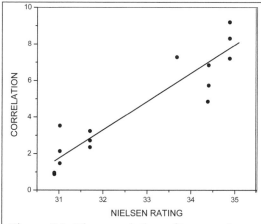

Figure 5.3. The correlation of two random event generators, 12 miles apart, as a national TV audience watches the Academy Awards. The rising slope indicates a strong correlation (Radin, 1996).

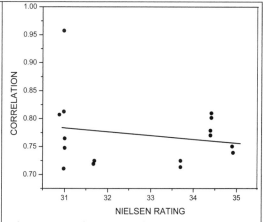

Figure 5.4. The correlation of two random event generators plotted vs. the Nielsen ratings 90 minutes later. There is no correlation (Radin, 1996).

The other surprising thing about this result is that there was no INTENTION on the part of the audience to directly affect these REGs. In this way, these experiments are different from the PK experiments of Chapter 3, in which the operator tried to make the

REG "go high" or "go low." Here the audience isn't thinking about the REGs and doesn't even know they exist. It is simply <u>the concentration of a large number of people on a commonly held thought</u> which influences the devices, causes them to become correlated and reduces their randomness.

The implications for physics and the understanding of consciousness are far-reaching. The randomness measured by these REG devices is supposed to be a fundamental constant of nature. It is not something that can be changed, according to present science. It is even more embarrassing for conventional science that what turns out to upset this "constant" of nature it is a few million people watching the Academy Awards!

There are some newer theories of physics which are discussed in Chapter 13, which may help to explain these revolutionary discoveries. They are based on the idea that quantum randomness is not just a constant but is due to the energy in space, the so-called "Zero Point Energy." Even in present day quantum mechanics, this energy is predicted to be present throughout all space. But physicists are taught to ignore it. However, some newer theories take the idea of this energy more seriously and consider it as composed of photons zipping through space in all directions. Normally the number of photons moving in each direction is the same, so we don't notice any effects from this energy until we look at the very small scale, at the quantum level.

These models offer a deeper explanation for uncertainty and randomness. It is this Zero Point flux of particles which must be affected by consciousness. This would explain how millions of minds focusing on the same thought can alter the level of randomness. These are new ideas, controversial in mainstream physics, but they offer a glimmer of hope that these surprising discoveries about consciousness will lead to a deeper understanding of the most basic laws of our universe.

This seemingly small change in viewpoint has far-reaching implications for the future of physics. Little did the viewers of the Academy Awards guess, as they were cheering for their favorite stars, that they were producing the data which may lead to a revolution in physics.

The O. J. Simpson Trial

Another example of this effect comes from the O.J. Simpson trial, which was one of the most highly watched events in television history. TV viewing was highest when the pre-show began, and then peaked again when the verdict was announced. At these moments, tens of millions of people around the world focused with rapt attention on their TV screens. Their collective consciousness was focused on one single event. And this collective focus had an enormous impact on the functioning of the Random Event Generators (REGs).

Figure 5.5 shows the behavior of a single REG at different times during the O. J. Simpson trial. As reported in (Radin, 1997) the random number generator behaved anomalously at key times when worldwide attention was most intense. When the TV pre-show began and at the moment of the verdict announcement, the behavior of the REGs was most anomalous, with odds against chance exceeding 200 to 1. At these moments it was estimated by Reuters News Service that a half billion people worldwide were focused on this event on their TVs or radios. The departure of the random event generators from normal chance behavior wass dramatic, as is clear in the graph. Once the verdict was announced, the REG quickly returned to normal random chance behavior.

This study and others (Radin, 1996; Nelson, 1996) show dramatically that the focus of human consciousness does affect the world around us. If many minds focus together the effect is greatly magnified.

Radin (1997) postulates that these experiments are consistent with the following set of properties:

- Consciousness extends beyond the individual and has "quantum-field" like properties, in that collective effects exist.

- Consciousness injects order into systems in proportion to the strength of the consciousness present.

- The strength of consciousness fluctuates from moment to moment and is regulated by the focus of attention.

- A group of individuals can be said to have a "group consciousness."

- When the members of a group are focused on different things the strength of the group consciousness is effectively zero.

- Physical systems respond to consciousness by becoming more ordered (less random).

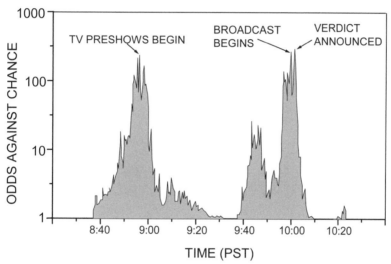

Figure 5.5 Results of the O.J. Simpson experiment. (Radin, 1997, p.167) When many minds focused upon the same thing, in this case the O. J. Simpson trial, random event generators were affected and began behaving unusually. The so-called random independent outputs of two REGs behaved as if they were coupled together. The graph shows the odds against such behavior occurring naturally. It became most unusual at times of peak interest, when the worldwide audience was largest. *Courtesy of Dr. Dean Radin*

Like the PK and remote viewing phenomena described earlier, the effect of group consciousness is very real, very dramatic, and has been scientifically measured and proven. And yet, these effects completely defy conventional physics. They show without a doubt that our present-day science is incomplete, and must change to account for such effects.

September 11 World Trade Center Attack
On September 11, 2001, an event occurred which focused the consciousness of hundreds of millions of people worldwide. On that day two passenger airplanes purposely crashed into the World Trade Towers in New York City and one into the Pentagon.

Thousands of people died in that tragedy. The attention of America and the world was riveted by these brazen acts of terrorism.

Figure 5.6. On September 11, 2001 the twin towers of the World Trade Center were attacked by terrorists. The event riveted the attention of hundreds of millions of people around the world. Several hours before the attack, the "random" outputs of REG devices around the world began showing anomalies (see Fig. 5.7 below), suggesting that some global event might be imminent.

At the time of the World Trade Center tragedy, Drs. Nelson, Radin and colleagues had established a network of 37 random event generators (REGs) in continuous operation at many points around the globe. This was called the Global Consciousness Project (GCP) and has since been extended to more than 50 REGs.

As we described earlier, the output of one coin toss should not affect the output of another coin toss. If you and I are tossing coins a thousand miles apart, and I toss heads, the chance for you to toss heads is still exactly the same: 50%. It should not be affected by my toss. It is said that the correlation between my toss and yours is zero. This is true for two subsequent tosses by the same person, and it is true for two tosses by different people. REGs should work the same way. Their "toss" is based on the output of quantum noise, and there should no connection between the outputs of two such devices. The correlation between them should be zero, according to known science.

However, as in the case of the Academy awards, when millions of minds focus on a single event, the outputs of the coin tosses or the REGs do become correlated. Figure 5.7 shows the correlations between the outputs of the global network of REGs. (Nelson, 2001) The bottom axis on the graph shows time, in days, with the September 11 tragedy marked by a box. It can be seen that, even a full day before the event, the global correlation of REGs was rising. After the event, as world attention concentrated on the TV coverage of the World Trade Center collapse, the global correlation continued to rise and reached very high values.

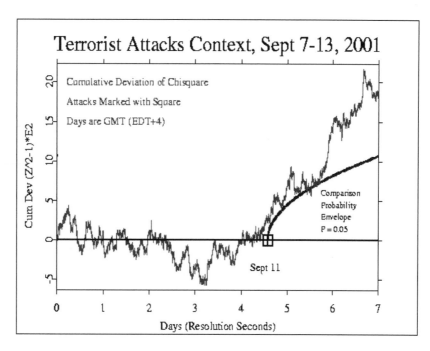

Figure 5.7. The time-averaged sum of the correlations between REGs. It indicates when independent generators in different locations start to move together, when their supposedly independent random outputs begin acting as though they are coupled. As the graph rises away from the centerline it indicates that something is disturbing the quantum noise and causing the REGs to be coupled together in many locations around the world. *Courtesy of Drs. Roger Nelson and Dean Radin of the Global Consciousness Project*

The smooth curve on the graph shows the 5% probability line. When the data curve is above this line, it indicates a probability of less than 1 in 20. It shows that the outputs of the 37 theoretically random REGs became partially correlated at the time of the attack. As Dr. Nelson commented:

"We do not know how the correlations that arise between electronic random event generators and human concerns come to be, and yet, the results of our analysis over the past three years repeatedly indicate such correlations."
(Nelson, 2001)

These graphs were produced by very precise, strict statistical procedures which we are describing in a simplified way for clarity. However, statistics is a precise science, and if the reader wishes to understand the details of the calculations, it is recommended that he refer to the websites cited in the following references: (Statistics, 2001; Radin, 2001, 2001a), (Nelson, 2003) and (May, 2001).

When the correlations shown in the graph above are converted to "odds against chance" it produces the graph in Figure 5.8. It shows very clearly just how anomalous the events of September 11 were. This is basically the same as saying that it plots the "odds against chance" of seeing this amount of cross-correlation between different REGs on that day (Nelson, 2001).

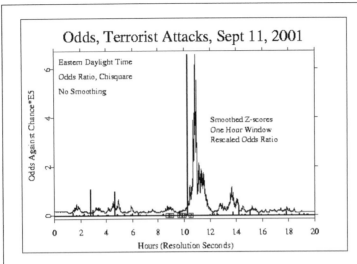

Figure 5.8. Odds against chance of obtaining the measured cross-correlation between REGs seen on September 11, 2001. Maximum peak is 200:1.(Radin, 2001b) *Courtesy of Dr. Dean Radin.*

As we can see from the graph, the signal is <u>huge</u> at the time of the attack. The horizontal timeline is calibrated in Eastern Daylight Time for September 11, and each of the five major events (the airplane crashes and tower collapse) is marked with a small box. The peak "odds against chance" seen in this event is over 600,000 to 1. The peak in anomalous behavior occurs just after 10:00 am, when the world television audience was probably the greatest.

A somewhat different approach taken by Dr. Radin involved examining the variance in the REG values for that day. Variance is a measure of how strongly the signal is fluctuating. "I'd predict something like ripples of high and low variance, as the emotional shocks continue to reverberate for days and weeks," said Radin (Nelson, 2001). This was implemented by computing the variance as a function of time and integrating it. This would show the "cumulative variance" which will grow steadily larger in times when the signals are fluctuating wildly. This parameter is plotted as the darker curve in the graph below, Figure 5.9.

For comparison, to compute the odds-against-chance, "pseudo-data" were generated by computer, and the same rules were applied to it. This is plotted as the light grey curve in the graph. It provides a visual indicator of just how anomalous the REG data were on September 11. One of the fascinating aspects of this data is that it begins to rise strongly hours before the event. The planes crashed into the World Trade Center starting at 8:45 am, and the event unfolded over the next several hours.

As the investigators are quick to admit, they do not understand how human consciousness can affect random event generators, much less when many of them are scattered around the world. Yet when we compare these new results to the older data shown earlier, we see that they are consistent. The focus of human consciousness is able to change quantum processes which should be inviolate. There are no mechanisms in conventional physics to explain this effect. It is a clear wake-up call to physicists to pay attention to these data.

The other interesting feature of these data is that the variance begins to <u>rise steeply at 6:00 am on the day of the attack</u>! Is this precognitive awareness? Are millions of people around the world subconsciously aware of what they are about to witness? We have seen in Chapters 1 and 2 that precognition often occurs in psychic phenomena. Is that what this graph indicates? And, if so, can this technology be used to WARN us of future attacks? We do not know at the present time. But the data suggest that the global network of REGs might well be a powerful early warning system against surprise attacks or other large-scale tragedies.

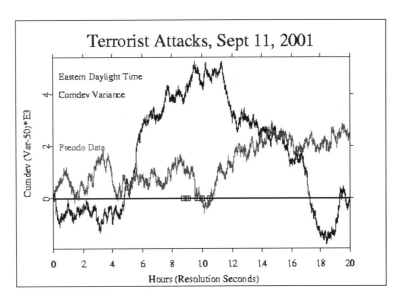

Figure 5.9. Behavior of the cumulative variance of the set of RNGs on the day of the World Trade Center attack (dark line) compared to a control data set (light grey line). (Radin, 2001b) *Courtesy of Dr. Dean Radin and Dr. Roger Nelson of the Global Consciousness Project*

In the early days of quantum mechanics there were debates between Einstein and Neils Bohr. Einstein believed that, at the deepest level, the randomness of quantum mechanics would be unmasked. He believed that events only appear random because we lack understanding of some other key effect or force which we are overlooking, the "hidden variable." If we discovered that, we could eliminate the fundamental random character of quantum mechanics. Bohr, on other hand, believed the randomness was fundamental, but he also stressed the effect of the observer. Bohr's view has become enshrined as the "Copenhagen interpretation," which implies that human consciousness is intimately involved in every physical measurement.

As we reflect upon the anomalous effects in this chapter, it may be that the ghostly debate between these two giants of physics has come alive again. It may be that both points of view are partly true, and are relevant to these recent discoveries.

In some way, human attention and human consciousness are affecting random quantum events. This means that the amount of randomness is not just some fixed constant of nature. It is due to forces, and it responds to forces. And one of those "forces" seems to be human consciousness.

In this way it is offering us a clue to the hidden mechanism which Einstein sought. At the same time, the power of global consciousness to affect so many REGs around the world reminds us of the importance of the human in the experiment, which was one of Bohr's main points.

The important lesson to learn from these experiments is that physics is not complete yet. It cannot explain these data. The data CAN provide powerful clues to a better, more accurate physical theory in the future. However, this will only happen if physicists take the data seriously. It will only happen if they step back from the present physics model and ask the question: "What kind of physics theory could predict the data that were seen on September 11?"

Meditation and Prayer

The power of human consciousness is not a new idea to meditators. It is also not new to those who pray. Both groups believe that the human mind is capable of reaching out beyond the physical limitations of the body, and bringing about change in the larger world. In recent times, these groups have sought to augment the power of meditation and prayer by doing it in large groups. Prayer groups and prayer circles have formed nationwide, with the goal of praying for healing for specific people, or for the larger and more general goal of world peace. The Internet has helped these groups to coordinate so they can all pray at the same time, even if separated by thousands of miles. Meditators in the past assembled in a single location or temple to meditate, but in recent times have more often coordinated their ceremonies over large distances. Again, they are seeking the multiplying effect which comes from a collective act, from coordinating intentions and synchronizing the focus of many individuals.

This phenomenon has been studied in experiments with thousands of meditators who practice Transcendental Meditation (TM). In several studies, they have meditated with the goal of reducing crime and violence in their community (Orme-Johnson, 1982, 1988). Thousands of experienced meditators gathered at the same time every day and focused on the same thought: to reduce crime and violence and bring about peace in their area.

These studies have found that <u>crime and traffic accidents were significantly reduced</u> under such conditions. Conflicts of various types were reduced as well. If one thinks of accidents and human conflicts as another form of the tendency toward chaos and randomness, then these experiments can be seen to be closely connected with those above.

Some data suggest that the strength of the effect increases as the square of the number of people involved. It probably also depends upon how strongly they are focused and the intensity of their concentration. Experienced meditators spend years developing the ability to control their concentration, so it is plausible that fewer of them would be required to have a measurable effect on the environment, as long as their concentration is unified toward one goal.

One such large-scale collective event is the global prayer for peace. Dr. James Twyman (Twyman, 2003) and several other individuals and groups have organized these coordinated world-wide prayer vigils. The Internet has been used to announce and coordinate millions of people around the world who, by agreement, all pray for peace on a certain day at a certain hour. This satisfies the requirement for collective conscious focus, which makes these events similar to those described above. By stating and focusing on a particular goal, it is hoped that the collective effect works to increase the likelihood of that goal.

Dr. Roger Nelson of the Global Consciousness Project has found that, during these world-wide prayer vigils, the network of REGs does indeed exhibit anomalous behavior. Posted on their website (Nelson, 2003) are the combined results of 17 such coordinated, large scale global prayer events. We recall that the outputs of the REGs are supposed to all be random and independent of one another. And of course, keep in mind that they are placed in many sites around the world, thousands of miles apart on the average. Any systematic correlation between their outputs is an indicator of a decrease in randomness, which indicates an anomaly on a global scale.

In Figure 5.10, we see how the correlation of the worldwide array of REGs behaves in response to these global prayer sessions. Again, the chart shown is the average of 17 such synchronized global prayer events. The horizontal time line is adjusted so it corresponds to the beginning of each prayer event. The parabolas corresponding to 5% and 1% probability are shown as dotted lines. The "control data" curve is based on a computer simulation to show what typical uncorellated data would be expected to look like. The actual REG data, averaged over the prayer sessions, is seen to be highly anomalous. The probability that such strong correlations could occur by chance is about 1 in 300.

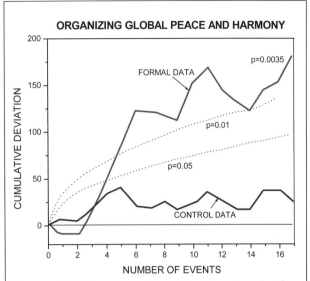

Figure 5.10. Response of worldwide network of REGs to coordinated global prayer by millions of people. (Nelson, 2003) *Courtesy of Dr. Roger Nelson, Global Consciousness Project*

Does this graph prove that prayer works? No, not exactly, because it does not address the specific goal of the prayer. But it does show two important things: first, that global prayer <u>does</u> have an effect. The effect is world-wide. The effect is physical and extends to the subatomic level. So it shows that prayer can be powerful. Secondly, the effect shown in Figure 5.10 suggests that the level of chaos, or randomness, is reduced following the prayer.

Is this the same as ensuring world peace? That is hard to say. We don't know how to measure global emotions on a worldwide scale with any precision. But a decrease in randomness, a decrease in chaos, as indicated by the graph, should be a step in the right direction.

Clearly the power and the global effect demonstrated by these events should be an encouragement to everyone that such efforts do have an impact on global consciousness, and the impact is in a positive direction. As our science evolves, we may learn to glean more specific information from such measurements. But in the meantime, the data suggests strongly that peaceful positive prayers and meditations are a good thing.

Implications

We have seen in this chapter powerful experimental evidence that thoughts influence reality. This is a central tenet of all religions: the power of prayer, the power of intention. Maintaining an attitude of goodwill and love is not merely a "nice thing to do," even though it is taught by many religions. Our attitudes, when summed over large numbers of people, actually change behavior and change the external world in physically measurable ways.

The central theme of many personal growth programs is similar: "Thoughts are things." "As a man thinketh in his heart, so is he." The power of positive visualization is used by athletes, actors, public speakers and businessmen who pay personal development coaches handsome salaries to train them in maintaining positive successful thoughts. The data in this chapter and preceding chapters show us that these practices are successful for a very powerful reason: <u>thoughts do affect reality</u>.

In older, traditional, "primitive" societies this is well known and is integrated into the rituals of everyday life. But "modern" Western industrialized societies have placed their faith in machinery, tools, electronics, and "science" as we know it. The discoveries in this and previous chapters show us that our "science" is missing some very important pieces. It does not understand consciousness, and does not include this force in present theories. We see from recent research that the power of consciousness can no longer be ignored. It must be studied seriously, and its force and power must be integrated into the present scientific structure.

When we do this, we may also begin to change our personal habits. Our Western culture has taught us that thoughts don't matter. If each one of us goes around each day carrying anger and resentment, the Western belief is that it has no direct effect on the world. As long as we refrain from overt violent actions, the dominant belief is that no harm will be done to others. But in view of the present evidence, this can no longer be maintained. We are truly tied to one another, and even our thoughts affect one another.

James Twyman has led several world-wide synchronized group prayers for peace. Those prayers had measurable effects, and even altered the physics of the quantum background and the level of chaos world wide for a time (see Figure 5.10 above). He observes the following:

> "...conflict in the world is the result of conflict within us. We project that feeling into the world because we are not ready to accept that we are the cause, and therefore the solution, to that conflict. Thus wars have raged in the world since the beginning of time, because we are not ready to deal with the conflict where it really is, within us." (Twyman, 1996)

Summary

In this chapter we have seen that, when many minds focus on the same thought, it can change the physical properties of space and time over a great distance, even over the entire planet. The mere fact that millions of people watch the Academy Awards at the same time across the country, and focus their attention on that event, has been found to reduce the level of randomness in random event generators (REGs). The outputs of these generators begin to become synchronized, so REGs thousands of miles apart act as though they are coupled together.

Random event generators are supposed to be based on the fundamental quantum noise which arises from the Uncertainty Principle of quantum mechanics. According to present physics, there is no way their outputs can become correlated in this way..

Clearly, when many minds focus on the same thought, it affects this background universal field of quantum noise. It reduces the level of chaos. This is a fundamental physical effect which challenges contemporary physics. It suggests that something is missing from the current physics model, and it is affected by human consciousness.

When the properties of quantum chaos are changed, it can result in real physical effects. In Chapter 3 we saw how an REG was used to operate a small robot which is affected by consciousness. When baby chicks were emotionally bonded to it, it hovered around their cage. There are many other applications for this newborn science.

In this chapter, we have seen that, as a major global disaster approaches, the global network of REGs gives a precognitive warning. It is as if the coming event, which will synchronize the focus of millions of people, is so huge that it begins to affect the background quantum noise before it arrives. Global consciousness seems to anticipate the event, and begins to change the quantum chaos hours or days before the event itself arrives. This has been seen in the data for 9-11 and other catastrophes. It opens up the possibility of predicting major terrorist events or other large scale tragedies, and perhaps averting or blunting their impact.

When the group consciousness of many people is focused on a specific goal, such as reducing violence or promoting world peace, then we have seen that violence can be reduced over a huge area. In such experiments, the correlation or synchronization of the global network of REGs gives off a powerful signal. It demonstrates that global prayer can reduce quantum randomness on a planetary scale, and bring about demonstrable reductions in crime and violence following the global meditation. Therefore it is seen that, by coordinating the focus of millions of people, not only are the noise properties of space and time affected, but the intended goal of peace and harmony is actually achieved for a time following the meditation.

One lesson to be learned from the research so far is that the human mind can indeed change the world. Another lesson is that, when many minds act in unison, the effect is multiplied and affects vast areas of the planet. It shows that large-scale prayer initiatives do have an effect, and it demonstrates once again, in a scientifically rigorous way, that thoughts have power to bring into reality that which they visualize.

In the research quoted so far, we have seen that the power of the human mind is breathtaking. Not only can it acquire information at great distances, but it can affect objects at great distances as well. These should not be matters for further dispute. The scientific evidence is solid. The protocols and the statistics have been rigorously done. If the scientific method really worked as it is supposed to, then these results would have already been accepted by the larger scientific community.

At the present time we do not know the limits of this new science. We have seen, for example, that the Russian psychic Mikhailova could levitate small objects without touching them. Others have demonstrated similar abilities. What is the limit of this ability? Could it be extended so that a few gifted individuals could lift even their own body? The dream of flight is as old as man. Many people experience dreams in which they fly. But there are reports, some very credible and well documented, that gifted individuals have demonstrated this ability, have done it repeatedly and in full view of crowds of witnesses. In the next chapter we will discuss some of these claims.

The reader may judge for himself if he finds these accounts credible. There is only one request. As in all these matters, approach the subject with a critical, but open, mind. We are on the threshold of a new science, and do not yet fully know what its limits are. We are certainly discovering that human beings are capable of far more than we previously believed. A few gifted individuals may show us what is possible. They may demonstrate the ultimate potential of the human being. If we are to explore and develop our own fullest potential, then we need to consider these remarkable people with an open mind.

CHAPTER 6 - LEVITATION

"On one occasion Medwick reports, the scourge was not enough, so Teresa donned 'a halter and a saddle weighted with stones' and was led by another nun into the refectory on all fours. But saddles and stones couldn't stop her increasingly frequent levitations; the Carmelite sisters were put under standing orders to yank her down should she begin to float upward. At communion, she would sometimes grip the altar grille to keep from scudding upward."
-- Liesl Schillinger, in The New York Times, December 26, 1999, review *of Teresa of Avila-The Progress of a Soul,* by Cathleen Medwick, (Medwick, 1999) describing the life of Saint Teresa, canonized by the Roman Catholic Church

DEFINITION-Levitation: The process of defying gravity and lifting up into the air without the use or assistance of conventional forces or means. It is seemingly a process in which the individual's body becomes immune to gravity, or develops antigravity properties.

Brother Joseph

Levitation is another spectacular and controversial paranormal ability. Numerous stories from reliable sources have come down through history which document human levitation. Brother Joseph of Copertino was one of the most famous. He was a Franciscan monk in the district of Copertino in southern Italy.

Born in 1603 as Giuseppe Desa, he was described as a strange and sickly child. As a teenager he often tortured himself for penance, and was notably modest and devout. At the age of 22 he took his vows and became a monk in the monastery at Copertino (Murphy, 1992).

But every so often, typically when he was praying, he began floating above the floor and could not control it. It would sometimes happen during Mass when the prayers or music were most intense. It would sometimes happen when he meditated, or sometimes even when he was taking his turn serving the tables at dinner in the monastery. It became such a distraction that he was prevented from joining his brothers in choir, because it was often during the singing that he would rise uncontrollably.

Figure 6.1. Painting from 1735 of Brother Joseph of Cupertino, levitating.

One day when he went off to a quiet corner of the chapel to pray, the other brother monks heard him let out a loud yell. They observed him rise straight into the air and fly to the altar. With another cry, he flew back to his corner in a kneeling position.

St. Joseph became understandably well-known for these feats of levitation, although he seemed to be embarrassed by the talent and unable to control it. He was observed in this state by hundreds of people during his lifetime, on hundreds of occasions. Perhaps most important for the credibility of this case, the Church conducted a thorough investigation of Brother Joseph and his feats of levitation. After interviews with many of the witnesses under oath, it absolved him of the charge of practicing false miracles.

Joseph's reported miracles were investigated by Prosper Lambertini, a high church official who had been deeply influenced by the European Enlightenment, and later became Pope Benedict XIV. He was initially skeptical of the levitation claims, but at the conclusion of an exhaustive investigation, wrote the following:

"While I discharged the office of Promoter of the Faith, the cause of the venerable Servant of God, Joseph of Copertino came up for discussion in the Congregation of Rites, which after my retirement was brought to a favorable conclusion, and in this eye-witnesses of unchallengeable integrity gave evidence to the famous upliftings from the ground and prolonged flights of the aforesaid Servant of God when rapt in ecstasy." (Thurston, 1952)

In the figure above, St. Joseph of Copertino is depicted flying in a religious rapture. This picture was published in 1735. St. Joseph was even said to have lifted others into the air with him in his ecstasies (Wilson, 1975).

David Dunglas Home

Another remarkable man who dazzled England with his paranormal exploits was Daniel Dunglas Home (pronounced "Hume"). He was born in Scotland in 1833. His abilities were witnessed by some of the most respected and eminent people of his day, including Lord Adare and the famous scientist Sir William Crookes, inventor of the forerunner of the vacuum tube and the florescent light, and discoverer of the element Thallium. Lord Adare and others observed that Home was able to change his apparent size: "Home grew, I should say, at least six inches. Mr. Jencken, who is a taller man than Home, stood beside him so there could be no mistake about it. Home's natural height is, I believe, 5 feet ten inches. I should say he grew to six feet four inches or five inches. I placed my hands on his feet, and they were level on the ground...He appeared to grow also in breadth and size all over, but there was no way of testing that." (Wilson, 1975a)

The poets Robert Browning and Elizabeth Barrett Browning entertained Home in their home, where he levitated flowers which settled on Mrs. Browning's hair. The novelist William Thackeray witnessed Home's mediumship in America and concluded: "I have seen what I would not have believed on your testimony, and what I cannot, therefore, expect you to accept on mine." (Stemman, 1975) Home performed for Emperor Napoleon III and the Empress of France, causing a hand to materialize in the air in front of them. The Empress claimed to recognize the hand as that of her dead father, because of a defect in one of the fingers.

Home cooperated with several European scientists who were initially intent on exposing him. Two of these were the royal physician, Dr. Ashburner, and the President of the Royal Medical Society, Dr. John Elliotson. They both had initially attacked Home, but after independently conducting extensive tests, were both won over and became public converts to spiritualist beliefs and the genuineness of Homes' abilities (Iverson, 1992).

The eminent scientist Sir William Crookes conducted extensive investigations of Home for many years. He began as a skeptic, declaring to the press: "The increased employment of scientific methods will produce a race of observers who will drive the worthless residuum of spiritualism hence into the unknown limbo of magic and necromancy." But after extensive tests, he concluded that Home's abilities were genuine. He declared:

"A medium walking into my dining room cannot, while seated in one part of the room with a number of persons keenly watching him, by trickery make an accordion play in my own hand when I hold its keys downwards, or cause the same accordion to float about the room playing all the time." (Iverson, 1992)

Figure 6.2. A drawing of D. D. Home levitating. "He most often rose perpendicularly with his arms above his head, and then would hover for about five minutes. He often asked his sitters not to look at him the moment he was rising, lest the trance be shattered." (Stemman, 1975). *Courtesy of Mary Evans Picture Library*

Home was most famous for his reported ability to levitate, which he did frequently in front of many people. On December 13, 1868, Home levitated outside a window, three floors above the ground. Lord Adare observed this event and recounted it:

"I went with him. He told me to open the window as it was before. I did so [Adare cracked the window open about one foot.] He told me to stand a little distance off. He then went through the open space, head first, quite rapidly, his body being horizontal and apparently rigid. He came in again, feet foremost, and we returned to the other room. It was so dark I could not clearly see how he was supported outside. He did not appear to grasp , or rest upon, the balustrade, but rather to be swung out and in...When Home awoke he was much agitated. He said he felt as if he had gone through some peril, and that he had a most horrible desire to throw himself out of the window. He remained in a very nervous condition for some time, then gradually became quiet." (Wilson, 1975a)

Dozens of witnesses have left written testimony to his levitation abilities. It was not uncommon for heavy pieces of furniture to levitate and go flying around the room during his seances. Even more amazing was that when tables went flying, the objects on them remained undisturbed.

In careful experiments conducted by the scientist Sir William Crookes, a board was placed on a weighing scale, and a glass of water was placed on the board. Crookes found that Home, by merely placing his hand in the glass of water, could change the measured weight virtually at will.

When Crookes began his lengthy investigation of Home, he was a skeptic: "At first, like other men who thought little of the matter and saw little, I believed that the whole affair was superstition, or at least an unexplained trick." (Picknett, 1987) But after many years of experiments and close observation, Crookes compiled a list of 17 separate anomalies which he witnessed Home create or manifest. These included levitation of himself and others, and of objects at a distance. These experiments were conducted in bright lighting and good visibility. Throughout all of them, Home actually encouraged the scientist to be skeptical and dubious, and to check for every possible trick. In all the years of observations by Crookes and many other people, Home was never detected in a fraud of any kind (Stemman, 1975).

Peter Sugleris
A modern example of levitation is described by Berlitz (Berlitz, 1988) in the case of a young Greek boy named Peter Sugleris. Sugleris was reported to have psychokinetic powers similar to the more famous Uri Geller. Sugleris' alleged ability to move objects and bend spoons and other metal utensils without touching them was been observed by many people. He frequently demonstrated to family members and close friends his ability to levitate. He could do it seemingly at will. On numerous occasions he demonstrated it for others as well. It required immense concentration and a vegetarian purification diet for several weeks before the event.

A recent occasion, in 1986, was photographed by his wife Ester. He is said to have risen off the kitchen floor a distance of eighteen inches and remained suspended for forty-seven seconds. During the levitation his face took on a frightening grimace which was similar to descriptions of Brother Joseph of Cupertino during his levitations. Afterwards, Sugleris broke out in a cold sweat and was exhausted. It took ten or fifteen seconds for him to regain normal consciousness. This example suggests that this ability, although unusual, may not be limited to saints from earlier periods.

The Yogis of India
Yogis are the Hindu Holy men of India. They are similar to the monks of the Middle Ages in Europe, to the extent that they lead simple lives of abstinence, prayer and

meditation. When Yogis reach a certain stage of enlightenment, they are said to often develop unusual, or paranormal, abilities. One of these was levitation.

During the time when the British Empire occupied India, stories of these feats were often brought back to England by British Colonial officials. Here is an account from the autobiography of a well-known yogi who came to America, Paramahansa Yogananda, about an experience which happened during his childhood in India (Yogananda, 1946):

> *"I saw a Yogi remain in the air, several feet above the ground, last night in a group meeting." My friend, Upendra Mohun Chowdhury, spoke impressively.*
>
> *I gave him an enthusiastic smile. "Perhaps I can guess his name. Was it Bhaduri Mahasaya, of Upper Circular Road?"*
>
> *Upendra nodded, a little crestfallen not to be a news-bearer. My inquisitiveness about saints was well known to my friends; they delighted in setting me on a fresh track.*
>
> *"The yogi lives so close to my home that I often visit him." My words brought keen interest to Upendra's face, and I made a further confidence.*
>
> *"I have seen him in remarkable feats. He has expertly mastered the various pranayamas mentioned in the ancient eightfold yoga outlined by Patanjali. Once Bhadura Mahasaya performed the Bhastrika Pranaya before me with such amazing force that it seemed an actual storm had arisen in the room! Then he extinguished that thundering breath and remained motionless in a high state of superconsciousness. The aura of peace after the storm was vivid beyond forgetting."*

In this description, the word pranayama refers to a specific breathing exercise practiced by yogis. Its purpose is, very generally, to fill the body with prana, or "life energy", also called "chi" or "qi" in Chinese medicine. It is also referred to in the West sometimes as "subtle energy," and will be described in much greater detail in Volume II of this series. The accumulation and control of the various forms of this energy appears to be one of the secrets by which a yogi achieves his powers. It may also be the key to understanding all paranormal phenomena.

In Volume II we will see how Robert Pavlita built devices which accumulate this energy. It can then be controlled by thought to produce minute movements in delicate devices. A normal human being, staring at such a device for many minutes, is able to store enough prana in the device to enable it to operate. Then the stored prana responds to mental intention, which generates forces and motion.

Pavlita showed that such concentrations of prana could produce very real forces which could lift, attract and move objects of any kind. Apparently the yogis are able to generate or collect prana much faster and in larger amounts through exercises such as pranayama. The concentrations appear to be so large that they can generate paranormal effects without the assistance of a machine. It would be naïve to suppose that this explains every aspect of a yogi's ability. But it does offer insight into what may be one mechanism used by yogis.

Other Cases

There have been many well-documented cases of public levitation. Saint Teresa of Avila was one of the most famous of these. When the Catholic Church grants sainthood, it goes through a careful process of research to verify the miracles attributed to the candidate. In the case of Saint Teresa, many witnesses vouched for her levitation to Church authorities under oath. A recent book, *Teresa of Avila-The Progress of a Soul* (Medwick, 1999) provides much supporting evidence.

One witness, Sister Anne of the Incarnation, stated in her deposition at the beatification proceedings:

"I was in the choir waiting for the bell to ring when our holy Mother entered and knelt down...As I was looking on, she was raised about half a yard from the ground without her feet touching it. At this, I was terrified and she, for her part, was trembling all over. So I moved to where she was and I put my hands under her feet, over which I remained weeping for something like half an hour while the ecstasy lasted. Then suddenly she sank down and rested on her feet and turning her head round to me she asked me who I was and whether I had been there all the while. I said yes, and then she ordered me under obedience to say nothing of what I had seen, and I have in fact said nothing until the present moment."
(Murphy, 1992)

An Italian medium, Amedee Zuccarini, was reportedly photographed while levitating 20 feet above a table. In Lynn Picknett's book *Flights of Fancy* (Picknett, 1987), there is a photograph in a well-lit room of a man levitating several feet off the floor. It is entitled: "Carmine Mirabelli, the great Brazilian medium, hovers near the ceiling without benefit of string, pulleys, or a safety net…"

Figure 6.3 Levitation photograph from Hill(1965) in Albert Hall (Photo credit: *Psychic News*

A British medium, Colin Evans, was also reported to have performed spectacular feats of levitation under carefully monitored conditions. Figure 6.3 shows a photograph of such a demonstration, reportedly conducted at Albert Hall in London. This was done

110

during a public séance in a tall room with observers on all sides. Fraud or fakery would have been very difficult because of the high ceilings and audience on all sides. The photograph itself is impressive (Hill, 1965).

More frequently, psychically gifted individuals have been able to demonstrate the levitation of objects. The famous Swedish psychic Olof Jonnson (born 1918-died 1998) is shown in Figure 6.4 with a group of people levitating a table. Jonnson is standing behind the table but no one is touching it. Supposedly the group energy of many people makes this feat easier. The physical mechanism seems to be similar to psychokinesis or PK, as described in Chapter 3. In commonly observed PK experiments, the medium may levitate small objects, such as matches or cigarettes. Such experiments were performed with the famous Russian medium Michailova, as described in Chapter 3.

Olof Jonnson was a well-known clairvoyant, with psychic abilities which had been tested extensively in laboratories in Europe. When he emigrated to the United States in 1953, he participated in ESP experiments at Duke University conducted by Dr. J. B. Rhine. He was a key participant in the famous long-distance telepathy experiments with Astronaut Edgar Mitchell during the Apollo 14 mission to the moon (see Chapter 2) which were reported to have been remarkably successful. He was also a member of the psychic team which recovered approximately two billion dollars in gold buried in the Phillipines by the Japanese during World War II. (Steiger, 1971)

Figure 6.4. Psychic Olof Jonsson, with help from several others in a carefully supervised seance in Copenhagen, levitating a table. (Steiger, 1974) *Courtesy of Brad Steiger*

When the writers Ostrander and Schroeder were in Russia conducting research for *Psychic Discoveries Behind the Iron Curtain* (Ostrander, 1970) they encountered a magazine article describing Mikhail Drogzenovitch, a fifty-three year old farmer from Bulgaria, who had frequently demonstrated levitation to the local villagers. He had been observed and tested by "scientific witnesses." He would sit down in a field and close his eyes, often surrounded by observers. Then, according to the article, he rose into the air to a height of about four feet, and remained there for ten minutes. Witnesses checked around him for ropes and mechanical contrivances, and found none (Ostrander, 1970).

And in America, today, there is a professional magician who may embody elements of "real magic" together with the usual arsenal of stage magic tricks. The performer David Blaine produced a video of performances of "street magic" in which he traveled to many cities and performed magic tricks for passersby, filming their reactions.

The resulting video, *Fearless* (Blaine, 2001), is fascinating because many of the tricks are performed in broad daylight on city sidewalks in major cities. There are no obvious special effects, and there is no place to easily hide a scaffolding or other prop which could lift him into the air. Yet, on several occasions he does appear to rise into the air with onlookers only a few feet away. Is this a magic trick or is it real levitation?

Figure 6.5. Is this a magic trick or real levitation? Although some skeptics have demonstrated a "false levitation" technique in which one foot is partially hidden and is used to lift off the ground by a few inches, we see here that the height above the ground seems too great to use such a fraudulent technique. The low camera angle, which shoots under his feet, also seems to preclude such a technique. (Blaine, 2001) *Courtesy of David Blaine*

On the one hand, Blaine is a skilled illusionist. Therefore the natural conclusion is that it is a magic trick, an illusion. There was no scientist there to check for hidden wires or cranes above his head, so we can never consider this a scientific experiment.

On the other hand, he did it in broad daylight, surrounded by pedestrians, on a busy sidewalk in a major city. The reaction of the witnesses is revealing. In several cases they become almost hysterical when they see this feat. This reaction by itself suggests something unusual is going on.

The photograph above, Figure 6.5, is a single frame from Blaine's video. Although his right hand is hidden behind a bystander, the frames immediately before and after show the sidewalk around him to be completely clear. There are no overhanging buildings or other structures from which a wire could be suspended to lift him up. His entire body is visible at close range on the camera as he talks to the bystanders before and after. And he is wearing a simple T-shirt (it is Atlantic City in the summer) which would seem to rule out any hidden harnesses or other mechanical structures.

On camera, he slowly rises into the air about one foot, and then descends again equally slowly. This is not a jump, and it certainly does not appear to be what some skeptics have suggested, that he is lifting himself on one foot. His foot would have to be extremely long to do this, and in the video frame one can clearly see beneath his feet to the ground below. In the full video this is made even more apparent.

Blaine himself does not call this levitation and offers no clarification about whether these events are real or the illusion of a gifted magician. He says that he does his tricks to open people's minds and stimulate them to think. Is it real, or is it a trick? Blaine does not say, but he offers this quote from Aristotle:

"It was through the feeling of wonder that men now and at first began to philosophize." --Aristotle

The feats of David Blaine certainly engender wonder and do stimulate the desire to understand.

The examples presented here barely scratch the surface of this subject. Even if some of these cases turn out not to be real, it takes only one legitimate example to prove the phenomenon. And there is a wealth of high quality testimony here to support the existence of this ability. Levitation seems to occur more often than we have been led to believe, and deserves serious study.

Summary

In this chapter we have seen evidence that a few gifted individuals, even in modern times, are able to levitate. Unfortunately, there is very little rigorous controlled laboratory evidence to substantiate this. Therefore we are left with first hand accounts, some very credible, and photographic and film evidence. In the case of the Catholic Saints Teresa of Avila and Brother Joseph, any witness falsely swearing to have seen these remarkable flights would be subject to the most severe Church punishments, both in this life and the afterlife. These investigations, as well as the others in this chapter, have the ring of sincerity and authenticity.

The closest thing to a scientific study would probably be the investigations carried out by Dr. William Crookes, the eminent British scientist, discoverer of Thallium and Fellow and former President of the Royal Society. He studied the abilities of the psychic D.D. Home for many years and devised numerous experiments to eliminate the possibility of fraud. In the course of those years, while being examined and tested by many scientists, Home was never detected in any fraud. And he demonstrated levitation on countless occasions.

In the author's opinion, the evidence is persuasive that this ability exists. However, this is one of those frontier areas of the new science, where we must resort to anecdote in lieu of rigorous scientific experiments. Hopefully these will one day follow.

Levitation is one of the abilities often ascribed to saints, yogis, and others of highly developed psychic and spiritual abilities. Another rare, controversial ability is that of teleportation, the ability to make an object disappear in one place and materialize someplace else. In Western culture we associate this with the trickery of the stage magician. But there is actually hard scientific evidence, carried out in controlled conditions in the laboratory, where such abilities have been demonstrated.

In Lewis Carroll's *Alice in Wonderland*, Alice was advised to think of six impossible things before breakfast every morning as a mental discipline. We have already seen that the strange forces associated with the paranormal can move objects, affect random processes, and cause levitation, all of which defy current physics. In the next chapter, we shall learn about one more impossible thing: the normal solidity of objects is not what we think.

Our modern science knows that the atom is not solid but is mostly empty space. However it still seems solid to the touch. Modern science also knows that matter has wave-like properties, and there has been much speculation about the possibility of transmitting or broadcasting matter as one would with radio waves. There have even been demonstrations in the physics laboratory of "teleportation" of photons and attempts at teleporting single atoms.

This is a far cry from having an operational transporter room resembling the one in *Star Trek*. Contemporary science is very far away from the ability to disassemble and reassemble solid objects, or to instantly transport them across distance or through solid walls. Teleportation seems to be a rare ability and there have been only a few laboratory demonstrations of it which have been made public. A great deal more research will be required before this subject is accepted by the scientific community. But in the next chapter we will encounter evidence that some gifted individuals seem to have these abilities. As in previous chapters, this information can help us understand what is possible in our universe. It may require us to modify our physical laws and theories, and it may lead to a heightened understanding of our true human potential.

CHAPTER 7 - TELEPORTATION

"Then the highest leader among them ordered that he [Zhang Baosheng] be locked up in a room. When this official went home, as soon as he opened the door, he saw Zhang Baosheng waiting there for him. He was stunned. From that time on, Zhang Baosheng has been working for the Defense Ministry...Zhang has the power to move shoes, hot water bottles, keys and other objects through wooden boards and walls, and make large objects move back and forth. On one occasion before a large number of witnesses, Zhang caused a hundred pound sack of sugar to move through walls of a storehouse, ending up in front of them."
- Paul Dong and Thomas E. Raffill, (Dong, 1997)

"In 1974 a group of distinguished physicists at the University of London observed renowned psychic Uri Geller apparently bend metallic objects and cause part of a crystal, encapsulated in a container, to disappear."
- U.S. National Research Council report, *Enhancing Human Performance-Issues, Theories and Techniques* (Druckman, 1988)

DEFINITION-Teleportation: The act of transporting objects or beings from one place to another, without the object seeming to exist in intermediate locations. Walls and structures are no obstacle to this process which usually occurs almost instantaneously. The object often seems to fade out or instantly disappear in one location and fade in or instantly appear somewhere else.

Chinese Experiments

The mainland Chinese government has demonstrated a strong interest in people who can manifest paranormal abilities. It has conducted open, massive, nationwide searches to identify highly talented individuals. These are called the EHF or "Extra-High Functioning" children (Dong, 1984). One such gifted young girl is Zhue Mei, a third grade pupil at the primary school attached to Shanghai Jiaotong University. She demonstrated in controlled experiments a form of psychokinesis which may better be qualified as teleportation. She is able to remove beans from a sealed bottle in a sealed box, without unsealing the bottle or, needless to say, touching the box in any way.

This ability was discovered during government tests in which she also demonstrated strong remote viewing abilities. She first volunteered to the scientists that she had the ability to unlock a lock inside a sealed box. Officials placed a padlock inside a cardboard box and sealed it with tape. She held the box while dozens of researchers looked on. In a moment she declared that the lock was now open. When the researchers unsealed the box, they found that, somehow, the key had been placed into the padlock and turned, thus unlocking the lock.

Then the third grader announced that she could also remove beans from a sealed bottle. A plastic bottle was filled with red beans, sealed with a cork, and again placed in a cardboard box sealed with tape. As she concentrated on the box, her mother explained to the scientists that this experiment would take some time, as she had to first open the bottle, then remove the beans. She objected, saying "But it doesn't" and announced that the beans were out of the bottle. When the box was opened, the beans were found to have been removed from the bottle, but the cork was still securely in place. This strongly suggests, as amazing as it seems, that the beans were teleported out of the bottle (Dong, 1984).

Hartwig Hausdorf, in his book *The Chinese Roswell* (Hausdorf, 1998), describes experiments which he was allowed to witness in China. These involved psychokinesis, moving objects from one place to another, combined with some demonstrations of teleportation, in which the object would actually disappear from one location and appear at another virtually simultaneously.

To perform these feats, the Chinese assembled a group of young people who had demonstrated these abilities previously. These were probably the EHF individuals described by Paul Dong (Dong, 1984, 1997). The Institute of High Energy Physics in Beijing collaborated with the Chinese military on the demonstrations which Hausdorf witnessed.

In one set of experiments, a mini-transmitter was teleported from one location to another. It was a small, battery powered, radio transmitter which could be tracked by its signals. It was placed in the pocket of one of the individuals. A second individual in a separate room had a sealed container attached to her body. The goal was to teleport the transmitter into the sealed container. Therefore it had to pass from the pocket of an individual in one room, through the walls of the room, and into the sealed container attached to the body of the receiver. At no time was either individual allowed to touch the container or the transmitter. The scientists taking part in the experiment were Drs. Lin Shu-long, Hsu Hung-Chang and Chen Shou Liang.

Figure 7.1. Illustration of one Chinese teleportation experiment in which a small radio transmitter was teleported from the pocket of one individual through a wall and into a sealed container attached to a second individual. The position of the transmitter was tracked by a radio receiver. As the teleportation occurred, the frequency of the transmitter dropped gradually to zero and then returned to its normal value in the new location (Dong, 1984, 1997).

At just the moment when the transmitter was supposed to be teleported, the scientists observed the transmitted signal fluctuate wildly and at times disappear completely. A second later, the signal became firm again and indicated that it was now coming from the container in the second room. When the container was examined, it was found that the teleportation had been successful. Somehow, the transmitter had indeed rematerialized in the sealed container attached to the subject in the second room.

I have heard of this same experiment, or one very similar to it, from other independent sources. I was told that the frequency of the transmitter slowed down and actually stopped for a brief moment during the transmission, then gradually returned to the original frequency. This suggests that time itself may have been affected by the teleportation, since frequency is a measure of time.

This behavior is reminiscent of what happens in quantum mechanics. If an elementary particle, such as an electron, stops in space its frequency becomes very low and its position becomes spread out over a large area. This is a consequence of the Uncertainty Principle. If this is true of the Chinese experiment, it suggests that the teleportation process involves quantum-like delocalisation of the object. Normally quantum mechanical effects are only seen for very small objects, not something as large as pocket electronics. An example of a recent laboratory teleportation of a very small particle, namely a photon, is described at this end of this chapter.

In another, similar, experiment, the object teleported was not a transmitter, but a roll of unexposed film. It started out in a sealed container in one room, and was teleported into a different sealed container in a second room. Because psychic phenomena can sometimes expose film, this was a significant experiment. The goal was to teleport the film without exposing it. (The applications for military and espionage use should be pretty obvious.)

Again, as in the first experiment, the subjects were completely successful in carrying out the teleportation. The film disappeared from the container in the first room, and virtually simultaneously appeared in the sealed container in the second room. The seals on both containers were unbroken. When the film was developed, it was found to be unexposed (Hausdorf, 1998).

Paul Dong and Thomas E. Raffill, in their fascinating book *China's Super Psychics* (Dong, 1997), describe one of the stars of the Chinese EHF program. This is Zhang Baosheng, who has been given the formal title of "National Treasure" by the People's Republic of China. The quote at the beginning of this chapter provides a glimpse of his powers. As with the other Chinese super-psychics mentioned above, he is adept at removing pills from a sealed bottle, and can even cause paper or other objects to appear in the bottle without breaking the seal. This is basic teleportation, since objects must pass through the walls of the bottle without opening it. Causing a one-hundred pound sack of sugar to pass through a wall in front of many witnesses would seem more difficult, but he as done that as well.

One trick he has developed, which we all might envy, is the ability to make traffic tickets disappear. He was given a luxury auto by Li Jiacheng, the richest man in Hong Kong. He habitually broke the traffic rules as he drove it around town. Initially he received numerous tickets from the traffic police, but invariably when they returned to the station, they found that their tickets had vanished without a trace! They were unable to prosecute him. Since then, they have given up trying to ticket him.

The Chinese military conducts active research on Zhang. There is said to be a $20 million research program underway to study his abilities. One foreign government reportedly sent an agent to China to offer him as much to defect, but he refused. Other Chinese super-psychics are not as well known, but have even more amazing abilities. They are part of China's classified military research program. It is rumored that one of them can move very large objects, and another can cause a normal person's blood pressure to rise to dangerous levels, even causing death. This can be done from hundreds of miles away (Dong, 1997).

The Geller New York Experience

Uri Geller, the famous psychic who burst onto the American scene in the early nineteen seventies, had several strange teleportation experiences for which there is good supporting evidence. In one dramatic case, described in his book *The Geller Effect* (Geller, 1986), he was in New York City and had just left Bloomingdale's. At this point he said good-bye to Maria Janis, the wife of Byron Janis, the well-known composer. As he walked along the sidewalk he felt as if he were being pulled backward into a dark tube. The feeling accelerated and he found himself above a house falling downward.

He crashed through a window and landed on a table top surrounded by broken glass. He was on the back porch of a house. As he regained composure and looked around, he noticed that the room looked very familiar. He was in the house of a scientist he knew, who lived in upstate New York, more than 90 minutes drive from New York City. The scientist, Dr. Andrija Puharich, heard the crash and rushed to the back porch to find Uri there. When he learned what had happened he insisted that Uri immediately telephone Maria Janis in New York to tell her and to document the event.

They began calling her apartment but she had not yet arrived home. In about ten minutes she arrived at her New York apartment, which was only about three blocks from the place where Uri had dematerialized. She said to Uri over the phone: "Where are you? Where did you go?" He said, "I'm with Puharich at his house". She said "That's impossible. I only left you ten minutes ago." She verified the time when she left Uri in Manhattan and when she received the phone call a few minutes later. This event appears to be genuine despite its very strange nature.

Geller was the subject of several experiments conducted at the Stanford Research Institute during this same period (Puthoff, 1974, 1976; Targ, 1977; Tart, 1979). In one experiment, which was reportedly preserved on film (Byrd, 1992), Geller was given the task of attempting to make an object teleport. The experiment was conducted with a transparent table and cameras shooting down from above. A small object, the size of a salt shaker, was at one corner of the table.

For four hours Geller tried to make the object teleport or dematerialize. He tried everything, holding his hands over the object, shouting at it, staring at it, everything he could think of. Then he gave up, slapped his hands on his thighs, and said "That's it. I give up." At that instant the film showed the object dematerialize from its location and rematerialize at another point on the far corner of the table. It took several frames of the film to do this, something on the order of a second or two. While it was dematerializing, it could be seen rematerializing in the other location.

The appearance of this object while it was dematerializing and rematerializing is reported to resemble the sparkling or twinkling seen when objects "transported" on the old *Star Trek* show. Sometimes truth is stranger than fiction.

On another videotape, a wristwatch owned by Dr. Puthoff was seen to materialize above a table, descend while decelerating, land on the table and bounce. The watch had, moments before, been in Puthoff's locked briefcase. Another incident occurred when Geller arrived at his hotel room to find a brand new outboard motor lying on his bed. He called a friend of his to ask where it had come from, and learned that no one had sent it to him. His friend traced the serial number to a sealed packing box in a warehouse. They found the packing box, which was empty but unopened.

A supporting account about Geller is offered by Colin Wilson in the book *Mysterious Powers* (Wilson, 1975). He relates one of their meetings in which Geller succeeded in placing images into Wilson's mind and performed other convincing feats. Here is Wilson's description of a subsequent event:

"A couple of months after this, Ted Bastin, a quantum physicist, and I appeared on a television discussion show about supernormal powers- a subject about which Ted is distinctly skeptical. When I mentioned Uri Geller, however, Ted told me that he had conducted extensive tests and was convinced that Uri was genuine. A few days later Ted rang me up to announce that Uri had just performed a most spectacular feat in his laboratory. He had dematerialized half a crystal that had been sealed in a metal container. Bastin said that there was no way in which Uri could have touched the crystal." (Wilson, 1975)

In further support of Geller's legitimate abilities in this area, a report by the U.S. National Research Council entitled *Enhancing Human Performance-Issues, Theories and Techniques* (Druckman, 1988), states:

"In 1974 a group of distinguished physicists at the University of London observed renowned psychic Uri Geller apparently bend metallic objects and cause part of a crystal, encapsulated in a container, to disappear."

If a crystal, encapsulated inside a container, disappears, then that is an example of teleportation.

Ancient Cases of Teleportation

Other examples of apparent teleportation have occurred throughout history. Berlitz (Berlitz, 1988) describes the case of a Spanish soldier stationed in the Phillipines in 1593. He was assigned to guard the Phillipine capital of Manila. On October 25 of that year, he suddenly appeared in the main plaza of Mexico City, some 9,000 miles away. He was dressed in a different uniform from those around him and attracted considerable attention. He was bewildered by what had happened. A moment before, he had been in the Phillipines as part of a Spanish garrison, with the assignment to guard the palace. He said the governor of the Phillipines had been killed the night before, causing the need for more guards.

Then he suddenly found himself in Mexico City. He did not know how it happened. He was placed in prison and kept there until a Spanish ship from the Phillipines arrived weeks later, completely confirming his information about the assassination of the governor. They stated that the man was exactly who he said he was. To this day there is no adequate explanation how he could have spontaneously teleported 9,000 miles in the year 1593.

In another extraordinary case, a Catholic nun, Sister Suor Marfa, became internationally famous in the 1600s. She was very devout and imposed upon herself a strict discipline which including fasting, sleeplessness and self-flagellation (Berlitz, 1988). She was famous for her ability to respond to the unspoken thoughts of others and her ability to levitate, which was often witnessed in the convent. However her most notable feat involved her ability to bi-locate. It is said that while living in the convent in Spain, she projected herself across the Atlantic and ministered to a poor Native American tribe of hunter-gatherers, the *Jumanos*, in West Texas.

As the Spanish began to immigrate northward from Mexico, a Franciscan priest, Father Alonzo de Benavides, encountered this tribe. To his surprise they had already been converted to Christianity. They claimed they had been converted by a mysterious "woman in blue," who had also given them rosaries and nursed their wounds. The priest sent a letter to "both Pope Urban VIII and King Philip IV of Spain, demanding to know who had preceded him in his ministry. He did not receive his answer until 1630, when he returned to Spain and heard of Sister Suor's miracles. He visited her convent in person, and learned that the habit of her order was blue." (Berlitz, 1988)

U. S. Defense Intelligence Agency (DIA) Assessment

A DIA document dating from 1972, *Controlled Offensive Behavior-USSR*, discusses the possibility of developing "apports" - a technique by which physical objects, such as documents, might be teleported from enemy territory (LaMothe, 1972). This same report quotes several eminent scientists, such as Sir William Crookes (1832-1919), the famous British chemist and physicist:

> *"I have more than once seen, first an object move, then a luminous cloud appear to form about it, and lastly, the cloud condense into shape and become a perfectly formed hand...sometimes appears perfectly life-like and graceful, the fingers moving and the flesh apparently as human as that of any in the room. At the wrist or arm it becomes hazy, and fades off into a luminous cloud. To the touch the hand sometimes appears icy cold and dead, at other times warm and life-like, grasping my own with the firm pressure of an old friend...it gradually seems to resolve itself into vapor and faded in that manner from my grasp."(Crookes, 1874)*

We remark that this strange "apport" or part of a human body, which materializes out of thin air, is reminiscent of the ability of some yogis to produce, at their convenience, a "second body," completely lifelike in appearance, which is able to travel elsewhere and carry out errands. As fantastic as this sounds, one should read the account of Yogananda later in this chapter, and to recall that Sir William Crookes had the highest credibility as a scientist. He was, however, conducting research on one of the greatest psychics of the day, David Dunglas Home, which probably accounts for why he witnessed this rare phenomenon that few of us ever encounter.

Another incident was reported by Lady Crookes, the wife of Sir William. She was attending a séance and sat a little apart from the other sitters, facing them. D.D. Home stood in the doorway to an adjacent room holding an accordion. According to her:

> *"The accordion was immediately taken from his hand by a cloudy appearance, which soon seemed to condense into a distinct human form, clothed in a filmy drapery, standing near Mr. Home between the two rooms. The accordion began to play...and the figure advanced toward me till it almost touched me, playing continuously. It was semitransparent, and I could see the sitters through it all the time. Mr. Home remained near the sliding doors. As the figure approached I felt an intense cold, getting stronger as it got nearer, and as it was giving me the accordion I could not help screaming. The figure immediately seemed to sink into the floor to the waist, leaving only the head and shoulders visible, still playing the accordion, which was then about a foot off the floor. Mr. Home and my husband came to me at once, and I have no clear recollection of what then occurred, except that the accordion did not cease playing immediately. Mr. Sarjeant Cox was rather angry at my want of nerve, and exclaimed: 'Mrs. Crookes, you have spoilt the finest manifestation we ever had.' I have always regretted that my want of presence of mind brought the phenomena to so abrupt a termination." (Stemman, 1975)*

Dr. Crookes' experiments with D. D. Home were corroborated by the work of a contemporary, Dr. Alfred Russell Wallace. He was the naturalist who, together with

Charles Darwin, enunciated the Theory of Evolution. He became convinced from his observations that many of the remarkable feats performed by Spiritists in England during this period were genuine, having observed a number of them first hand. He believed they were the evidence for "an unknown power" and began conducting research to attempt to understand it. He carried out a number of experiments on a medium named Agnes Nichol, later the well-known Mrs. Guppy, who exhibited remarkable paranormal abilities.

In seances with her, levitation was reported to be a common occurrence. Sometimes the medium was lifted along with her chair right up onto the table. Her apparent ability to teleport objects, or to materialize them, was even more remarkable. In experiments conducted with Wallace, she was able to produce, on request, virtually any object. This happened on hundreds of occasions. When a friend of Wallace asked her to produce a sunflower, a six-foot tall sunflower with earth still clinging to its roots fell out of the air onto the table. Such experiences, duplicated hundreds of times under close scrutiny and scientific control, convinced Wallace that such phenomena "are proved quite as well as any facts are proved in other sciences." (Stemman, 1975)

After recounting these events, the Defense Intelligence Agency (DIA) document concluded its analysis:

"If any of this highly questionable material is true then it can be inferred that organic matter can be transformed into "ectoplasm," and this can be rendered invisible and impalpable and thus converted into something which, for all practical purposes, amounts to force. If organic matter can be converted into such "force-matter," it seems reasonable to assume that a physical object, if similarly converted, could travel through space…One is faced with the possibility that the human mind can disintegrate and reintegrate organic matter…in view of the very real Soviet threat in this sector, the science of parapsychology should be investigated to its fullest potential, perhaps to the benefit of national defense." *(LaMothe, 1972)*

Abilities of the Yogis -Teleportation and Bilocation

As Western scientists study the remarkable evidence of paranormal phenomena, there is always the temptation to believe that we are discovering something NEW. But further research reveals that these remarkable capabilities are actually very old, and have been developed to a high degree in certain ancient cultures. One of the most extraordinary of these are the yogis of India.

The culture of India is very old. The Vedas are the historical poems which record the history and important stories of the culture. They are believed by many scholars to have originated at least 6,000 years ago, and are therefore older than the Bible. This tradition includes many disciplines of body and mind training, called Yogas. Wise men who become expert at these practices are said to develop capabilities which we in the West call paranormal.

In the old culture of India, these capabilities were not considered extraordinary. They were a natural consequence of the yogic disciplines of meditation, breathwork, and exercise. These enabled the expert to control his bodily needs, to endure great cold or heat, to go without food and even without breathing, to achieve a state of suspended animation in some cases, to extend his awareness, and even to affect events in far off places.

Yogis are similar to monks in that they have renounced worldly possessions and spend all of their time in meditation and prayer. Their wisdom states that there are many levels to the universe above the physical. The yogis, through a lifetime, or they would say many lifetimes, of training have attuned themselves to these higher dimensional forces, and they say that this is what enables them to accomplish amazing feats.

One person who bridged the cultural gap between East and West was a true yogi himself. He was born in 1893 and grew up in India, was trained by some of the greatest Yogis of his time, and came to America in the 1930's with the specific mission of making this knowledge available to the Westerner. His name is Paramahansa Yogananda. He established the Self-Realization Fellowship in California in 1935. The story of his life, *Autobiography of a Yogi*, includes many first hand accounts of the extraordinary abilities of yogis in India. (Yogananda, 1946) A sketch of Yogananda, on the right, with his guru Sri Yukteswar is shown below in Figure 7.2.

Figure 7.2 A sketch of two yogis, Yogananda, on the right, and Sri Yukteswar, his teacher and guru, by H. Shapero.

The ability of a true yogi to transcend the limits of ordinary matter is illustrated in the following story, told in greater detail in his book. When Yogananda was a teenage boy his father, who was an official with the British Indian Railroad, often sent him on errands, even to distant cities in India, using the railroad as his means of transportation. This was in the first decade of the twentieth century and there were no telephones, so a personal messenger was often needed to convey a message.

Once his father asked Yogananda to travel to the distant city of Banaras to carry a message to Kedar Nath Babu, a friend of his. His father had lost the address and the city was large, so he told Yogananda that when he arrived in Banaras, go to the house of a mutual friend, Swami Pranabananda, a powerful yogi. He would help locate Kedar Nath Babu.

When Yogananda arrived at the Swami's house after a long train ride, the Swami instantly knew what he desired. Instead of explaining where Kedar Nath Babu could be found, or going to look for him, the Swami immediately entered a deep state of meditation. Yogananda was puzzled as to what he should do, so he sat quietly before the yogi and waited. In half an hour, the yogi came out of his trance and said that Kedar Nath Babu was approaching the house. A moment later he did indeed enter the Swami's house.

Yogananda was puzzled. How was it that Kedar Nath Babu had been summoned to the Swami's house, when the Swami had been seated before him in meditation for the previous half hour? Kedar Nath Babu explained that, less than a half hour before, he had been bathing by the river Ganges, when Swami Pranabananda came to him. He had no idea how he found him. The Swami said that Yogananda was at his house and desired to meet with him.

The Swami began walking with him back to the house, but in a few minutes decided to run on ahead and left him, walking at a rapid pace. So Kedar Nath Babu, following as fast as he could, had just arrived at the house. Somehow, the Swami had been in two places at once. He was meditating in front of Yogananda, and he was walking through the streets of Banaras with Kedar Nath Babu (Yogananda, 1946).

This phenomenon is called "bilocation." It is reported that yogis are frequently able to manifest this ability. They appear and are seen by others in two places at once. It is one of many extraordinary abilities they have, including great clairvoyance and precognitive powers.

Another example comes from a British railroad superintendent in India, who happened to have as an employee a modest young man named Lahiri Mahasaya, who later became famous throughout India as a great yogi. Despite his lowly position in the British office, his supervisor respected his unusual abilities. One day he confided to Mahasaya that his wife, back in England, was critically ill and he was worried about her health. The yogi replied:

"I shall get you some word about her." Lahiri Mahasaya left the room and sat for a short time in a secluded spot. On his return he smiled consolingly.

"Your wife is improving; she is writing you a letter." The omniscient yogi quoted some parts of the missive.

"Ecstatic Babu [said the British supervisor addressing the yogi] I already know you are no ordinary man. Yet I am unable to believe that, at will, you can banish time and space!"

The promised letter finally arrived. The astounded superintendent found that it contained not only the good news of his wife's recovery but also the same phrases that, weeks earlier, the great master had uttered.

The wife came to India some months later. Meeting Lahiri Mahasaya, she gazed at him reverently.

"Sir," she said, "it was your form, haloed in glorious light, that I beheld months ago by my sickbed in London. At that moment I was completely healed! Soon after, I was able to undertake the long ocean voyage to India."
(Yogananda, 1946)

In this story, Mahasaya either bilocated or teleported himself to London, appeared before the superintendent's wife, performed a healing, and returned a few minutes later to report to her husband the detailed contents of a letter which she was just then writing to him. This all occurred during a time before radio and before trans-oceanic telegraph. News required weeks to reach India from England. And upon her arrival in India, the wife recognized Mahasaya as the man who had appeared before her in her English hospital room and performed her healing!

Skeptical Westerners may well scoff at such stories. Yet many of these were supported and vouched for by the participants, and this carries more weight when the participants themselves were initially skeptics. Some yogis apparently can transcend the limits of space and time that we Westerners take for granted. In so doing they offer us a revelatory glimpse of the larger dimensions of the universe which are available to us. In so doing, they also make a mockery of twentieth century science, breaking at will the laws of physics we thought we knew.

Teleportation Across a Continent

The fakirs and holy men of Arabia and North Africa have much in common with the yogis of India. They too practice magic and are reported to be able to accomplish paranormal feats which should be impossible based on our known science.

One example is recounted in a book by Adrian Clark titled *Psychokinesis-Moving Matter with the Mind* (Clark, 1973). The author of this book is a scientist associated with the Skylab project and several other important NASA programs. He was instrumental in the development of America's first satellite launch vehicles, including the Vanguard rocket and the Saturn 5. He was also an advisor to the Marshall Space Flight Center. He recounts an incident, originally described by Ayling (Ayling, 1968), which demonstrated, for those present, the reality of teleportation.

It seems that a French medical officer, a Captain Dubois, had inoculated an Arab village against diphtheria. The local head man, Abdul, was very impressed with this feat and offered to demonstrate his power to Captain Dubois. First he caused mineral water to change into fine champagne. Being a man of science, Dubois was skeptical of the paranormal and believed it was a trick. The head man, to make a demonstration which defied any possibility of trickery, then caused a picture to appear in the Captain's hands. The Captain examined the picture closely and determined that it was no illusion. It was the exact same picture which had been, moments before, in the Captain's home thousands of miles away. Meanwhile, at the same time in Paris, someone noticed that the picture was missing and the apparent theft was reported to the Parisian police, who tried to locate it. After holding the picture for 48 hours, Abdul caused it to return to the captain's home in Paris. This story was reported in the French newspapers and the *London Times* (Clark, 1973).

Scientific Teleportation

Although matter may seem perfectly solid, and the claims of teleportation may seem wild, even mainstream physics is beginning to contemplate the possibility. The characters on *Star Trek* do it all the time, of course, as Captain Kirk asks Scotty to "Beam me up." But the peculiarities of quantum mechanics and the wave-like nature of matter have caused some physicists to begin experimenting with teleportation in the laboratory.

Associated Press science writer Malcolm Ritter has described an Austrian experiment in an article titled "Teleportation achieved in Lab?" (Ritter, 1997). He recounts a report published in *Nature* by Anton Zeilinger and colleagues at the University of Innsbruck in Austria. It is actually an "entangled photon" experiment, but it has elements which some feel may be the key to teleportation. Ritter describes the experiment:

"In an Austrian lab, scientists destroyed bits of light in one place and made perfect replicas appear about three feet away. They did that by transferring information about a crucial physical characteristic of the original light bits, called photons. The information was picked up by other photons, which took on that characteristic and so became replicas of the originals...The work is the first to demonstrate 'quantum teleportation', a bizarre shifting of physical characteristics between nature's tiniest particles, no matter how far apart they are... When two photons are entangled they have opposite luck...Whatever happens to one is the opposite of what happens to the other. In particular the polarizations are the opposite of each other."

So actually the polarization of one photon was transferred to another photon, which is a far cry from teleporting an object. Still, it is an interesting phenomenon and it may be related.

"Quantum entanglement" is an important effect which is finding applications in many areas of science. It makes use of a basic quantum principle in which a pair of particles is produced in a coupled quantum state, so the overall state of the pair is known but the state of each particle is unknown (see Figure 7.3). Pairs of photons are used in this case, so that the state of polarization, or spin, of the pair is well-determined, but the spin of each photon is unknown. This is called an entangled state.

Then the two photons are allowed to travel off in different directions. It may be a few feet away, or it may be light years. Then, if the spin of one of the photons is detected by a measuring device, we instantly know the state of the other photon, because the two spins must add up to the total state, which is known. Therefore, instantly we know the spin of something which can be light years away. Furthermore, once the spin of one is known, the other is determined so it is no longer uncertain.

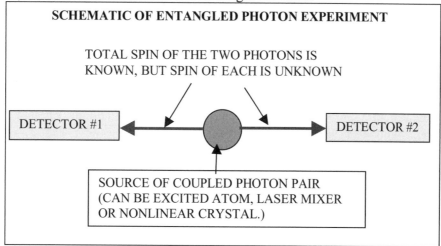

Figure 7.3. Schematic description of a photon entanglement experiment. By various means, a coupled state of two photons is produced, so the total spin (or other parameter) of the pair is known, but the spin of each photon is unknown. The photons propagate away from their mixing point in different directions. When one is detected by Detector #1, then its spin is known. Then the spin at the other detector will be instantaneously known, no matter how far away it is.

Dr. Akio Motoyoshi (Motoyoshi, 2000) has published a theoretical paper in *Physics Letters A* entitled "Teleportation without resorting to Bell measurement." This again refers to a method of teleportation in which a set of particles is created in an entangled state. Their wave functions are constructed with some uncertainty built into them. Then two or more beams are created in which the wave functions can be projected in different directions. At their destinations, a selection or detection of one beam can force the instantaneous untangling of the other beam. This can lead, theoretically, to instantaneous transmission of information about the quantum states and can be used to affect the quantum states of a set of electrons at a distance.

It is a far cry from beaming up Captain Kirk, and even the name "teleportation" may connote a slightly different meaning from its popular usage. Nevertheless, these experiments do point out that quantum mechanics can give rise to some very strange effects, including the instantaneous linking of material states over great distances. This is related to teleportation, even if in a very limited form. As science continues to explore this strange new land in which matter can materialize and dematerialize, and be transmitted like radio waves, perhaps some day we will learn that even the science fiction of *Star Trek* is not so far-fetched after all.

Summary

This chapter has reviewed some of the evidence for teleportation. As with levitation, there are very few scientifically controlled studies, at least which are publicly available. The National Research Council's report of Uri Geller teleporting a crystal out of a sealed container under the close observation of scientists is one clue that the United States government has taken an interest in teleportation research. The Defense Intelligence Agency report cited in this chapter also reveals military interest in this subject. However, both of those reports date from the early nineteen-seventies, when the U.S. government was just beginning research programs into psychic phenomena. Since that time very little has been made public.

A somewhat different picture is seen in China. The books by Paul Dong (Dong, 1984, 1997) have shown that research in teleportation has high-level support by the Chinese military. Their government has taken a very different approach from the American. Instead of trying to ridicule and classify research on teleportation, the Chinese government publicizes gifted psychics, and conducts nationwide sweeps to locate talented psychic practitioners and induct them into the EHF program. The experiments cited above are but a small sampling of the experiments which were probably conducted. They provide valuable scientific evidence about the nature and functioning of teleportation, which seems to be completely real and genuine.

Teleportation is of enormous scientific value, because it provides information about the true nature of matter. Modern physics knows that the elementary particles, electrons and quarks, which are the building blocks of all matter, are essentially point particles. They have no fundamental width. They take up space because they travel at high speed and exert forces on other particles. In this way the electron, for example, by zooming around the nucleus of the atom at high speed, makes the atom seem to take up volume, appear solid and have a certain diameter.

But in fact, almost all of the atom's volume is empty space. It is just vacuum. Because of this, it has been speculated that there might be a way to allow atoms to pass through other atoms. If one could synchronize the electrons in the two atoms so they did not collide, for example, this might be possible. In Chapter 13 we present a scientific model which would explain how this might be done.

From the available evidence, it seems that certain gifted psychics are already able to accomplish teleportation, including transmitting objects through walls and across distances of many miles. The strength of this evidence suggests that open, public science should investigate this phenomenon with an open mind, and that our theories of physics need to be reconsidered in the light of what this tells us about the true nature of matter.

In this book, we have encountered individuals with truly unusual abilities. These abilities give the possessor enormous power, and could serve the society in valuable ways. The present government of China seems to have realized this, and is carrying out its EHF program to locate and train such talented individuals. In the past, the ancient Greeks and Egyptians maintained similar programs to identify and develop those with strong paranormal talents. In those days they were called "Mystery Schools," or "Wisdom Schools" and were associated with spiritual centers.

One of the chief purposes of this system was to train talented students to heighten and master these abilities which we call paranormal. Graduates were called "adepts" or "initiates." They frequently exhibited all of the super powers we have discussed so far.

Although development of their psychic power was an important indicator of their advancement, an even more important element was the development of wisdom and spiritual awareness. Without this, their powers might be misused. In the next chapter we will describe some of these gifted individuals and the programs of training which created them.

CHAPTER 8 - ADEPTS

"We Westerners are rightly proud of our achievements in 'face-lifting' this world of ours, but we get a little disturbed sometimes when we hear of a half-naked fakir performing a feat which we can neither match nor understand."
–Paul Brunton, in *The Quest of the Overself* (Brunton, 1970)

"All creation is governed by law. The principles that operate in the outer universe, discoverable by science, are called natural laws. But there are subtler laws that rule the hidden spiritual planes and the inner realm of consciousness; these principles are knowable through the science of yoga. It is not the physicist but the Self-realized master who comprehends the true nature of matter. By such knowledge Christ was able to restore the servant's ear after it had been severed by one of the disciples."
--Swami Sri Yukteswar (Yukteswar, 1949)

DEFINITON-Adept: Someone who, in traditional societies might be a yogi or a shaman: a master of the paranormal, often displaying unusual powers from a young age.

What is an "Adept"?

Men or women of amazing paranormal abilities are often called "adepts." It is an ancient term describing one with advanced development of psychic and paranormal abilities, often capable of performing what we call "miracles." Yet they would say that they are simply manipulating the universe using natural laws which are not well understood or recognized by present-day science. When one considers the power displayed by such an adept, it is fortunate that the average person is not capable of such feats. There is such anger and violence present in the average man (one only needs to watch the road rage on the highway) that we can be thankful that these abilities seem only available to highly evolved individuals who have first mastered their own emotions.

Adepts are found in all cultures. In ancient and traditional cultures they were especially prized and honored. Special schools were maintained to identify and train them. In Greece and Egypt, these were called the Mystery Schools. In the Middle Ages, secret societies often attempted to continue these traditions. Some monasteries maintained strict regimens to develop such individuals. And today, in China, with the EHF program, we see a modern effort to locate and train people of extraordinary psychic abilities.

These societies recognize that we all have these abilities, but they must be trained in order to develop to the fullest. In traditional cultures adepts were often revered,

Figure 8.1. Apollonius of Tyana, a famous adept from the first century A.D., from copper engraving by Johannes Theodorus de Bry (Hall, 1981).

and their help was sought for leadership, guidance and healing

In Africa they might be called witch doctors, in Siberia they would be called shamen, in the Far East, yogis, and in the Middle East they are referred to as fakirs. In ancient cultures they were the Wise Men and the Viziers. The Wise Men in the Bible who traveled to Bethlehem were probably examples of such men. Through psychic ability or astrology they were able to predict the time and place of Jesus' birth. Unfortunately, in Western cultures today, such abilities are often denied or ridiculed, and their appearance is attributed to the supernatural or to fraud.

Adepts often manifest unusual abilities from a young age. However, rigorous training with a guru or teacher is usually a part of the education, as well. Buddha was considered an adept, as was Apollonius of Tyana. These men appeared to be human just like you and me, according to the accounts, and yet capable of miracles which are astonishing. It would be easy to ignore the stories, except that they often come from highly credible sources. The stories of Apollonius recounted below, for example, were recorded by the Roman governor at the time. Adepts show us what is possible in man.

In many ancient cultures, schools were established to maintain a supply of these psychically gifted individuals. Graduates were "Initiates," which usually signified that they had survived rigorous tests and emerged in control of paranormal abilities. Often the final tests were so severe as to induce an out-of-body or near-death experience, and this was considered an important part of the training. (Hall, 1981)

In the Middle Ages, due to Church suppression in Europe, some of the practices were maintained in secret among Hermetic societies, which gave rise to the Rosecrucians, Freemasons and other mystical groups. And yet some monasteries, in both the Western and Orthodox Christian churches, maintained similar disciplines and practices.

Adepts, by whatever name, were often useful to rulers. They were the advisors to kings; they were the Wise men, foretelling the future, interpreting dreams, healing, and advising on the best time to begin a battle or a war. But because of their power they could also be dangerous, and therefore were also frequently suppressed.

The accounts of adepts of the past are made more credible when we realize that adepts exist today. In India, though the tradition is waning, there are schools which teach spiritual development with the goal of developing yogis, often called "spiritual supermen." Before the Chinese invasion, the culture of Tibet also supported such education, and indeed it was the backbone of the civilization and the government. In China today, the Communist government supports well-organized programs to identify paranormally gifted children and to develop their powers, but unfortunately, this effort may lack some of the spiritual and ethical controls of traditional development programs.

The existence of such profoundly gifted individuals has served to assist the scientific study of the paranormal, because they can manifest unusual phenomena seemingly at will. In Russia, Siberian shamen, Tibetan priests, and Mongolian *qi-gong* masters have been thoroughly tested and measured, to determine how they produce the phenomena they do. The yogis of India, who have understood and developed these skills for thousands of years, and can manifest a wide range of abilities, have been of great help to Western science in studying these phenomena (Murphy, 1992).

Famous Adepts of History

Jesus Christ exhibited the abilities of an adept. The miracles he performed, such as turning water into wine, feeding the multitudes with loaves and fishes, and even raising the dead, are examples of miracles which some adepts have also been able to perform. Buddhists note, for example, that when Buddha became enlightened, he too could perform miracles. Christians today are often taught that only Jesus had these abilities, but he taught his followers that anyone has this potential, if they will properly prepare themselves:

"Verily, verily, I say unto you, He that believeth on me, the works that I do shall he do also; and greater [works] than these shall he do; because I go unto my Father." (John 14:12, The Bible, *King James Version)*

Jesus is a controversial case, because parts of the Christian Church after his death adopted the philosophy advanced by Paul, that Jesus himself was to be worshipped. Other groups have focused more on the teachings of Jesus, believing that his real goal was to teach us to be better people.

The actual lessons he taught emphasized that we are all children of God, therefore all sons and daughters of God. Jesus never called himself the <u>only</u> son of God, and never told his followers that they should worship him as a God. In the Lord's Prayer, he explicitly teaches his disciples that God is "<u>Our</u> Father."

His actual words are consistent with the teachings of the adepts of many cultures. They are identical to the lessons of the Near-Death Experience: Love is most important. Forgiveness. Letting go of hate and fear and difference. "Judge NOT, that ye be not judged." "If someone strikes you, turn the other cheek." These lessons are universal. It was because they went against the prevailing Roman and Judaic law that he was crucified. Governments cannot rally their citizens to fight in the army if they truly believe and put into practice the lessons Jesus taught.

Jesus spoke of Heaven as one who has been there. "In my Father's house are many mansions." Yet, if one reads the descriptions of certain adept yogis, such as Sri Yukteswar, in Volume III, who describes the Astral realm, one sees a great similarity. Read the description by Dannion Brinkley (Chapter 11), as well as others who had Near-Death Experiences. They describe a realm in which departed loved ones are still alive. It is a realm of overwhelming beauty, peace and love…"Peace that passeth all understanding." Crystal cathedrals and other buildings made of light are found there.

And a Being of Light meets them when they enter. Chistians often interpret this Being of Light as Jesus. But his face is not visible. He projects great love. Dannion Brinkley describes his appearance as a "bagful of diamonds." Those of all religions encounter this same being, whether they be Hindu, Moslem, Buddhist, Jewish, or even Atheist. It is the universality of Jesus' teachings that are most important. He did not come and die so humans would have another cause to hate and fight over. His mission and his teachings were exactly the opposite of that.

In the years immediately following Jesus' death, another great adept appeared on the scene. He was Apollonius of Tyana, and some considered him the equal of Jesus in his ability to perform miracles (Hall, 1981). He was born in 16 AD in the city of Tyana in Cappodocia and exhibited great intelligence and paranormal abilities from a young age.

As a young man he went through the Pythagorean training of Euxenus into the mysteries, including a five-year period of silence, avoiding of animal foods, and meditation. He traveled extensively, even to the Far East, and his life was recorded by the Roman historian Philostratus, compiled under the patronage of Empress Julia Domina, wife of Septimus Severus. According to this history, Severus regarded Apollonius as virtually a god, and placed a statue of him together with those of Jesus Christ, Abraham and Orpheus and performed his religious rituals before these statues (Conybeare, 1912).

One of the early Fathers of the Catholic Church in Ante-Nicean times, Father Justin Martyr, acknowledged in print the reality of the miracles produced by Apollonius:

"How is it," he said, "that the talismans of Apollonius have power in certain members of creation, for they prevent, as we see, the fury of the waves, and the violence of the winds, and the attacks of wild beasts; and whilst our Lord's miracles are preserved in tradition alone, those of Apollonius are most numerous, and actually manifested in present facts, so as to lead astray all beholders?" (Hall, 1981).

In a famous trial during the time of Nero, Apollonius was accused of numerous crimes, but when he was brought before the Court and the charges against him were about to be read from a long scroll, the Justices found that the words had suddenly faded from the paper. He was then released for lack of charges. In another court trial in his later years, he was about to be arrested when he wrapped his cloak about himself and vanished in a flash of light in the middle of the court room. That was the description of events from Roman records of the time. (Mead, 1980)

Part of Apollonius' philosophy can be summed up in a note written by him to Consul Valerius when the consul had lost a son:

"There is no death of anyone, but only in appearance, even as there is no birth of any, save only in seeming. The change from being to becoming seems birth, and the change from becoming to being seems to be death, but in reality no one is ever born, nor does one ever die. It is simply a being visible and then invisible; the former through the density of matter, and the latter because of the subtlety of being - being which is ever the same, its only change being motion and rest."(Mead, 1980 ; Hall, 1983)

The Yogis of India

Dr. Paul Brunton, born in London in 1898, deserves much of the credit for introducing yogis to the West. In the 1920's and '30's, as a young British journalist, he traveled extensively in the Far East and Middle East. He went first to India to find out if true yogis really existed, and to learn about their abilities. Stories had filtered back to England about the unusual feats of these Holy Men. Rumors of their great psychic ability, as well as feats of levitation, psychokinesis, bilocation (being in two places at once), an ability to seemingly master and transform matter, and to remain buried underground without breathing for days were just a few of the strange talents reported of yogis. At a deeper level, Brunton was intrigued by the possibility that they also possessed a spiritual wisdom which underlay their amazing abilities.

Brunton spent many years researching yogis in India, seeking out the greatest of them, and describing what he found. His book *A Search in Secret India* (Brunton, 1935) describes the results of this quest. Not only did he find men of astonishing abilities, but he himself became profoundly changed in the process, and he began to learn the ancient practices himself.

Dr. Elmer Green, a physicist, went to India to scientifically study the yogis. Green was one of the pioneers of the science of biofeedback in the United States, and realized that yoga is a discipline which has much in common with biofeedback. Part of the yogic discipline involves training the involuntary, unconscious parts of the body. For example, in Figures 8.2 and 8.3 below, he measured the electrocardiagram of an Indian yogi, Swami Rama, as the yogi demonstrated his ability to control the muscles in his heart (Green, 1977).

In the first graph, Swami Rama demonstrated his ability to suddenly change his heart rate. At the top of the chart is the EKG trace of his heart, the electrical record of the heart monitor. The lower line shows the heart rate in beats per minute. The yogi indicated the time at which the heart behavior changed. The heart rate rises suddenly from 60 to 80 beats per minute, and the EKG shows that two different heart muscles suddenly change their behavior at that point. Not only does his heart rate change, but the action of two different heart muscles are varied independently, according to the EKG record.

According to Dr. Green:

"In the normal heart record, using the electrical pickup from the right ear to left hand, the R wave is taller than the T wave, as shown in the diagram. But note that, just before the heart rate suddenly increases, the T wave becomes larger than the R wave. Since the T wave and the R wave represent functions of different parts of the heart, the record indicates that the Swami had developed differential control over sections of the heart..." (Green, 1977)

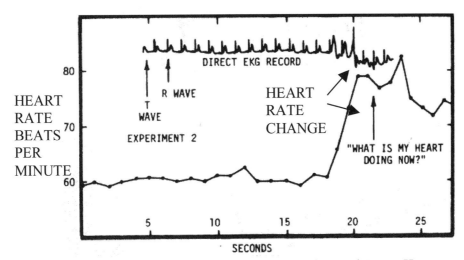

Figure 8.2. Electrocardiogram (EKG) of the Indian yogi Swami Rama. He demonstrated the ability to change his heart rate at will, and in the process changed the actions of two different heart muscles independently. *Courtesy Dr. Elmer Green*

In the next figure, Figure 8.3 below, the yogi demonstrates his ability to induce and stop fibrillation of his heart on command. Fibrillation is a state in which the heart undergoes very rapid beating, three or four times the normal heart rate. It is accompanied by a change in synchronization of the heart valves, so less blood is pumped than under normal circumstances. In normal individuals, it can be a fatal condition, and is impossible to control by conscious will. But as the graph shows, Swami Rama was able to start and stop fibrillation when he wanted to.

In another test, the same yogi demonstrated his ability to independently vary the temperature at two points on his skin. Two points on the palm of his hand were chosen, and temperature measuring devices (thermistors) were attached there. The arrangement and the resulting temperatures are shown in Figure 8.4. Initially there was about a two degree difference in the temperature at the two points. However, when Swami Rama began trying to make one point on his hand warmer and the other point cooler, the temperature difference increased dramatically.

The region on his hand which he wanted to cool <u>dropped an additional five degrees Fahrenheit</u> at its largest excursion. The other point, which he wanted to make warmer, <u>rose</u> an additional four degrees Fahrenheit. The temperature difference between these two points on the hand, only two inches apart, increased from two degrees Fahrenheit to eleven degrees. This is a very large and unusual temperature difference, and was measured under conditions that preclude fraud or deception.

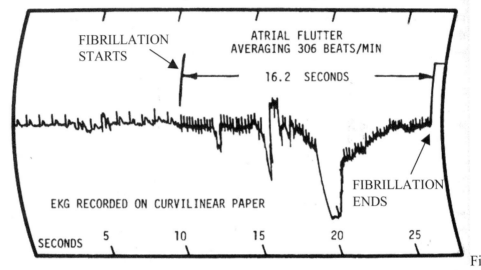

Figure 8.3. The Indian yogi Swami Rama demonstrates his ability to start and stop heart fibrillation on command. This is an EKG record conducted under scientifically controlled conditions by physicist Dr. Elmer Green (Green, 1977). *Courtesy Dr. Elmer Green.*

In another demonstration, Swami Rama demonstrated his psychokinetic ability. He demonstrated his ability to move a physical object at a distance without touching it or using any other known means of influence. The object he moved was a specially built pointer consisting of two aluminum knitting needles, attached rigidly to one another to make a cross-shaped indicator. This device was designed and built by Dr. Green. Since it was made of aluminum, it would not be influenced by magnetic fields. It was free to turn horizontally on a vertical support, with a base marked in degrees to indicate its orientation.

The room chosen was a small basement room, free of any air circulation or other disturbing influences. Under normal conditions in the room, the needles remained perfectly stationary. The swami sat at one side of the room, several feet from the indicator, as shown in Figure 8.5. He wore a mask which consisted of a painter's filter mask, over which was attached sponge foam and a transparent plastic sheet to completely prevent the generation of air currents by his breathing. A sheet was also placed over his body, so only his eyes and the top of his head were uncovered. This prevented any possibility of generating air currents to influence the needles.

The swami prepared for this experiment by meditating for nine days. When the time came for the test, the mask was carefully inspected by scientists. The swami intoned a mantra for about fifteen seconds, after which he gave a word of "command." The needles were seen to rotate about ten degrees. The tip of the needle at which Swami Rama had been staring moved toward him by that amount. While still sitting in the same posture he repeated the procedure, and for a second time the needle indicator rotated, in the same direction and by the same amount, ten degrees, for a total motion of twenty degrees. (Green, 1977)

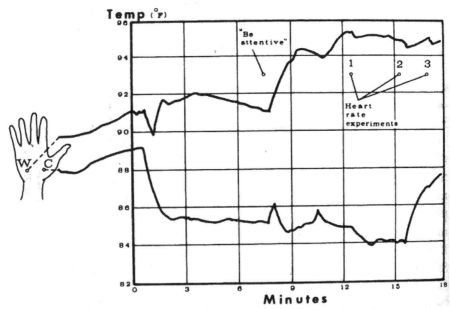

Figure 8.4. The temperature variation between two points on the palm of one hand were measured during experiments with Swami Rama. He demonstrated the ability to control the temperature of the two points, making one point warmer and the other cooler. He achieved a maximum temperature difference of nine degrees between the two nearby points. (Green, 1977) *Courtesy Dr. Elmer Green.*

This type of ability is called psychokinesis, the ability to move objects at a distance. Many examples were described earlier, in Chapter 3. It is considered to be a normal talent of yogis, and is often developed during their process of training and discipline.

As far as how yogis are able to achieve these feats, much depends on meditation and Yoga, including exercises to quiet the mind. The practice also involves learning to manipulate the flow of subtle energy through the body, including the awakening and purification of the chakra centers. The yogis explain that this "force" is caused by a form of subtle energy or *prana* which they build up in their body through the process of meditation and breathing. They say it can be projected by the eyes and hands, among other methods, and that it is the "cause" of the motions demonstrated in this test. Volume II of this series will describe subtle energy in greater detail.

According to Yogananda, who himself was a yogi:

"Awakening of the occult cerebrospinal centers (chakras, astral lotuses) is the sacred goal of the yogi. Western exegetes have not understood that the New Testament chapter of Revelation contains the symbolic exposition of a yogic science, taught to John and other close disciples by Lord Jesus. John mentions (Rev. 1:20) the "mystery of the seven stars" and the "seven churches"; these symbols refer to the seven lotuses of light, described in yoga treatises as the seven "trap doors" on the cerebrospinal axis. Through these divinely planned "exits", the yogi, by scientific meditation, escapes from the bodily prison and resumes his true identity as Spirit. (Yogananda, 1946, n. 184)

In recent years, as paranormal research has become of interest in industrialized countries, more yogis have been studied scientifically. The work just described was conducted by Dr. Elmer Green, and was carried out in the United States and India with limited private funding. The Soviet Union, in a larger program during the nineteen-sixties, made arrangements with the government of India to bring yogis into Russia to study them in scientific laboratories. If we in the West hope to ever develop a science which can understand the subtle energies, we would be well advised to study the yogis and to learn from their teachings.

Figure 8.5. Sketch of experimental arrangement in which a yogi, Swami Rama, seated at right and wearing a specially devised mask to prevent airflow, attempts to move a compass needle on the table. The mask consisted of a plexiglas plate and foam rubber insert, making it impossible to influence the compass needle by air currents. This experiment was designed and conducted by a team of U.S. scientists headed by former physicist Dr. Elmer Green (Green, 1977).

Paranormal abilities are not the goal of a yogi's development. They are rather a by-product of years of training and deep meditation, in which they come to a more profound understanding of the true nature of reality and the illusory nature of what we Westerners call the "physical universe." Consciousness seems to have a power over matter when this deep perspective is understood. To a yogi, the physical levels of the universe are seen as only the lowest level of a hierarchy of dimensions, and they develop the ability to move effortlessly between and within such dimensions. They are now focusing on the higher spiritual layers and their own evolvement. Manifestation of the physical is child's play once its *understanding is fully comprehended.*

The Education of an Adept
Throughout history there have been schools to educate young people to become adepts. In ancient Egypt and Greece they were called Mystery Schools. Some were maintained at the important oracular sites of the Mediterranean, such as Delphi and

136

Eleusis. The later Christian churches maintained some esoteric teaching in monasteries, where chanting, prayer, abstinence and even self-flagellation were used to promote the development of adepts. Such monasteries were also maintained, even in modern times, by the Greek Orthodox and Russian Orthodox Churches. In the Islamic world, similar schools for adepts were operated by the Sufis.

In India and other parts of the Far East there was a system of gurus and yogis which taught carefully selected students the arcane arts. Many years of hard practice were usually involved, including physical disciplines of yoga and abstinence, and continuous meditation. In Tibet the teaching and development of adepts was integrated into the governmental structure of the country until the Chinese invasion. Before that, it was a church-state in which the ruling hierarchy, overseen by the Dalai Lama, supervised the education and development of Buddhist priests and yogis.

The prevalence of Mystery Schools throughout history is significant. In the five thousand years of recorded history, almost every major culture and religion has maintained them in some form. Sometimes they played a prominent role, such as in Tibet. At other times they operated in secrecy. But they have always been with us.

The question is why? Why have powerful quasi-governmental bureaucracies like the Eastern Orthodox Church and the Tibetan Buddhists maintained such schools? One reason, I believe, is that the graduates of such schools can be very useful. Their abilities as advisers, seers, healers and prophets make them a valuable asset to any government. But in most cases the true goal of such schools has been to promote spiritual advancement in the students, even if this involved beliefs which were incompatible with the popular culture.

Figure 8.6. Illustration of a stage in the initiation process of an adept. The initiate has his head veiled. (Schreiber, 1895)

A variety of techniques were employed in their education: "In Greece, the kundalini initiation in the tholoi or temple involved isolating an initiate in a subterranean maze. At Epidauros, there was a labyrinth under a rotunda, or ethilos, as it is called…An initiate would be dropped into the labyrinth through the hole made by the removal of the keystone (or capstone). Then the capstone would be replaced. Underground there was a series of concentric passageways cut in such a way as to form a maze, and within that maze were snakes. The initiate was required to live in that underground maze for nine days in total darkness with no food or water — and to avoid the snakes. If the initiate survived when he was brought out, he was to report what had occurred in and around the country while he was in the labyrinth. Thus, staying alive was only the first part of the test. Proper use of inner sight and psychic awareness was an additional part of the challenge." (Bruyere, 1994)

The goal of such difficult rituals was to teach the student how to have an out-of-body experience and control it. When in this state, one's consciousness can travel instantly anywhere in the world, see distant lands and acquire further knowledge. Such initiations could trigger a near-death experience. In this state, the initiate was said to encounter spirit beings who do not have a physical body and yet are very conscious and often very wise. Those who go through initiation processes or Near-Death experiences acquire a heightened sensitivity and awareness of these spirit beings, and of the "other side" in general.

The "other side" is referred to in Hindu literature as the Astral realm, where we go, or our souls go, after death and before our next incarnation. This realm is often described as a parallel dimension (see Volume II). It is the realm in which souls find themselves when they arrive at the "other end" of the tunnel (see Chapter 11). It is the spirit realm, where they meet departed relatives, and experience their panoramic life review. In that realm, time and space are not limited as they are in the physical. Beings have access to far greater knowledge and understanding. It is said to be a realm filled with love.

It is also a realm in which the soul undergoes education to help it advance in its spiritual evolution. The initiation process enhanced the ability of the initiate to contact this realm, and to receive guidance and knowledge from it. As with Dannion Brinkley and so many who experience NDEs, it also greatly enhances psychic ability. However, these graduation trials could also be painful and frightening. Some initiations were truly life threatening, and the initiates did not come back from the "other side." They died.

In order to graduate, the students must develop the ability to go out of body at will, and control the experience. This gave them access to knowledge of their physical surroundings unavailable to most people. It certainly made them useful as advisors to rulers. Such adepts often developed precognitive ability. They received knowledge about the future, which made their advice even more valuable. They often learned esoteric arts such as astrology, which was used to evaluate people and plan events.

In Biblical times such men were called "wise men" and "prophets," and in the days of the Arabic Caliphs, they were called "viziers." Down through the years they have served as advisors to kings. During the Presidency of Ronald Reagan, important events were planned and timed down to the minute with the advice of Astrologer Joan Quigley, as has now been disclosed by Presidential advisor and Secretary of the Treasury Donald Regan. (Regan, 1988, 1989) The development of the military remote viewing program also appears to be a rediscovery of the usefulness of such talents.

One of the keys to becoming an adept was the "rising" of the *kundalini* energy. This did not always occur, but when it did, it conferred upon the adept the entire range of paranormal abilities described in this book. Kundalini is related to the subtle energies, the various types of "prana" or "chi". However, the *kundalini* appears to be a coupling together of all these energies, so they work in harmony when properly controlled. Here is a brief description of the *kundalini*, according to Rosalyn Bruyere, a noted healer who has also participated in important scientific research into these energies:

"In the mythologies of China and India and in particular those of Greece and Egypt, the myth of the snake as part of this kundalini initiation process is predominant. ...the purpose of these initiations was the same in all cultures: the function of all lesser mysteries, or the lower grades of initiation, was to convey to the initiates information about the nature of the higher worlds, while the purpose of the greater mysteries, or the higher degrees of initiation, was to bring the initiate into direct contact with the beings who inhabit these higher worlds."
(Bruyere, 1994)

As we shall see in the next section, some clues to the physics of the kundalini are beginning to emerge. It appears that the rising of the *kundalini* is probably linked to the synchronization of the chakras. All chakras rotate at certain frequencies. When they synchronize, then energy is transferred smoothly from one to the next, from the feet to the head. The chakras themselves are higher dimensional structures, as we will see in Chapter 13. When they are linked together smoothly, they form an even higher dimensional structure which can coordinate and access energy which is not normally available.

By forming an energetic structure which crosses many "physical" dimensions, it gives the adept power to tap energy from those dimensions, and to coordinate phenomena across those dimensions. This enables him to manifest physical effects which we would normally call "miraculous." The rising of the *kundalini*, and the mastery of this powerful energy, is key to this development.

As with any object of power, the rising of the *kundalini* is also said to be fraught with danger because it is difficult to control. This is one reason why adepts only pursued its awakening under the close supervision of a wise and experienced teacher.

The "Physics" of an Adept

Understanding the science of how an adept performs his miracles is a challenge to modern physics. Since he manipulates matter and energy, a complete science should be able to account for how he does this. Present day science has hardly begun to ask the question, much less answer it. Therefore, we would not pretend here to offer a comprehensive answer. But a few hints have emerged from experiments with individuals in altered states. They are clues to the origin of the adepts' remarkable abilities.

The healer Rosalyn Bruyere describes the development of an adept in terms of the subtle energy systems of the body. In her book *Wheels of Light* (Bruyere, 1994) she shows how the seven primary chakras alternate in polarity. The first, third and fifth are positive, meaning they output energy from the front of the body. The second, fourth and sixth are negative, meaning that energy flows into the front of the body there. She calls these the "intake" chakras.

This arrangement is shown in Figure 8.7. The chakras alternate in spin direction. Therefore, some chakras intake energy from the back, and others intake energy from the front. The intake direction alternates as one goes up the spine. Likewise, the spin directions of the chakras also alternate as one goes up the spine.

Therefore, the natural path for energy flow is to be drawn in by the root chakra at the bottom, where it then exits at the front, and is taken in at the front by the second chakra. This naturally leads to a winding or serpentine path up the spine.

Each chakra contributes additional energy to the flow as it moves upward. This results in a coiled, serpentine path for the energy. Because the front and back of each chakra forms two sides and two polarities, there are really two serpentine paths: one leading from the base chakra to the crown and the other leading back down.

Each chakra has its own frequency and its unique form of subtle energy with which it interacts. In later chapters we will say more about the possible fundamental nature of this form of energy. However, it comes in many different types analogous to different colors. Each chakra can be thought of as gathering in and controlling energy of a different color.

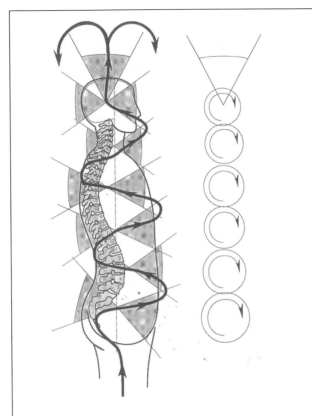

Figure 8.7. Illustration of the unification of the chakras as the kundalini rises up the spine. (Bruyere, 1994) *Courtesy of Rosalyn Bruyere.*

The entire set of chakras gathers in the complete spectrum of colors. As the *kundalini* moves up the spine it gathers together these different types of energy and unifies them. This can be thought of as white light, which contains all the colors. More correctly, it takes on a higher dimensional form because of the way it combines all of the chakra energies.

When this path is clear, then subtle energy can flow freely, and powerful effects begin to occur. In this state, the spinning of all the chakras is <u>synchronized</u>, so they operate coherently. This maximizes their efficiency in collecting energy and making it available to the body. The synchronization of spins suggests that, in modern scientific terms, the entire subtle energy system of the body has entered a <u>coherent, macroscopic quantum state</u>. In the language of the yogi, it would be said that the *kundalini* energy has begun to flow.

Evidence that the *kundalini* energy represents a coherent quantum state of all the chakras can be seen in the measurements by Hunt and Bruyere (Bruyere, 1994). In one case a subject had a *kundalini* experience while wired to their electrodes. They saw the signals for all of the electrodes change to the color white, which represents all the colors This meant that each chakra carried all of the colors of the spectrum, and indicated that each chakra was so closely coupled to the others that they all carried the full spectrum of vibrations.

Even more interesting, a shift in the <u>DC voltage</u> of the chakras occurred at the moment when the kundalini rose. All of the measurements were geared toward AC signals, which means they were looking for the vibrations in each chakra. But a DC shift means the *actual constant background voltage changed.* This suggests that the actual overall voltage of the subject suddenly changed by a constant amount. This output is shown in the graph in Figure 8.8, below.

In quantum mechanics, when the voltage changes for a macroscopic object, like a person, it implies that all the charged particles in the system have changed their frequency. It is as though there is a sudden overall shift in the frequency of the subject. This is a coherent shift, since a shift in voltage will change the base frequency of all the particles in the system.

As we will see in Chapter 13, an overall shift in vibration rate corresponds to a slight shift "out of this dimension". When the quantum oscillators of each chakra are in synchronization, this will result in a net average voltage shift.

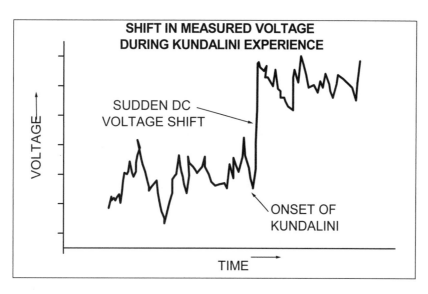

Figure 8.8. This is a plot of the voltage versus time from a subject who undergoes a kundalini experience. At the moment when this began, a shift occurred in the average voltage measured at the electrode. This change in the average DC value of the voltage was not observed under any other conditions. It is consistent with the idea that a coherent quantum state occurs which changes the overall frequency of the subject. This may be one way of beginning to understand the kundalini phenomenon, which is so important in developing the paranormal powers associated with adepts (Bruyere, 1994).

This synchronization of the chakras is a key event in the initiation of an adept. *Kundalini* energy gives the adept powers which we would call magical. They are due to his interaction with other nearby "dimensions", or nearby systems which have a different synchronization frequency than our own "dimension". When the adept is in this state, this coherent connection with nearby dimensions makes it possible to create forces and access energies which are normally impossible.

This gives rise to his unusual abilities. The Hindus called them the *siddhi* powers. These include clairvoyance, clairaudience, telekinesis, precognition, levitation, telepathy, clairsentience, invisibility, bilocation, materialization and healing, among others. In other words, most of the anomalous phenomena we are studying in this book become available to the adept once he masters the flow of the *kundalini*.

The *kundalini* is sometimes represented by one or two serpents rising up the spine. According to Bruyere, this is because, when all the chakras are synchronized, energy is carried upward from one to the next on one side, and then downward on the other side. It is the nature of the chakras that their spin direction alternates going up the spine from one to the next. This gives rise to a serpentine pattern of the energy as it rises. (Bruyere, 1994)

This pattern of the kundalini energy flow up and down the spine gave rise to the symbol of two entwined serpents on a staff. It represented the initiate, or a key step in the initiation process. It has become the modern symbol for medicine (See Fig. 8.9).

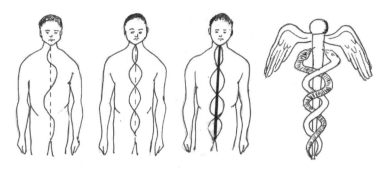

Figure 8.9. The three views of the energy flow up the spine.

In Chapter 13 we offer the beginnings of a scientific model which can account for these energies and abilities, and how they relate to our familiar three-dimensional reality. The "material world" is composed of a "synchronized" component of energy. It vibrates in phase with the other matter we see in the universe. Their vibrations are locked together so when we look outward, this is the matter we see. This matter seems permanent and solid.

But other energy components can exist at different rates of vibration and different phases. Because of the phase difference, they only appear as random noise to us. The analogy here is a flashing strobe light aimed at a rotating electric fan. When the strobe and the fan are synchronized, the blades seem to stand still. They appear solid and stationary. When the strobe light is out of sync with the fan blades they seem to disappear, as though they are not there. This is what other "adjacent dimensions" are like. They are really very close by, but because of our different synchronization, we do not see them.

One of the goals of an adept is to learn to synchronize the mind so he can perceive these other dimensions, and even access them and use them. In the *kundalini* state, the adept is able to couple his vibrations together, to synchronize them and use them to access forces and energy from these adjacent dimensions. This gives rise to his paranormal power.

This viewpoint is diametrically opposed to Western materialism, which assumes that matter is real and solid, and that spirits are an illusion. When we consider the "synchronized universe" model, we begin to understand that our so-called physical reality is based on particles which just happen to be in a certain state when we look at them. Our reality describes only the matter which is synchronized with us. There is a vast universe of other matter and other movement which is not in phase with our particles. These are just as real as we are, but we don't see them and we assume they are not there. This is the origin of parallel dimensions. There are also said to be higher dimensions which are combinations of these various synchronized systems. The eyes of the initiate are opened so he is able to access this higher dimensional world, of which our physical reality is but a thin slice.

Summary

We have seen in this chapter that extraordinary psychic abilities are not a new discovery. The psychic abilities of remote viewing, ESP, psychokinesis, levitation, teleportation and many others were well known in ancient times. An important part of the training of an initiate was the development of these powers. The yogic system of training has persisted until very recent times, and today the government of China appears to be pursuing a systematic program of identifying and training psychically gifted individuals.

The existence of organized schools and their persistence over thousands of years is further evidence that these abilities are not illusory. They are very real, and many societies through history have understood the value of cultivating those abilities.

Two common features found in the education of adepts are the "near-death experience" (NDE) and the "out-of-body" experience (OBE). The "final exam" often consisted of a harrowing and dangerous test, bringing the candidate near death. Snake pits, drowning, fire, and tortuous pain were often components of this test. The fear was sometimes so great that it initiated an out of body experience. In some cases, actual death resulted.

One can get an inkling of this process from the Native American Sundance ritual, which required young braves to hang for days suspended by hooks though their pectoral muscles. A realistic depiction of this was given in the movie *A Man Called Horse*. Days of pain and exhaustion while suspended in this manner usually brought on an "out-of-body" or "near-death" experience. The initiate would find himself out of body and experience transformative events. This would awaken his psychic abilities, often permanently.

The initiates' awareness of the spirit world would be heightened through such an experience. He would often meet guides and ancestors, and might travel in the out-of-body state to other dimensions or other locations on the earth. For those who survived the ordeal, sensitivity to psychic phenomena and awareness of these other dimensions was invariably heightened. In later chapters, Chapters 10 and 11, we shall learn from first-hand accounts what a near-death experience and an out-of-body experience are like, and the long term changes that result.

But before that, we will describe a different kind of adept, a "natural" adept. We call them "prodigies." They are as familiar as the calculating genius played by Dustin Hoffman in *The Rain Man*. He was an "idiot savant," born with severe developmental handicaps, and yet able to solve mathematical problems faster than the most brilliant mathematician. Such prodigies often have no training, no education, and may even be unteachable in any conventional manner. And yet they seem to be born with full knowledge in certain areas, and abilities which transcend those of highly educated and trained experts. Their existence and abilities are impossible to explain based on our conventional models of the brain and of learning. Their existence suggests that the brain has other ways of knowing, other means of acquiring information from the universe which defies present science. Some of their amazing and puzzling abilities are described next.

CHAPTER 9 - PRODIGIES

"When less than two years old he would recite all he heard his sister read while conning her lessons. He sings and counts in different languages, has mastered an appalling array of statistics, and is greatly attracted by music."
–William Corliss, *The Sourcebook Project* (Corliss, 1976)

"More and more scientists are expressing doubts about the neurologists' brain-mind model because it fails to answer so many questions about our ordinary experiences, as well as evading our mystical and spiritual ones. Studies in distant mental influence and mental healing also challenge the notion of a mind localized within a brain."
-- Dr. Larry Dossey, M.D. (Dossey, 1994, 1996a; Atwater, 1996)

DEFINITION-Prodigy: Someone who reveals unusually advanced abilities, talents or powers at a young age.

Child Prodigies

Prodigies are a kind of "natural" adept. Their unusual powers are present from birth. Their abilities usually appear before they receive training or education. These abilities often extend far beyond those of average, "normal" humans, and in this sense they are reminiscent of the adepts. While the powers of adepts are often paranormal, involving levitation, teleportation, ESP, and psychokinesis, the powers of prodigies are mundane: adding, subtracting, multiplying, playing or writing music. They are skills we all have to a degree. But what is inexplicable about prodigies is the degree and manner of their talent. They often have a fully developed skill, far in excess of normal abilities, and without the benefit of any training. It is as though they were born with the knowledge or breathed it in with the air. And their talents so far exceed the norm that it raises the question: What is the source of their abilities? How did they acquire their skill? What is the source of their knowledge?

In many cases science can offer no explanation for such abilities. Sometimes the talent is quite common but the circumstance makes it unusual. For example, multiplying two numbers together is something almost anyone can do. But the ability to multiply two very large numbers instantaneously, in one's head, when one has had no previous training in mathematics, defies normal experience. It suggests that the brain is processing the problem in an unusual way.

Dr. William Corliss is a physicist whose *Sourcebook* Project collects examples of puzzling but well documented events. He recounts the following story from *Science*, Volume 17, page 353, printed in 1891:

"Dr. S. V. Cleavenger, in the <u>Alienist and Neurologist</u> for July 1890, describes an infant prodigy, Oscar Moore. Two little colored children were reciting the multiplication table at their home, a little cabin in Texas, as they had repeatedly done before, and one of them asserted that four times twelve was fifty eight, whereupon a thirteen-month old baby, Oscar Moore, who had never spoken before, corrected the error by exclaiming "Four times twelve is forty-eight!" There was consternation in that humble home until the family became reconciled to the freak...When less than two years old he would recite all he heard his sister read while conning her lessons. He sings and counts in different languages, has

mastered an appalling array of statistics, and is greatly attracted by music."
(Corliss, 1976)

There are numerous well-documented cases of this type, children who can play piano concertos at the age of three or can carry out complex arithmetic calculations instantly in their head. Upon close examination, these cases cannot all be explained in a rational way by our present scientific paradigm. In the case of Oscar Moore, the 13-month old baby, he had never even spoken before, much less gone to school to learn multiplication. Many of these *infant savants* seem to be in full mastery of certain fields of knowledge, without the benefit of any education at all. Others perform feats which exceed the normal ability so greatly that they argue for the existence of some unconventional means of reasoning and acquiring knowledge.

The movie *Rain Man* with Dustin Hoffman dramatized a prodigy of this type: a young man who seems mentally retarded and with limited education, yet is able inexplicably to perform lightning fast mathematical calculations and compute calendar dates hundreds of years ahead. When asked how he does it, he replies that the answer just comes to him.

Tom Fuller, an African slave, was captured at age 14 and brought to America in 1724. Fuller never had educational instruction of any kind. Although he lived to be over eighty, he never learned to read or write. Yet, he could do complicated arithmetic problems in his head much faster than educated men could with pen and paper (Corliss, 1976).

Figure 9.1. Some childhood prodigies are fully functional and become successful in adult life. One of the most famous was the mathematician Karl Friedrich Gauss. At the age of three with no instruction whatever in mathematics, he corrected his father's addition of a long table of numbers. In adulthood, he became the most prolific and creative mathematician of the nineteenth century. It has been said that if he had published all of the discoveries he had made by age nineteen, mathematics would have advanced fifty years. Here he is memorialized on the German 10 mark note.

Corliss recounts other mathematical prodigies such as Jerah Colburn: "Questions in multiplication of two or three places of figures, were answered with much greater rapidity than they could be solved on paper." The extraction of the roots of exact squares and cubes was done with very little effort; and what has been considered by the mathematicians in Europe an operator for which no rule existed, finding the factors of numbers, was performed by him and in the course of time he was able to point out his method of obtaining them.

Colburn was asked the following question: "Supposing I have a corn field, in which are 7 acres, having 17 rows to each acre; 64 hills to each row; 8 ears on a hill, and 150 kernels on an ear. How many kernels are on the corn-field?" The boy's answer: 9,139,200. At this time he was only a child of six, unable to read and ignorant of the names or properties of one figure traced on paper. When asked the number of seconds in 11 years, it took him only four seconds to answer: 346,896,000.

Another famous example comes to us from Dr. A. F. Tredgold, who wrote a monumental study on mental deficiency based on studies conducted at an insane asylum in Armentiers, France (Tredgold, 1937). In one case a patient, M. Fleury, had been born blind and feeble-minded. His parents were syphilitic, which probably caused his physical defects. He had been abandoned as a young child and been institutionalized most of his life. He was emotionally stunted, and proved incapable of learning the social norms of interaction, or indeed most of what was explained to him. However, he did show a precocious and inexplicable gift for arithmetic (Edwards, 1961).

In one celebrated examination by twelve European scientists who came to visit him, he was asked a series of mathematical questions. A typical question was "If you have a series of sixty-four boxes and you place one grain of corn in the first box, and twice as much in each succeeding box as the box it follows, how many grains of corn must you place in the sixty-fourth box?" At first he giggled and hid his face in embarrassment from his examiners, but after less than half a minute of calculating in his head, he gave the correct answer: 9,223,372,036,854,775,808.

In his day, it would have taken many hours for a skilled mathematician to compute such an answer. Fleury's success in this examination as well as many others defies our conventional model of how the brain thinks. A young man with no training, and deficient in most aspects of mental functioning, was able to somehow perform mathematical calculations far faster and more accurately than the best trained mathematicians of Europe.

History records thousands of such gifted individuals. Some of the great mathematical and musical geniuses of history have displayed such prodigious abilities as children. They seem to "know" information which they have not been taught. They seem to have access to another information channel unavailable to the rest of us.

At the age of three, Karl Friedrich Gauss corrected his father's addition of a column of numbers, without having received any mathematical training (see Figure 9.1). There is no conventional explanation for this. Reuben Fields (Corliss, 1976) was "able to solve almost any problem involving arithmetic, fractions, and anything in the higher branches of mathematics." His answers came instantly. He was also able to tell the time of day or night without a watch. His answers were accurate to the second. At the same time he was "perfectly illiterate," having never attended school a day of his life.

The Flash of Inspiration, the Stroke of Genius

Information seems to come to these people from "outside". It is not usually based on their training, education or experience. There are no satisfactory conventional explanations for such abilities. Two possible non-conventional explanations are:

(1) the child is remembering knowledge learned in a previous incarnation, which is "past life memory", or

(2) the child is able to somehow psychically tap into a universal data bank of information which has the answer he seeks. The ancient Hindus had a name for this universal data bank: the "Akashic Record."

Although the conventional scientist will balk at either of these suggestions, science has been unable to offer a satisfactory alternative explanation.

The dextrous and mature way that Mozart took to the piano, mastering it at age three and writing complete sonatas and touring Europe at age six, could be more easily understood if we accept the possibility of reincarnation and past-life memory. This is also true for Raymond de Felitta, who in 1971 began playing piano at age six. The first time he sat at the piano, he found that he already knew how to play. He said that his fingers "were doing it themselves," and he found himself playing jazz in the style of the great Fats Waller, who died in 1945 (Cockell, 1996).

It is difficult to understand how such abilities occur unless we consider the possibility that these young children bring with them knowledge they gained in a previous life. The work of Dr. Ian Stevenson, Professor at the University of Virginia (Stevenson, 1966, 1975), shows that, in many cases, past life memory is retained in young children. Sometimes the information is so specific that the location and relatives from the previous incarnation can be located and interviewed.

Such an explanation may be attractive when we try to explain cases such as the young Tom Wiggins, a six-year old mentally retarded blind boy, born to a slave girl in the community of Bethune, Alabama in 1849. Because of his deficiencies he was allowed to stay in the manor house, where he crawled around on his hands and knees. One night, the plantation owner's family was treated to a piano performance by two of the local Bethune ladies, one them the wife of the plantation owner and the other her daughter-in-law. Both had studied at Boston conservatories and were excellent pianists.

Later that evening the younger lady was awakened to the sound of piano music. At first she thought her mother-in-law had returned to the piano. But when she went down to investigate, she found the small boy, Tom Wiggins. He had crawled through an open window to get into the piano room, and then, unable to see, had felt his way across the room and up to the piano. He was playing from memory the piano pieces he had heard that evening. Although he never had a single piano lesson and never touched a piano before, she watched in fascination as he felt his way across the keys to find the notes he had heard in the concert that evening. Then he began again and played the entire piece from beginning to end with the correct timing and tempo. His imitation of the earlier concert was flawless.

He became a well-known musical prodigy, famous for his ability to listen to a great pianist and imitate the performance flawlessly. However, the means by which one can instantaneously acquire such a talent has never been explained. It defies our conventional models for how the brain is wired up and how it learns. Most of us can spend a lifetime practicing piano and never acquire the gift that little six-year-old Tom Wiggins displayed that night in Alabama.

Although past-life memory may be helpful in understanding part of the ability, math prodigies seem to require something more. It is as if they are able to tap into some universal data bank and retrieve the answer they seek. They are frequently uneducated, illiterate children, often sub-par in other functioning. In most cases they work the answers out in their head without writing down any calculations. This further buttresses the idea that their thinking processes are anything but conventional.

The mathematician Sir Roger Penrose has observed that the "stroke of genius," which comes to scientists and mathematicians when they least expect it, may be a form of information exchange in which the answer is received from "outside" (Penrose, 1989). A man may apply his logical mind for weeks or even years to the solving of a problem. Then one day, "in a flash", the answer is revealed to him. The idea comes instantly when it comes. This is similar to remote viewing, where image and information about the target comes in sudden flashes, called "thought-balls". Information comes instantly as a complete concept or idea.

This is consistent with the Hindu idea of the "Akashic Record," a universal data base in which one can access any event which has ever occurred anywhere in the universe. Supposedly, every event creates a record in the vibrational patterns of the distant matter of the universe. These vibrations can be accessed or "tuned in to" at other times and from other places, just as we tune into a radio station by turning the dial to the correct frequency. For psychics the description of insights is very similar. When information comes, it comes as an instantaneous revelation, like a "flash of lightning."

Figure 9.2. In a famous story, the scientist Archimedes was given the task by the king of determining if his new crown was made of gold, or if the goldsmith had substituted a cheaper metal. As Archimedes settled into his bath and the water sloshed out, he realized that the same principle could be used to test the crown. The idea came to him in a flash, as most great ideas do. He was so excited, according to the story, that he shouted "Eureeka!" and leapt out of the bath, running through the streets of the village. Great ideas often come in a flash, and defy the cognitive model that the brain does all of its thinking by logical deduction.

Penrose points out that this type of information transfer, which is often described by scientists as the source of their deep insights, is not consistent with the methodical and systematic working of the logical mind. It is more consistent with the idea that information has been received from outside. In other words, flashes of genius may be psychic in nature. From this one may conclude that computers will never match humans unless we learn how to make machines which can tap into this great sea of psychic knowledge.

Superlearning and Lozanov

Such accounts raise the question of whether ordinary people can learn to acquire these extraordinary abilities. The ancient training system of adepts suggests this might be so. A modern researcher, Dr. Georgi Lozanov of Bulgaria, discovered systematic procedures by which anyone can learn at a much faster rate, performing mental feats which previously were considered impossible. These methods, which are related to hypnosis, unlock the enormous latent abilities of the human mind. They offer clues which help us to understand prodigies, adepts and supernormal functioning.

Dr. Lozanov's method is predicated on the idea of "holistic learning." The left brain is thought of as the "analytical side," the right side as the "creative side." It is often said that we only use 10% of our brain. Lozanov reasoned that maximum results could be achieved if the left and right sides of the brain were simultaneously engaged in learning, together with the body. He designed an integrated system of education in which the teacher varies voice and intonation to address and engage the whole person.

Lozanov's technique uses suggestion, or autosuggestion, which is a form of self-hypnosis, to prepare the student for learning. Positive ideas are planted that learning will be easy and fun, and that the student will remain relaxed throughout. In the classroom session, a steady relaxed rhythm of a certain tempo is used, combined with classical background music. The teacher speaks the key words in synchronization with the rhythm. In a four-beat rhythm, the most important concept is given on the second beat.

In a typical Lozanov language class, the teacher begins by reading phrases in different intonations. He alters his voice, sometimes barking out the phrase, sometimes soft, sometimes businesslike. The music and the regular, stately pace lulls the students into an almost hypnotic state. In this state, which Lozanov calls *hypermnesia*, students develop the ability to learn and remember with almost 100% accuracy (Ostrander, 1979).

This process goes on all day. At the end of a typical class, the students are tested on the 1,000 words which were the subject of the day's lesson. The class average is 97% correct! A working vocabulary is estimated to be approximately 2,000 words, so they have learned half in a single day, with almost perfect memory retention.

Sheila Ostrander and Lynn Schroeder were among the first Americans to become interested in Lozanov's techniques. They traveled to visit him in Bulgaria in the 1960's and began to introduce his methods to the West. In fact, this was one of the reasons they visited Czechoslovakia in the Prague spring of 1968, which led to their monumental book *Psychic Discoveries Behind the Iron Curtain*. But even before their interest in psychic research in the Soviet Union, they were interested in Lozanov's *Superlearning* techniques. In fact, they discovered that the two are closely related (Ostrander, 1979).

Using these methods, languages are now being taught in a couple of weeks in special schools. In 1977 at a conference in Iowa, Dr. Lozanov explained that learning 500 words per day has now become the standard in all his schools. The Canadian government, using his methods, announced that they were able to routinely teach 400 words a day in their language courses. Swedish educators who visited the Bulgarian schools found third-grade students working at a sixth grade level in math. Science students in Iowa being taught by the Lozanov method found that their accuracy in science and math shot up dramatically. Two Spanish classes using this method learned more than a full year of Spanish in ten days (Ostrander, 1979). There is overwhelming evidence the method works.

Another fascinating aspect of this teaching method is its side-effects. A woman studying French suddenly discovers her sinus troubles have cleared up. A man learning chemistry discovers his intuition has improved. Health, creativity, and even improved psychic ability are some of the unintended consequences of the Lozanov method.

In a way it is not surprising that Lozanov's teaching methods would stimulate paranormal abilities or that the learning ability of his students would begin to rival adepts and prodigies. Lozanov was a student of the paranormal and developed his teaching methods in part from studying the yogis of India. He noted that some yogis memorize all of the sacred Hindu texts, so if some disaster destroys the books, they can preserve the memory. In fact, the foundation of ancient Hindu culture, the Vedas, have been passed down by memory in this way for thousands of years. To memorize thousands of pages of text requires "hypermnesia": supermemory. The yogis had developed techniques for doing exactly this.

Lozanov studied how they did it. The traditional method used by the yogis is called Raja Yoga. It is geared toward governing the mind, and uses visualization, concentration and breathing to achieve altered states of consciousness. Graduates of this training were said to develop *siddhis*, the miraculous paranormal powers ascribed to adepts. Among these powers are supermemory, and instant calculating.

In Bombay, he met Yogi Sha. After practicing Raja Yoga every day for a year, Yogi Sha developed supermemory. He could instantly recall many columns of eighteen-digit numbers, tell the day of the week for any day of any century, and exhibit perfect photographic (eidetic) memory. There were dozens of people in India who had developed these abilities in the same way.

We begin to see a connection between the prodigies described above and these adepts. The abilities are the same. The yogis developed them by training. The prodigies were born with them.

Lozanov realized that most Westerners would not have the discipline or patience to follow years of rigorous Raja Yoga, so he adapted the ideas for the Western classroom. The meditation of the yogis was replaced with soothing, rhythmic music which promoted a relaxed, trance-like state. This was combined with hypnotic suggestions, which reinforced the altered state. The shifting of rhythm and emphasis strengthened concentration. The combined effect resulted in enhanced memory and often triggered other yogic powers. Thus the awakening of intuition and psychic ability in graduates of the Lozanov course was not unusual. It was the natural result of the awakening of the deeper powers which we all seem to have.

Experiments by Canadian neurophysiologist Dr. Wilder Penfield have shown that the brain has an enormous capacity to remember. During brain operations, Penfield discovered that touching certain parts of the brain caused the patient to remember a past event vividly. In fact, the recall of the event was complete. Every sound, smell, feeling, sight and emotion of the event was played back in the patient's mind, just as if he were experiencing it again. The brain seems to remember everything that happens. The difficulty is accessing it. Lozanov found that, by teaching in a relaxed, positive emotional atmosphere, he greatly enhanced the ability of the student to access and recall the information being taught.

The success of these methods illustrates again that our minds have immense untapped ability. It remains for science to explain how these methods work and why they are so much more successful than traditional methods. The hypnotic rhythmic state of the procedure creates a trance state and suggests that the subconscious mind is the key. As we have seen in earlier chapters, the subconscious mind is the gateway to paranormal and psychic communication. We also have seen that yogis achieve their paranormal abilities after they learn to go into deep trance states. Once again, there is a key connection between deep trance and supernormal functioning. Could it be that childhood prodigies are naturally in this state from birth, and this gives them access to these other channels of information and their unusual abilities?

151

Does Thought Take Place in the Brain?

These accounts of people with unusual abilities should cause us to question our present theories of the brain. If it is really the neurons in the brain that do the thinking, and if the wiring gets developed over time like a neural network computer, then how can we explain people who are fully trained the FIRST time they sit down at the piano? Neural networks, which are thought to mimic the brain, take a lot of trials and errors to get trained. This model may fit the normal child learning to ride a bike. He falls off a lot until he learns. It may work for that kind of learning.

But what about the prodigies who are dysfunctional in many ways and yet can calculate the answer to difficult mathematical questions almost instantly? And worst of all, from the neural network model point of view, they often have NO mathematical training. Their brains seem to work very differently from what these theories would predict. The lack of training and the instantaneous way these prodigies acquire their skills force us to ask another radical question: Do the important activities of thought take place solely in the brain? What if there is another, very different, way by which we are able to access information?

This possibility is highlighted by cases of people who experience severe damage to large parts of their brain and yet continue to function normally. In one case reported to the American Psychological Association, Dr. Jan Bruell and Dr. George Albee performed an operation on a 39 year-old man in which they removed the entire right half of his brain. This man was of above average intelligence. To the doctors' astonishment, he was able to leave the operating room after the operation without assistance, and recovered normally. His intellectual abilities were found to be virtually unimpaired by the operation. (Edwards, 1961)

In another case, a 14 year-old boy was treated for abscess of the brain. He had complained of violent headaches, but otherwise his behavior and intellectual ability were normal up until the time of death. Upon performing the autopsy, the doctors were astonished to find that his brain mass was entirely disconnected from the bulb, or the brain stem. Therefore his brain had no hard-wired connection to his spinal cord at all. How had he been able to function, to think, to talk? The abscess had destroyed all of the cerebellum and part of the cerebrum. Yet up until the moment of death, his intellectual functioning appeared normal. (Edwards, 1961)

Another case was recounted by a noted German brain specialist, Dr. Hufeland, who performed an autopsy on a paralyzed man who had been in full possession of his intellectual faculties until his death. (Edwards, 1961) The man had no brain and instead had eleven ounces of water in his brain cavity. These examples suggest that the brain possesses other means of acquiring knowledge that do not agree with the conventional "neuron wiring" picture.

According to F. Holmes "Skip" Atwater, who is Director of Research at the Monroe Institute and a graduate of the military remote viewing program:

"There is no neuro-physiological research which conclusively shows that the higher levels of mind (intuition, insight, creativity, imagination, understanding, thought, reasoning, intent, decision, knowing, will, spirit, or soul) are located in brain tissue (Hunt, 1995)...More and more scientists are expressing doubts about the neurologists' brain-mind model because it fails to answer so many questions about our ordinary experiences, as well as evading our mystical and spiritual ones. Studies in distant mental influence and mental healing also challenge the notion of a mind localized within a brain" (Dossey, 1994, 1996a; Atwater, 1997)

Perhaps the brain has a means of sending and receiving signals from the outside world, so that it can acquire knowledge without the laborious step-by-step logical deduction of a computer. In addition to computer-like functions, the brain may work like a radio transmitter and receiver. This might explain how it is able to access knowledge about playing a piano or find the answer to complex mathematical problems, or how it can jump over the conventional step-by-step educational process and go directly to the answer.

In Eastern philosophy the "Akashic Record" is described as a universal storehouse of knowledge which we can access. Is it possible that these examples are hints that the brain is much more than a tangle of neurons and much more than a computer? If it is able to somehow transmit and receive knowledge from the external world, then this may be a clue to how we can access this storehouse of knowledge.

This model seems more likely when we consider recent discoveries about how cells and biological molecules communicate. It has been found (Frohlich, 1983; Kroy, 1989; Popp, 1989) that they radiate and receive electromagnetic signals of many frequencies. Biomolecules are in constant communication with one another. This enables them to carry out biochemical processes very efficiently. As we will see in Chapter 13, even DNA transmits and receives electromagnetic waves in many bands. We found from the Backster experiments that some of this signaling is not conventional electromagnetic radiation. It passes through shielding and does not weaken with distance, and therefore cannot be conventional electromagnetic energy. But it is a form of communication, nevertheless. Is it possible that the brain does something analogous to this, sending and receiving information from the rest of the universe? This would certainly help us understand prodigies.

Modern physics must figure out how such knowledge can be stored, transmitted and received. The mechanisms may be at the heart of a deeper understanding of thought, memory and consciousness. We can learn from these accounts of highly gifted people that we as humans have extraordinary abilities as yet untapped.

Summary

Prodigies may seem to be a strange subject to include in a book on the paranormal. After all, everyone has heard of prodigies. The movie *The Rain Man* was widely popular and told the story of an "idiot savant" who was retarded in almost every way. Yet he could solve mathematical problems in his head faster than the most brilliant mathematicians. The ability of prodigies to compute the day of the week far into the future or past and to carry out mind-boggling mental computations has been a source of curiosity for centuries. The historical record is clear that such people exist. And yet their abilities are difficult to explain using our present theories of the mind.

Many prodigies receive little formal training. Like Karl Friedrich Gauss at age three, they just seem to already know how to add, subtract, multiply, play music or even write music. It highlights a question which is central to this book: Do we have OTHER WAYS of knowing things besides the conventional methods of learning? Is there a means of receiving knowledge DIRECTLY, as in ESP? Or perhaps do these young children retain their knowledge from a past life, through reincarnation?

Although prodigies are accepted and taken for granted in our society, these questions are seldom asked. How is it possible that a prodigy can do what he does? How does he arrive at the answer so quickly? How does he master a field of specialized knowledge, such as mathematics or music, virtually instantly with little or no training?

It leads inexorably to the idea that the brain does not function according to the conventional model of a computer or a neural network. Certainly our brains contain billions of nerve cells, and their interconnections and firings explain part of the process.

But the brain is also electrical. There are currents flowing within it. We know that it is affected by electric and magnetic fields of various frequencies. And the Backster experiments in Chapter 4 show us that cells also send and receive information by some other, unknown, form of energy. This energy is unique to each individual, and it can be received or transmitted over hundreds or thousands of miles without weakening.

Is it possible that the brain is a receiver of such energy? Is it possible that thoughts may come into the brain not solely as the result of a logical, computer-like deduction, carried out by the neurons? What if the brain is also a receiver, and can sometimes receive thoughts from the outside world, just like a radio receiver? Is this the origin of the "Aha!" experience when we solve a problem or make a discovery? Is this why it feels different from the laborious answer we worked out so methodically? Perhaps there are really two very different processes by which the brain acquires information, by which it "thinks." Maybe one of them is much like a logical computer calculation.

But when the inventor shouts "Eureeka!", when the light bulb goes on in your head at the moment of an exciting idea or discovery, this is a very different feeling. It is instantaneous. There is a thrill when it happens. It feels completely different from the laborious logical deduction. The logical deduction is tedious, like adding up a row of numbers or solving an algebra problem. An idea or discovery or insight is nothing like that. It strikes like joyful lightning.

Idiot savants and child prodigies may operate more in the altered state which promotes receiving inspiration and telepathic information. Certainly great inventions and discoveries have this character. The great inventor Thomas Edison purposely kept himself on a regimen of two hours sleep twice a day in the hope that sleep deprivation would keep him in an altered state. He believed that it was the key to receiving creative ideas. And he was the most prolific inventor in history.

This theory promotes the concept of a "thought-ball," a coherent complete thought that can be transmitted or received by the brain. When it is received, it occurs instantly. Great ideas are almost always described this way. They are received instantly: "It hit me like a ton of bricks" or "I was struck by lightning."

Prodigies are the familiar evidence for the unfamiliar idea: that thoughts can be transmitted and received from outside the brain, and that this phenomenon may be far more widespread and commonplace than we would have guessed.

In the next chapter we explore further the idea of "information from outside." We have seen that remote viewing and other psychic processes allow the brain to receive information from "outside" in unconventional ways. In many remote viewing sessions, the subject speaks as though his brain itself, or his center of consciousness, has actually <u>traveled</u> to an external location. It is as though his center of consciousness is no longer in his body, but is actually present at a distant location witnessing the event. This is called an "out of body" experience. The evidence for the reality of these events is discussed next.

CHAPTER 10-THE OUT-OF-BODY EXPERIENCE

"A controlled out-of-body experience is the most efficient means we know to create a Different Overview. First, and perhaps most important, among these Knowns is survival of physical death. If there is a better way than the OBE of knowing that this takes place - not just hoping, having faith, or believing, but knowing - we are unaware of it."
--Robert Monroe, in "The Ultimate Journey" (Monroe, 1994)

"Thousands, if not millions, of people alive today have had the experience of existing outside the space of their physical bodies for a brief period and experiencing this separated state as *real*, not as a dream or imaginary experience. A typical consequence of such an out-of-body experience is on the order of 'I no longer *believe* that I have a soul, or that some part of me will survive death, I *know* it!'"
-- Dr. Charles Tart (Rogo, 1983)

"As predicted, the average strain-gauge activation level for the period immediately following target generation -- that is, when the subject was reportedly 'looking' at the target -- was significantly higher for trials which were hits than for trials which were misses...The average activation levels over all eight sampling periods showed a significantly higher degree of activation on occasions when hitting occurred...Therefore, it is our opinion that the results can most likely be attributed to the subject's OB [out-of-body] presence in the shielded chamber."
-- Dr. Karlis Osis and Dr. Donna McCormick (Osis, 1980)

DEFINITION-OUT-OF-BODY EXPERIENCE, also called OOB, OBE, and "ASTRAL TRAVEL." Refers to the experience in which the conscious awareness of the individual is no longer located in the physical body. Often, the individual recalls looking back and seeing his body from outside. During the OBE, the "person" i.e. the consciousness, can move almost instantly anywhere in the world, simply by willing it. In genuine OBEs, the astral body can pass through walls and floors, bringing back detailed information. Usually invisible, the person during astral travel sometimes is seen as a ghost, a shadow figure, or a small rapidly moving "orb."

Proof of the Physical Reality of the OBE
During an out-of-body experience, the consciousness can seemingly move at will. It gives the impression to the experiencer that it is moving freely to various locations at high speed. When the subject sets his intention, his consciousness immediately seems to go to the place of interest. It is able to fly and to pass through walls. Loved ones can be visited, or new places can be investigated. The ability to move effortlessly at high speed, through barriers, while invisible, makes the out-of-body experience an attractive topic for study by military intelligence. But is it real? Does "something" really go to these places?

Several experiments have been performed to answer this question. Mitchell (Mitchell, 1981; Carrington, 1975) describes the experiments of Dutch scientists who weighed the physical body before, during and after subjects began an OBE. They found an average weight loss of 2 ¼ ounces for the subject during the OBE. This is very similar to the findings of MacDougall (MacDougall, 1907) who weighed patients before and after the moment of death and found a weight loss of a little over one ounce. The weight loss occurred suddenly at about the moment of death. This supports the idea that there is a physical energetic component to the part of the body which travels during an OBE.

Most convincing of all are experiments in which, during a remote viewing session, a strange "energy" was detected at the target which was being remote viewed. This unexplained energy has been detected by the weak light it gives off, by its effect on strain gauges, and by its effects on animals and people in the vicinity. These important experiments verify that the out-of-body state is something "real" and is associated with an unknown form of energy which apparently travels outside the body and is detectable by physical sensors. These experiments are described below.

The PRC and SRI Experiments

The astral body is one name for the energetic component which is believed to be the center of consciousness, which leaves the body during an out-of-body experience. The hypothesis is that, when a psychic subject attempts to remote view a target, he does this by sending his astral body, his center of consciousness, to the desired target. A number of experiments have been done to attempt to detect this astral body during remote viewing sessions. They have apparently achieved initial success.

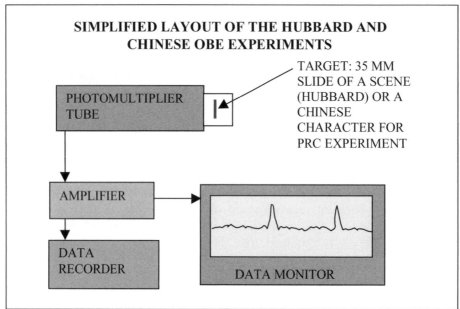

Figure 10.1. In experiments conducted in the People's Republic of China and replicated by Hubbard et al. (Hubbard, 1986), a remote viewer attempted to see a target placed very near to sensitive camera film, or to a photomultiplier tube. Either device can detect small amounts of light. The remote viewing target was kept in the dark, so the light could be measured. The Chinese used characters from their alphabet as the target. Hubbard used a 35 mm slide of a scene. The data monitor measures the light output at the target. It was found that, <u>when the remote viewer was accurately describing the target, anomalous pulses of light were measured in its vicinity.</u>

In 1982, scientists in the People's Republic of China (PRC, 1982; Yonjie, 1982) reported a remarkable scientific result. They used some of their highly talented remote viewers to attempt to view a small target, a Chinese alphabet character. These remote viewers were said to have "exceptional vision," and therefore were probably some of the EHF young people we encountered in Chapters 2 and 3. Most Western remote viewers have difficulty identifying letters of the alphabet, but the Chinese viewers reportedly were able to do it.

The unique aspect of the experiment was that the target was monitored by x-ray film or by a sensitive photomultiplier tube. This device can measure very small amounts of light. The Chinese discovered that, at the moment when the remote viewer said he was "looking" at the Chinese letter and identified it correctly, they measured unexplained light being emitted from the vicinity of the target.

The photomultiplier tube and the target were shielded in a light-tight compartment away from the remote viewer. The layout of the experiment is sketched in Figure 10.1. When successful remote viewing was occurring, light pulses were observed in the vicinity of the target. They were between 100 and 1,000 times greater in intensity than the background noise. This amounts to as many as 15,000 counts for the largest pulses seen.

Such large, relatively bright pulses indicate the presence, at the target, of some anomalous form of energy. When it is present, it causes a large pulse of energy or light which is measured by the photomultiplier.

This indicates that, when the viewer is able to place the center of his consciousness at the target so he can describe it, at that time strong energy pulses of some unknown form are measured at the target. Presumably this unknown energy is associated with the consciousness, the "astral form," of the remote viewer.

An American group of scientists attempted to duplicate the experiment (Hubbard, 1986). They used a high-quality photomultiplier tube and a 35 mm slide of a scene, instead of a Chinese character, as the target. They received excellent results, with probabilities of detection far exceeding chance. Therefore it can be said that they reproduced the effect. However, their signals were not as strong as those measured by the Chinese. The strongest pulses they measured were only 20 to 40 times larger than the noise level. An example of their results is shown in Figure 10.2.

As with the Chinese experiment, they counted pulses of light emitted during periods of accurate remote viewing and compared them to periods when there was no remote viewing or when the viewer was not describing the target accurately. The bar graph at the bottom of Figure 10.2 shows the times when remote viewing was occurring, and the gaps show when it was not occurring. The upper curve shows the intensity of light measured at the target.

A large pulse is seen toward the end of a run. It occurred during a period of successful remote viewing. This pulse is much larger than the noise and has no conventional explanation. The most likely explanation is that it is caused by the presence of some anomalous form of energy, probably the astral body of the remote viewer, which is hovering very near the target at this moment.

Hubbard et al. concluded:

"When remote viewing was good, there was an increase in the signal detected by the photon counting system. When the viewing was less accurate, a smaller signal was detected by the counting system." (Hubbard, 1986)

In trying to understand why the results were not as good as the Chinese, they suggested two possibilities: first, that the Chinese remote viewers are better, since they are the product of a systematic, open, nationwide sweep for talented remote viewers; second, by using a slide photograph of a scene instead of a Chinese character, the remote viewer might send his consciousness to the actual site depicted in the photograph. This often happens in remote viewing and would greatly diminish the measured signal at the photomultiplier.

157

Hubbard's group also suggested that the large pulses might be due to anomalous energy *inside* the tube. In that case, the OBE energy form would not have to give off light, but might just affect the electrons inside the photomultiplier tube. In either case, <u>some form of unusual, anomalous energy is present near the target when remote viewing occurs.</u>

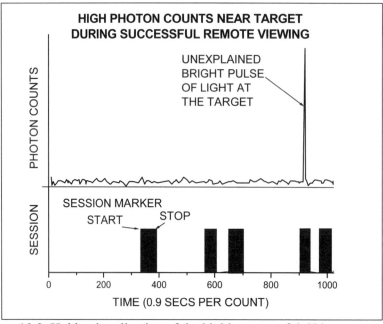

Figure 10.2. Hubbard replication of the highly successful Chinese experiments in measuring light emitted at the target during OBE/remote viewing (Hubbard, 1986).

The Osis - Tanous Experiment

Drs. Karlis Osis and Donna McCormick (Osis, 1980) conducted a series of OBE experiments in which the subject, a gifted psychic named Alex Tanous, was asked to remote view a specially designed target. The target consisted of several displaced pieces inside a box, which would only line up to form an image when seen from a particular location. This required that Tanous move his astral body into a specific position in order to "see" and correctly identify the target. Optical devices and strain-gauge sensors were located there to measure any unusual physical phenomena.

The remote-viewing target and sensors were protected in a chamber which was shielded to prevent any stray electrical or vibrational interference. The laboratory layout is shown in Figure 10.3. The remote viewer, who would attempt to leave his body, remained in one room fully wired to sensors which recorded his physical and brain-wave activity. The researchers monitored the experiment from a second room, and the target and strain gauge sensors were kept in a third, sealed room.

The strain gauge sensors consisted of two metal plates suspended from a plexiglas rod inside a double-shielded container (Figure 10.4). The strain gauges connect the hanging metal plates with the horizontal plastic rod. Any slight disturbance of the metal plates would cause a signal on the strain gauges. The idea was that if the remote viewer, Tanous, came near the optical image device, his astral body, or "consciousness," would pass near the strain gauge sensor and disturb it.

The important control on the experiment was that Tanous had no idea what the target looked like. It also was changed at various times. The researchers, Osis and McCormick, could evaluate whether Tanous' OBE was "real" or not by how accurately he described the target. What they discovered, and this is highly significant, is that, when he was describing the target accurately, there were many more disturbances of the strain gauge sensor. These results are shown in Figures 10.5 and 10.6.

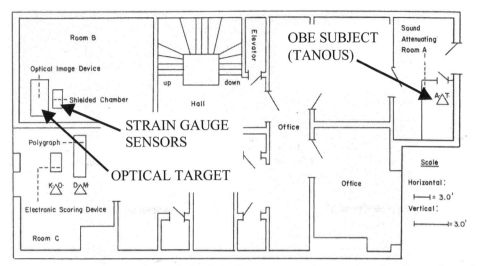

Figure 10.3. Physical layout of the Osis-Tanous experiment, showing floor plan of the laboratory. The OBE subject, Alex Tanous, was isolated in a sound-attenuating room on one end of the building (far right). The optical image device, to which he attempted to go in the out-of-body state and view, is at the opposite end of the building (far left in the diagram). Also located there were the strain gauge sensors in a motion-isolated shielded cage.

The correlation of a strain gauge signal with Tanous' correct answers indicated that "something" approached the target window at the times when the viewing information was correct. The optical sensors showed that this "something" was invisible. Yet the strain gauge sensors indicate that it had electrical properties or was able to induce mechanical disturbances. This suggests that the "astral body" has detectable physical attributes, even though it is usually invisible to humans.

We have testimony from many sources (Targ, 1984) of a small sphere or "orb" which is sometimes seen during OBEs. We have the measured weight loss of an ounce or two during the OBE (Mitchell, 1981; MacDougall, 1907). And we have indications from strain-gauge sensors that electrical and/or mechanical disturbances occur (Osis, 1975) when the astral body is nearby. The similarity in physical characteristics between this astral or "soul body," and the orbs witnessed in ghostly hauntings is remarkable. In both cases, orbs are seen which move rapidly. In both cases anomalous electro-mechanical effects are observed. We have indications that both objects have physical mass of one or two ounces. In some cases the OBE form is seen as a pale or white human figure, and at other times as a moving orb. It is reasonable to suspect that this energetic form, seen in OBE cases, in remote viewing experiments, and in ghostly hauntings, is probably the same thing.

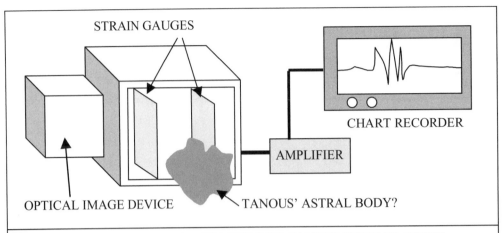

STRAIN GAUGES

CHART RECORDER

AMPLIFIER

OPTICAL IMAGE DEVICE

TANOUS' ASTRAL BODY?

CONCEPTUAL EXPLANATION FOR THE OSIS-TANOUS RESULTS. WHEN TANOUS WAS REPORTING THAT HE WAS "OUT OF BODY," AND VERIFIED BY BRAIN WAVE MEASUREMENTS, AND ACCURATELY DESCRIBED THE TARGET, STRAIN GAUGES INDICATED THAT "SOMETHING" UNUSUAL WAS AFFECTING THE STRAIN GAUGES NEAR THE TARGET.

Figure 10.4. Conceptual interpretation of the Osis-Tanous experiment. During an OBE there were measurable physical disturbances in the strain-gauge sensors. These disturbances occur near the optical target, which the subject, Tanous, was describing at the time. The strain gauge detector is shown at left. The outer box of the detector was shielded against electromagnetic disturbances, and suspended from the ceiling by elastic bands to reduce vibration. Two sensor plates were suspended inside, attached by strain gauges to a horizontal wire. Any disturbance inside the chamber would cause the sensor plates to move slightly, and this would generate a signal on the strain gauges, and be displayed on the chart recorder.

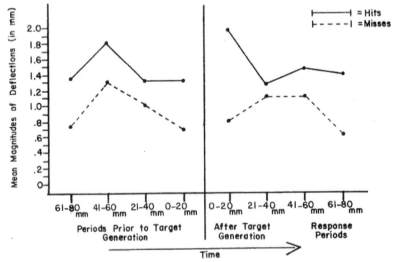

Figure 10.5. Results of the Osis-Tanous experiment. Graphs show activation of the strain gauges in the vicinity of the OBE target. When the viewer, Tanous, was unable to see the target accurately ("miss") there was less activation of the strain gauges. When he was able to accurately "see" and describe the target ("hit"), then the strain gauges were disturbed more strongly and more often. The disturbance of the strain gauges was greatest of all immediately after the target was generated and Tanous was told to go look at it.

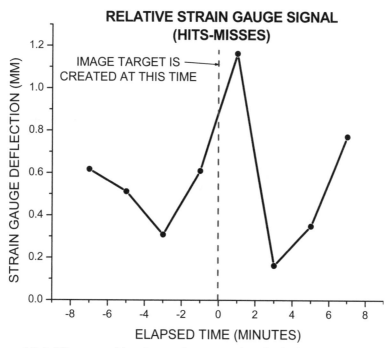

Figure 10.6. If we consider the strain gauge signals during a target "miss" as due to random noise, then this may be subtracted from the strain during a target "hit". This graph summarizes this result, derived from the data in Figure 10.5. There were more strain gauge signals at all times during hits versus misses. This suggests that Tanous' astral body, or OBE body, was present in the vicinity of the target even before the image was generated. However, immediately <u>after</u> the image was generated, at time zero in the center of the chart, the number of strain gauge hits goes up dramatically. This is consistent with Tanous' astral body being in proximity with the remote viewing target.

Figure 10.4 depicts a conceptual explanation for these results. They are consistent with the conclusion that, during a remote viewing session, as Tanous attempts to view the target from the special designated position, some energetic part of him leaves his body and is present at the target viewing location. The special target designed by Osis and McCormick can only be properly recognized when it is viewed from a particular position. Therefore the "hit" data requires that Tanous' awareness must be located at that precise position.

Recall, from Figure 10.3, above, that Tanous' body is at one end of the laboratory complex resting in a chair and fully instrumented with electrodes. The target he is describing is at the opposite end of the laboratory, many rooms away, in a sealed room and a sealed container. Therefore, when we say Tanous must "view" the target from a certain spot within the container, we are saying that his OBE form, his astral form, must do this. His body is far away, unable to move, and unable to gain access to the room in which the viewing target and strain gauge sensors are found.

Therefore it appears that there is an energetic manifestation near the OBE target at the time the target is being observed. This supports the conclusion that there is an energetic "substance" or "structure" which goes out-of-body and goes to the vicinity of the target at the time the target is being viewed. This is similar to Ingo Swann's performance in Chapter 3, when he "placed his consciousness" inside a highly shielded secure magnetometer at the Stanford Research Institute. In that experiment, the magnetometer itself showed Swann's presence. Swann's body was on an upper floor of the building, being supervised by Hal Puthoff. The magnetometer was in the basement immersed in many layers of shielding and a bath of supercold liquid Helium. But it did not stop Swann from projecting his conscious down into the device.

The Morris-Harary Experiments

One way to overcome the subjective aspect of the OBE is to avoid using humans as observers. Robert Morris (Morris, 1978) among others, devised experiments which used a kitten to detect when an OBE was occurring. The kitten belonged to Dr. Keith Harary, a well-known psychic researcher who also has a talent for going out of body at will. The kitten had shown a strong affinity for Harary, and it was thought that perhaps it might be sensitive to his out-of-body presence, as well. There is abundant anecdotal evidence that felines are able to detect OBEs.

A very talented natural psychic as well as a parapsychologist, Harary has authored several books about his experiences, including *Mind Race* with Russell Targ (Targ, 1984). In the North Carolina experiments, his respiration, heart rate and other parameters were monitored while he entered the out-of-body state.

The kitten was placed in an open box enclosure measuring 30 inches by 80 inches on the sides, with walls three feet high. This is shown in Figure 10.7. The floor of the box was marked off into 10-inch squares. The motions of the kitten, as well as its vocalization (meowing), were recorded. A record was kept of the kitten's movements from one square to another, based on the rule that two front paws in a square counts as being in the square.

Figure 10.7. Artist's impression of the Harary kitten experiment. One kitten belonging to Harary was placed in a special box. Harary was a half-mile away inside a laboratory and was instrumented to monitor his physiological state. During Harary's OBEs, he attempted to visit the kitten. Its behavior changed significantly during those periods when Harary's physiological measurements indicated he was "out-of-body" and attempting to visit the kitten (Morris, 1978).

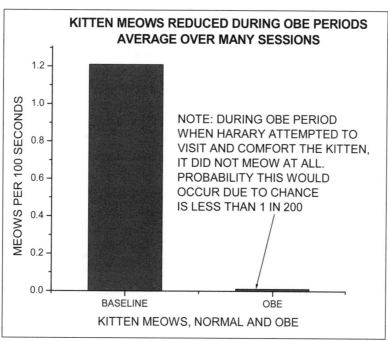

Figure 10.8. During the Morris-Harary experiments involving Harary's kitten, the average number of meows per time period are plotted on the vertical axis. The first column shows the number of meows during a normal time period. The second column shows the number of meows when Harary went out-of-body and was trying to comfort the kitten. During that time it did not meow AT ALL. Probability of this occurring by chance is about 1 in 200.

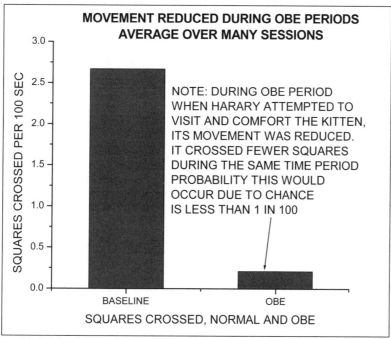

Figure 10.9. Normally the kitten crossed about 2.5 squares in a 100 second time period. During the time when Harary went out-of-body and tried to comfort the kitten, it moved only ONE TENTH AS MUCH. The probability of this occurring by chance is less than 1 in 100.

163

Harary, in a remote laboratory location, attempted to go out of body and "visit" the kitten during the experiment. Harary's biological functions, EEG, heart rate, etc., were monitored during the tests. The kitten's movements and vocalizations ("meows") were then compared to the times Harary believed he was out-of-body (and confirmed by EEG measurements), and to the times when he was in a normal state.

It was found that the kittens meowed 37 times during the eight control periods, but <u>not once</u> during the eight out-of-body periods. The number of squares they crossed was also greatly reduced, meaning the kittens tended to move much less during the OBE periods. An experimental period was 100 seconds long. <u>The odds against seeing such changes in the kitten's behavior by chance was 200 to 1 on the vocalization, and 100 to 1 for the movement.</u>

The results are highly significant. The change of the kitten's behavior during Harary's OBE strongly indicates that it detected "something" that greatly quieted it. The odds of <u>both</u> of these changes in behavior occurring due to chance alone would be 1 in 20,000. Therefore the results are strongly persuasive evidence that the OBE was "real."

The Mitchell-Swann Experiments

Ingo Swann has been one of the key figures in the development of our understanding of the OBE because of his participation in many experiments. He also assisted in the development of the military remote viewing program, both as a talented viewer and an advisor who suggested a curriculum of study.

Swann's interest in the out-of-body state grew out a natural talent which he first displayed at the age of three. At that time, he was anesthetized for a tonsillectomy. He remembers finding himself floating above his body watching the entire operation. Afterwards, he was able to recall numerous details from the operation. (Mitchell, 1987)

In later years, he practiced the skill to develop his ability to go out of body when he wanted to. He would decide to place his consciousness at some specific location, and note what he observed there. Later he would travel to that location to test his accuracy. In 1971 he began working with Dr. Janet Lee Mitchell, of the American Society for Psychical Research. She conducted a series of scientific experiments to determine if his ability was real, and if so, to learn how it worked and what its limitations were.

One early test consisted of placing an object in a container ten feet above the floor. The container was open at the top, but not at the sides and the bottom. Swann, sitting below it in a chair, was given the task of psychically describing the object. There were potentially several different methods of viewing the object. If he went out-of-body, he could hover over the box and look down into it. On the other hand, if he were viewing it telepathically or clairvoyantly, he would not need to be above it, and his viewing perspective would not be relevant.

To distinguish between these possibilities, a partition was placed in the middle of the box, and different objects were placed in each half of the box. Then, looking at the box from one side, he would see one of the objects. Looking from the other direction, he would see a different object. By using perspective in this way it was possible to tell whether his perception was similar to normal viewing. If it were telepathic, he could presumably look through the box, and would see both objects. Careful controls were placed on Swann's movements in the lab to insure that fraud was not a factor.

Dr. Mitchell found that Swann's accuracy in describing the objects varied with the lighting of the object. Harsh lighting cast shadows and decreased his accuracy. The best lighting, in terms of his accuracy, was soft and diffuse. Primary colors were easier to see than pastels, and two-dimensional cut-outs were easier than three-dimensional objects. This suggests that depth perception may be absent. This would be expected if he were viewing the target from a single eye, for example. Simple shapes were easier for him to recognize than complex shapes, and letters and numbers were often not seen at all. These tests were all conducted "double blind," meaning that Dr. Mitchell did not know the target either. This alleviated the concern that Swann would get it by "reading her mind."

Afterward, Swann's descriptions of the target were given to an independent judge, who did not know the nature of the tests. The judge attempted to match the descriptions to the targets to determine accuracy. In an example cited in (Mitchell, 1987), one judge found that the eight descriptions provided by Swann correctly matched the eight targets he had viewed. The probability of this happening by chance was 1 in 40,000.

During these tests, Swann was wired up to an array of instruments which measured his brain waves, heart rate, skin resistance, breathing, and many other factors. These measurements were compared to periods in which Swann felt he had been out of body, or was trying to go out of body. Dr. Mitchell found that, during these periods <u>there was an overall lack of electrical activity in his body</u>. (This has also been seen in other OBE experiments with Hindu yogis.) There was a decrease in alpha waves, and the decrease was more pronounced in his right hemisphere. The probability of this occurring by chance was 1 in 1,000 on the right side of his brain and 1 in 200 on the left side. In other words, the reduction of alpha waves in this pattern seems to be a real effect which accompanies the OBE.

This remarkable decrease in electrical activity has been confirmed by other independent researchers. Joel Whitton, in Canada, analyzed the EEG data of psychic Alex Tanous when he reported being out-of-body.(Whitton, 1974) He too, showed a decrease in electrical activity. Using sophisticated computer analysis, Whitton found that the relative amounts of energy at different brain wave frequencies shifted, so most of the energy was in the very low frequencies between 1 and 4 cycles per second. This is associated with the delta-wave, which for normal humans indicates unconsciousness.

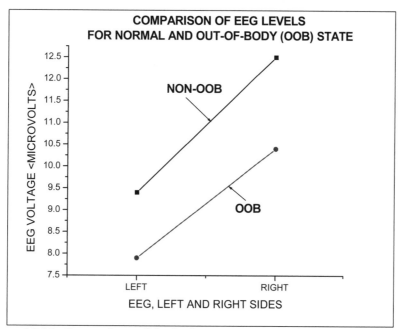

Figure 10.10. Comparison of the brain wave patterns of Ingo Swann in normal state (non-OOB) on the upper line, and in the out-of-body (OOB) state, on the lower line. There was a significant drop in voltage in the out-of-body state.

Along with the loss of electrical activity, there was a decrease in eye movement, or REM. Other OBE researchers have observed these same effects. Mitchell (Mitchell, 1987) cites research by Green (Green, 1970) on a Hindu Swami, who exhibited a similar decrease in EEG voltages when in the OBE state (see Chapter 8). Studies by Tart (Tart, 1968) and Morris (Morris, 1978) confirmed the decrease in rapid eye movements when in this state. At the same time, Mitchell found a speed up of brain waves in the visual region of the brain. Since her subject, Swann, was trying to see a physical object, this makes sense.

In Mitchell's discussion about the OBE measurements, particularly the fact that brain wave voltages decreased when the subject was in the OBE state, she suggested that the rest of the room be instrumented with voltage measuring devices. She proposed that perhaps, when the voltages in the body decrease, an increase would be found elsewhere in the room corresponding to the location of Swann's consciousness, his "astral body," at that moment. From other experiments, such as the Osis-Tanous experiment (Osis, 1980) and the Chinese experiments (Yonjie, 1982; PRC, 1982) described above, this appears to be the case.

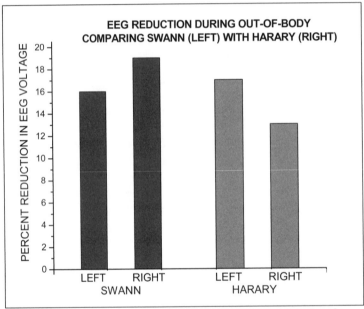

Figure 10.11. Comparison of the brain wave patterns (EEG) of two talented OOB subjects. The data are measured on the two sides of the brain, the left and the right. Data for Ingo Swann are shown on the left side of the graph. Data for Keith Harary is shown on the right. Data plotted are the per cent reduction in average brain wave voltage during their OOB, compared to their normal readings. In both cases, both sides of their brains show a drop of between 12% and 19% in brain wave voltage during out-of-body periods

This idea is consistent with whole body Kirlian photography, which shows that, as a person begins an OBE the location of electrical activity shifts away from the body. If this is indeed the energy arrangement when an OBE begins, then we can see why the voltages within the body would be reduced. The major electrical activity tends to follow the energy ball (variously called the astral body, the second body, the soul body, etc.). Sensors placed around the room should pick up its energy as this energy ball passes nearby. At the same time, the electrical activity within the physical body is significantly reduced.

Appearance of the "Astral Body"

When an OBE or "astral visit" takes place, and is so clear that the visitor is afterwards able to describe it in great and accurate detail, how is he perceived by those who are at the scene? In many cases the visitor is not perceived at all, but in some cases, a very definite and clear interaction occurs which is remembered later by all parties.

In one example, recounted by Berlitz (1988), a man named Wilson fell asleep and "dreamed" he visited a female friend who lived forty miles away. In his dream, he knocked on the door and was greeted by the maid, who told him the woman he sought was not at home. He asked to come in and have a glass of water, and the maid obliged. Later Wilson and several friends traveled to the house to investigate. The maid recognized him as the man she had given water to!

This case is similar to others in which the person, in the out-of-body state, is perceived to be physically real and normal and present. The Landau case described below is another in which the out-of-body entity, namely Mrs. Landau, appeared human, except that she was pale white and glided across the floor without walking. There are many cases like this, when the astral form is perceived as a specific person. In others, all that is seen is a shadowy figure, a "shadow person," without distinguishing features. More commonly, what is perceived is a small orb moving quickly about in the vicinity.

Berlitz (1988) relates such an example involving Keith Harary. During one of his out-of-body sessions, Harary visited a doctor who was not expecting the visit. The doctor later reported seeing <u>a small red glowing orb, about an inch in diameter</u>, flash across his field of vision at about 3:15 am, exactly the time Harary had been conducting the out-of-body visit.

Figure 10.12. Photograph of a haunted house at night. The upper, white streak in the photograph appears to be an "orb," a small spherical object which often moves rapidly. The end of its track, seen at the upper left in the figure, reveals that it does have a round shape, and that the track is caused by its rapid motion during the time the camera shutter was open. The lower, yellow streak coming out the window is believed to be the light of a lamp inside the house. Paranormal phenomena seem able to bend light beams, thus distorting the lamp image so it generates the lower streak. This is another controversial and important anomaly.

These small glowing orbs are sometimes seen or photographed when out-of-body events are taking place. They move rapidly and can be easily missed. They are very similar to the small glowing orbs seen in haunted houses when ghosts are reported present. In several documentary episodes of *Sightings* and *Unsolved Mysteries*, these orbs have been photographed at locations of high paranormal activity.

One experienced ghost hunter stated that he had tried on hundreds of occasions to photograph a ghost in haunted houses and he had always failed: "All I ever got on film are these darned little glowing orbs zipping around in the scene." (Holbert, 2000)

Based on the similarity in appearance between the fast-moving glowing orbs seen in out-of-body experiences and those seen at haunted houses, it must be considered a reasonable hypothesis that they are the same thing. This may be the appearance of the "soul" or the "consciousness" of another being when in the out-of-body state.

The Landau OBE Experience

The following was originally reported in 1963 in the *Journal of the Society for Psychical Research*. (Landau, 1963) The author of the report, Lucian Landau, described his experiments and observations of his wife, who frequently experienced controlled OBEs when asleep. In a typical example, his wife wanted to check up on a friend of theirs who was vacationing in Cornwall, and would try to pay a visit there in an out-of-body state while sleeping. The next morning she reported to him that their friend was photographing a "rock plant" when she "arrived." She described in detail the surroundings and a gentleman who was with their friend. Later, this information was completely confirmed. Their friend stated later that he had been vaguely aware of a "shadowy figure" passing him at the time of the OBE visit.

For Lucien Landau, OBE experiences were not something bizarre and unusual. He had many times witnessed his wife "visit" others in an OBE state, and had subsequently been able to confirm crucial details.

Therefore, on one occasion when Mr. Landau was ill and spending a lot of time in bed, he devised an experiment to test his wife's ability. Referring to the diagram below, Mr. Landau was in the bedroom on the right, and Mrs. Landau was staying in the bedroom on the left. The compass needle marks north, and various objects and locations in the account are labeled with letters.

Mr. Landau wanted to test his wife's ability to move a physical object while in the out-of-body state. He asked her to pick up his small diary, weighing 38 grams, which he left on her desk (marked "G" in the diagram, and bring it with her into his room when she came. Since he could hardly expect her to make the address book pass through a closed door, he left both bedroom doors opened. He made a note to wake himself should anything unusual happen during the night.

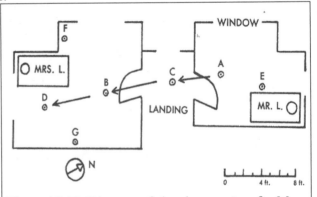

Figure 10.13. Diagram of sleeping quarters for Mr. and Mrs. Landau for the OBE experience described.

The following account describes, in Mr. Landau's words, what he saw that night:

"I woke up suddenly: it was dawn, and there was just enough light coming in through the partly drawn curtains to enable one to read. At the point marked "A" [see Figure 10.13] stood the figure of Eileen, facing north-west, and looking straight ahead towards the window. The figure was wearing a night dress, its

face was extremely pale, almost white. The figure was moving slowly backwards towards the door, but it was otherwise quite motionless; it was not walking. When the figure, progressing at the rate of about one foot per five seconds, reached the position "C," I got out of bed and followed. I could then clearly see the moving figure, which was quite opaque and looking like a living person, but for the extreme pallor of the face, and at the same time the head of Eileen, asleep in her bed, the bedclothes rising and falling as she breathed. I followed the figure, which moved all the time backwards, looking straight ahead, but apparently not seeing me. I kept my distance and ultimately stood in the door of the spare bedroom [Mrs. L's bedroom] when the figure, now having reached the position "D," suddenly vanished. There was no visible effect on Eileen, who did not stir, and whose rhythm of breathing remained unchanged..

"I moved quietly back to my room, and at point "E," on the floor, found a rubber toy dog, which belonged to Eileen, and which stood on a small chest of drawers in position marked "F" when I last saw it. This dog weighed 107.5 grams.

"In the morning, after breakfast, I questioned Eileen about the diary. She said that she first went to the desk (position "G") on which it was, and somehow could not pick it up. She then thought that it would be easier to carry something that belonged to her, and she decided on the rubber toy, which she managed to take with her to my room. It was a pity that I woke up some thirty seconds too late." (Landau, 1963; Mitchell, 1974)

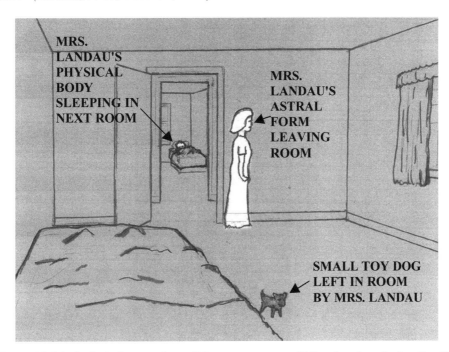

Figure 10.14. Artist's impression of the appearance of Mrs. Landau during the OBE, as described by Mr. Landau (Landau, 1963).

Mrs. Landau added that she had been taught as a young girl not to handle other people's letters or diaries, which may be why she was unable to pick up Mr. Landau's diary. She remembered choosing the rubber toy dog, instead, and she remembered carrying it into Mr. Landau's bedroom. She did not find it difficult to hold or carry the dog. She saw her husband sleeping comfortably when she entered the bedroom.

However, she did not recall using her legs to move, nor about moving backwards out of the room. It is interesting that she did not remember walking, and her husband noticed that she seemed to glide along.

In many respects, this experience resembles encounters with ghosts. The body is pale or white. It glides, rather than walks. During the time that "she" was moving between bedrooms, Mr. Landau could see her physical body asleep in her bed. He could see this at the same time that he could see the pale white image of her moving back into her room.

Since she was able to move objects using her ghostly, presumably non-material body, this phenomenon also resembles poltergeist phenomena. In a poltergeist event, objects can move or fly around the room seemingly by themselves, with no physical, visible person causing the movement. We see from this example that in out-of-body cases, the same effect can be achieved by the "astral body" of the individual.

Charles Tart, Professor of Psychology at the University of California, and highly respected expert in paranormal phenomena, says of this report:

"OOBE's are one of the world's most important and most neglected phenomena. Even psychic researchers generally do not pay attention to them. But their importance in understanding man cannot be overestimated." (Tart, 1974)

Tart points out that OBEs in which one is able to move objects are unusual, but certainly not unheard of. This case provides an interesting overview of the wide class of problems these cases pose for conventional physics.

The Wilmot Case

Another apparent out-of-body case occurred in the nineteenth century. It was described by one of the foremost paranormal researchers of the 1930's, Sylvan Muldoon, in the book *The Case for Astral Projection*. (Muldoon, 1936):

Mr. S. R. Wilmot sailed from Liverpool to New York, passing through a severe storm. During the eighth night of the storm he had a dream in which he saw his wife come to the door of the stateroom. She looked about, and seeing that her husband was not the only occupant of the room, hesitated a little, then advanced to his side, stooped down and kissed him, and after gently caressing him for a few moments, quietly withdrew.

Upon awakening from his dream, Mr. Wilmot was surprised to hear his fellow passenger, Mr. William J. Tait, say to him: "You're a pretty fellow to have a lady come and visit you in this way."

Pressed for an explanation, Mr. Tait related what he had seen while wide awake, lying in his berth. It exactly corresponded with the dream of Mr. Wilmot!

When meeting his wife in Watertown, Conn., Mr. Wilmot was almost immediately asked by her: "Did you receive a visit from me a week ago Tuesday?"

Although Mr. Wilmot had been more than a thousand miles at sea on that particular night, his wife asserted: "It seemed to me that I visited you." She told her husband that on account of the severity of the weather and the reported loss of another vessel, she had been extremely anxious about him. On the night of the occurrence she had lain awake for a long time and at about four o'clock in the morning it seemed to her that she left her physical self and went out to seek her husband, crossing the stormy sea until she came to his stateroom.

She continued: "A man was in the upper berth, looking right at me, and for a moment I was afraid to go in; but soon I went up to the side of your berth, bent down and kissed you, and embraced you, and then went away."

In this case we have the corroborating testimony of three individuals, each with his or her own perspective on the event. Yet all three were consistent. If we are to believe them, then this is one more remarkable piece of evidence that OBEs can occur over great distances.

Robert Monroe

In modern day America, we are not blessed with a tradition of yogis or adepts as in some ancient cultures. However, technology has come to the rescue. An invention by businessman Robert Monroe may help us achieve similar altered states. Monroe was developing an electronic method of inducing sleep in order to perfect a sleep-learning technology. He reasoned that since certain brain wave patterns correspond to sleep, if he could induce those patterns in the brain, he could make it go to sleep. He used stereo headphones and beamed sounds of slightly different frequencies into each ear. A difference frequency, or "beat" frequency, would be created inside the head, and if properly designed might induce sleep. This was the origin of *hemi-sync* technology. It is in wide use today, not for inducing sleep, but for inducing altered, very relaxed states of consciousness.

Working in the 1950s, Monroe lay down one evening listening to his newly created hemi-sync tape. The next instant he found himself in an unfamiliar place. When he looked to his side, he saw the light fixture emerging from what he thought was the floor. When he looked up at what he thought was the ceiling, he saw a bed with a body lying in it. It looked like <u>his</u> body. Slowly he realized that he, or his consciousness, was on the ceiling looking <u>down</u> at his physical body. He had never heard of an out-of-body experience before, and so concluded that he must be dying or going crazy.

A subsequent physical exam revealed him to be in excellent health. In the 1950's in America almost no one knew about out-of-body experiences, or OBEs. Monroe had no one with whom to share his experiences. He did notice that in many of these sessions he witnessed events which he was able to later verify, so he could not dismiss these experiences as mere hallucinations. In some cases he traveled out of body to other rooms of his house or to other parts of the country and was able to look in on friends and loved ones.

Monroe eventually learned that in other cultures and other parts of the world, these abilities are not so unusual. They are an accepted part of life in many older traditions. Even today there are many yogis, fakirs, and other adepts in Asia who are able to go out of body with ease. Among such groups, this ability is considered an ordinary, even essential, talent for survival.

Monroe was, in his heart, an engineer and scientist as much as he was an explorer. He methodically investigated this strange "new country" of the out-of-body state, and documented his experiences in his books. (Monroe, 1971, 1985, 1994) He continued to develop electronics and audio technology so he could control these out-of-body states. He refined the methods until he was able to identify several distinct levels of consciousness, and could determine which hemi-sync signals would cause each of the various states.

By 1978, the technology was sufficiently mature that he decided to create The Monroe Institute, a facility about 40 miles south of Charlottesville, Virginia which provided accommodations and laboratory capability for others to come and share these experiences (see Figure 10.15). In specially designed sound proofed chambers, visitors could listen to the hemi-sync tapes and have their own direct experience with altered states.

Monroe's work attracted the interest of the U.S. government when the military remote viewing program was being developed. They were searching for ways to increase the performance of remote viewers.

The altered states, which could be produced almost on demand and in a controlled way by Monroe's technology, seemed to be just what they were looking for. Starting in the late 1970's, every remote viewer in the military program was cycled through the Monroe Institute to acquire experience in the out-of-body state, and to improve his ability to relax quickly and enter the altered states required for remote viewing (Schnabel, 1997).

Figure 10.15. The Monroe Institute, in Faber, Virginia, was founded by Robert Monroe. It has been a pioneer in research of the out-of-body state. Hemi-sync audio tapes are used to induce alpha and theta brain wave states conducive for deep meditation and OBEs. The Monroe Institute also assisted the CIA and DIA in the military remote viewing program, by training remote viewers to reach deep altered states.

Monroe's explorations of the out-of-body state have added immensely to our knowledge of what appear to be other dimensions, spiritual or non-physical beings, and the existence of the "spiritual" or "soul-body" of man which can exist more or less independently of the physical body. In describing these other, more subtle, dimensions Monroe wrote:

"Exploration out-of-body is a prime means of functioning outside the physical universe. The 'second body' of the OB state is certainly not physical. It is part of another energy system that commingles with the Earth Life System but is <u>out of phase</u> with it. The clue lies in how easy it is to find those who have left physical existence." (Monroe, 1994)

This last statement suggests that some of the terrain explored in these OOB trips is the same territory described in Near-Death experiences. In this altered state, or "other dimension," the OOB traveler often encounters the spirits of those who have died. The skeptic might reasonably ask whether such beings are really being encountered, or whether it is just the imagination of the person having the out-of-body experience. The best answer here is that the information acquired during these experiences can be checked and verified afterwards. In many cases the information has a high degree of accuracy which suggests that the encounters are not imaginary.

Parallel Dimensions

While there is abundant evidence, as shown above, that the OBE is something "real" with measurable properties, at the same time there are unreal and dreamlike aspects to it which are difficult to understand. Keith Harary described an OBE he had in which he awoke in his bed, floated above his body, and then noticed that he had left a candle burning. He floated over to it, put his face very near it, and attempted to blow it out. After several attempts, he succeeded, then returned to his body, reentered it and slept through the night. Upon awakening the next morning he discovered that the candle had burned all night. He had not "really" blown it out. Experiences like these convinced him and Dr. Scott Rogo that the OBE takes place in a sort of mirror image of reality:

"Rather reluctantly, I had to accept the theory that during the OBE, we contact only a parallel of the real world -- a plastic interactional world that may alter when we physically alter our own. If I place a picture on a wall, for instance, the same object may well appear in the parallel world. But this plane is more tenuous and less stable than the physical world of the five senses...the universe we normally perceive is only a substructure of a vast realm of dimensions that lie beyond it. These higher worlds can be contacted only psychically. During an OBE we perceive a mirror image of the real world..." (Rogo, 1983)

Not only does our familiar physical reality seem to have a parallel dimension, a "mirror world," as Rogo describes here, but there many other, less familiar parallel worlds which are also encountered in OBEs. In Robert Monroe's journeys, he encountered many strange and unfamiliar places. They were not exotic locales on this planet, but rather places which do not exist in our world. Monroe meticulously catalogued these different realms, not quite sure whether they were real or imaginal. But their characteristics did seem to remain static over time, allowing him to revisit them. This lends credence to the idea that they are, in some sense, parallel dimensions.

Monroe describes how he first came upon the entrance to one of these peculiar domains. It appeared to be a hole in his wall:

"That's the only way to describe it. To my sense it seemed to be a hole in a wall which was about two feet thick and stretched endlessly in all dimensions." (Monroe, 1971)

Monroe revisited this place in subsequent out-of-body journeys, and eventually explored it. It seemed to be a parallel universe, similar to our own but much more beautiful. He later discovered another "dimension" which was dreary and distasteful.

These two realms have been reported by other out-of-body experiencers, lending credence to the idea that they have some sort of "real" existence. Physicist J. H. M. Whiteman, who was very adept at going out of body, described an experience which sounds similar to Monroe's. His OBE began with:

"...a 'spatial opening' in which the surface of a whitewashed wall, two feet away, was studied, with a full clarity of perception and the visual impression of precise spatial position...The opening then changed to one in which a heathlike country was seen in a wide panorama, with steep ground in front, and almost at once I was conscious for a few moments of being catapulted amid that scene" (Whiteman, 1961)

Like Monroe and Harary and numerous others, Whiteman described a "spatial opening," a hole, about two feet wide, which led into "another dimension." There is a consistency among many OB experiencers about this tunnel between dimensions, as well as about the characteristics of some of the realms seen at the other end of the tunnel. This same tunnel, or one very like it, is encountered in the near-death experience (NDE). It connects this world with another world in which the dead are still alive, and there is much beauty and love.

Keith Harary found himself in one such world during his experiments with his kitten, described above. Although it was a successful experiment and his kitten became quiet during his OBE, he reported that, from his perception, he had not been with the cat "but had been caught up in a whole new dimension - a barren, dry, dreamlike world from which he escaped by returning to his body." (Rogo, 1983)

Despite the elusiveness of these supposed "parallel universes," they have several properties which make them likely to be real. First of all, OB experiencers like Monroe were able to revisit the same reality repeatedly, and it always had the same characteristics. Secondly, many OB experiencers have described realms which sound identical. The "dreary, nasty" realm and the "beautiful, peaceful" realms referred to above have been visited, apparently by many remote viewers, who come back with similar descriptions.

The third reason to believe in the "reality" of such realms is because there are many cases when more than one person has visited the realm simultaneously, and they returned with shared memories of the event. Harary describes one such OBE in which, during the evening after retiring for bed, he went out of body. He wanted to visit an old friend of his in a different part of the country, in Maine. He was prompted to invite, while in the OBE state, another friend, George, to accompany him. That person was asleep, but his astral body joined Harary and they went to visit their friend in Maine. The realm they traveled through was not the familiar physical world. Harary says: "George and I passed through some sort of an atmospheric barrier and entered another level of existence."

Harary describes encountering strange pools of bubbling pink liquid, which he knew were dangerous even in the OBE state. They met their friend and had an eventful evening. The next day, initially George remembered nothing. But later, spontaneously, George recalled almost every detail of the journey. The beginning and ending of the trip involved a passageway into or out of a "higher world." Again this idea of a hole or tunnel appeared. As we will note later, in Chapter 12 on time travel and prophecy, tunnels also appear there. The Native American medicine woman "No-Eyes" and the writer Mary Summer Rain describe traveling through a "time tunnel" to witness events in the future. The description is very similar.

Our science lacks the knowledge at the present time to reliably tune into this second state, or build a receiver for these signals. If this is ever done, such realms may become just as real and commonplace as radio and television signals are today. In the meantime, we must rely on the testimony of talented individuals who have learned to make this transition, or we may elect to receive the training ourselves, so we can experience these realms directly.

In the meantime, the apparent reality of parallel dimensions, which are intimately connected with OBEs, may offer valuable clues in understanding the out-of-body state and its connection to remote viewing, time travel, and the near-death experience. In Chapter 13, we will present the beginnings of a possible theory of the paranormal. We call it the "Synchronized Universe" model. The existence of parallel dimensions, accessible by phase shifts, is a natural consequence of this model.

The Effect of High Voltage on an OBE

In Robert Monroe's first book, *Journeys Out of the Body* (Monroe, 1971), he recounts an experiment he did in 1960. He was in a Faraday Cage in which he had conducted numerous other out-of-body experiments. A Faraday cage is a box made of wire mesh, which in this case was embedded in the walls of the room. Normally it was grounded, which makes it effective at shielding out disturbing electromagnetic signals and enhancing the ability of the subject to relax.

But this time was different. The walls of the Faraday cage, instead of being grounded, were charged to 50,000 volts DC. Monroe doesn't say if it was positive or negative voltage. Then he went through his usual routine inside the cage, lying on a bed. Listening to his tapes, he relaxed deeper and deeper and soon found himself outside his body. So far, everything was normal.

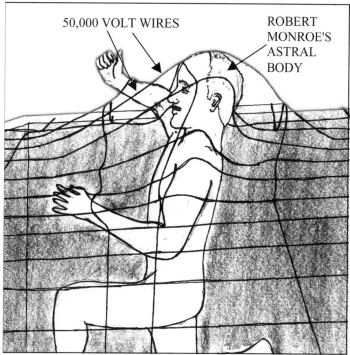

Figure 10.16. Illustration of Robert Monroe's out-of-body experience trying to pass through the ceiling of a Faraday cage charged to 50,000 volts. Under normal circumstances, Monroe, in his out-of-body state, was able to pass through the ceiling of the chamber effortlessly. However, when the wires in the walls and ceiling were charged, they seemed to entangle his astral body like a net as he tried to pass through them. He was unable to leave the chamber in his out-of-body form when the walls were charged to high voltage.

But when he tried to leave the room by going through the walls or ceiling, he kept running into and becoming entangled with many WIRES. He was unable to get out of the room! He was trapped. Normally his astral body just passed right through the wires built into the walls of the Faraday cage. For some reason, when they were charged to a high voltage, this did not happen. Suddenly the wires became impenetrable to his astral body. They became like a net ensnaring him and holding him inside the chamber.

175

This is a highly significant observation. It suggests that the process which allows the astral body to pass through matter is affected by VOLTAGE. At a high enough voltage, the astral body no longer can pass through matter.

In quantum physics, we know there is a relationship between voltage and frequency. The higher the voltage, the greater the frequency difference. If we assume that the astral body is at a different frequency than normal matter, then we shall see in Chapter 13 that this could explain how it can pass through matter effortlessly. But when the voltage of the wires in the wall is raised it changes their frequency, so now they may come into synchronization with the energy making up the astral body. So far, this is only the sketch of an idea. It is developed in more detail in the last chapter of this book.

Monroe's experience is consistent with many of Keith Harary's out-of-body experiences. Harary demonstrated his ability to leave his body and describe distant events many times. But he

"...was adamant about one thing. He would not project during thunderstorms or when such a storm was threatening. He felt that the electrical buildup in the atmosphere hampered his abilities and disoriented him. He also disliked approaching any kind of powerlines during his projections. Sometimes, he told me, he would get 'caught up' by the lines and become stuck to them." (Rogo, 1983)

Rogo also recounts an independent story which supports this observation:

"One woman described how she had approached some powerlines during one of her OBEs, had become stuck to them, and had to travel down them before ultimately breaking loose."(Rogo, 1983)

These experiences remind us of the "ghost trap" used in the movie *Ghostbusters*. It, too, was a Faraday cage charged to high voltage. It was used to contain the ghosts and spirits captured by Dan Akroyd and his fellow ghostbusters. Although the movie is fictional and a great deal of fun, it is surprising that their technological solution is so similar to actual cases. A Faraday cage charged to high voltage apparently is able to contain one's astral body and prevent it from escaping. There is circumstantial evidence, to be discussed in Volume II, which suggests that a real "ghost" is little more than that, an astral form. Therefore a charged Faraday cage might well be able to trap and constrain a ghost. When one learns that Dan Akroyd's father, and Dan himself, reportedly have a serious long term interest in paranormal research, then it seems reasonable that they may have used this knowledge in suggesting the technology used by the "ghostbusters."

Summary

The experiments of Osis and Tanous (Osis, 1980), Hubbard (Hubbard, 1986) and Yonjie (Yonjie, 1982) show that, during an out-of-body experience, a real physical manifestation leaves the body and can be detected as it moves about. It causes electric and magnetic disturbances and registers on strain gauges. For lack of a better term, we shall call this the astral body, which is the traditional Hindu term for the consciousness as it moves in the OBE state. When in that state, the experiments of Harary show that certain animals, such as cats, are aware of it. It has also been photographed in certain circumstances, and some humans have reported seeing it.

The appearance of the astral body has two basic forms. Some people see it as a ghostly form of the actual person, as in the Landau case. In fact, in some cases, it appears in color and fully natural as in the Wilmot case. But the most frequent form is as a small orb which moves quickly. In this form it has been photographed and registered on electromagnetic detectors. When the person is in the OBE state, physiological functions such as EEG, the electrical activity of the brain, are greatly reduced. Whole-body Kirlian photographic images support this conclusion, as we will see in Volume II. It is as though a portion of the electromagnetic structure and activity leaves the body and goes with the astral body.

The challenge for science is that there is no known form of energy which creates stable energetic spheres which can travel autonomously. The fact that this sphere also seems to be the seat of consciousness and awareness is a much greater challenge to science. As the Mitchell-Swann experiments show, during an OBE the subject behaves as if his "eyes" are located at the astral body, not the physical body. In the Osis-Tanous and Hubbard experiments, when the remote viewer reported being able to see the target, sensors at the target were set off, indicating that an unexplained energy was present. The most reasonable conclusion is that the viewer's visual information was somehow coming from his externalized consciousness, his "astral" body, which was causing disturbances at the sensor.

In the next chapter, the OBE state will be extended to cases where the physical body was actually declared dead. In some cases, the subjects were declared legally dead and remained so for minutes to hours. In the most extreme case, that of Dr. George Rodonaia, he was declared legally dead and lay in the morgue in Moscow for three days. When the surgeon began cutting into him during his autopsy, he suddenly became "alive", sat up and protested. In the majority of near-death cases, many of which include full legal and medically validated death, the subjects report an out-of-body experience at the beginning of their near-death experience. There have been many attempts by skeptics to explain away these experiences. But the difficult part to explain away is that the patient, while dead, is able to report moving around the hospital room or even outside the room, and can accurately describe detailed events which took place.

The near-death experiencers describe another realm, another "dimension," in which deceased relatives and loved ones are very much alive. In this realm there is enormous love. They describe loving and wise spirit beings, as well as crystal cities and extensive pastel landscapes. Ancestors and loved ones who have died before are there to welcome them. Near-death experiencers invariably return from the experience transformed.

Dr. Rodonaia was an avowed atheist before he died. After his experience he devoted himself exclusively to the study of spirituality. He said:

"...God showed me that the universe in which we live is a beautiful and marvelous mystery that is connected together forever and for always. Anyone who has had such an experience of God, who has felt such a profound sense of connection with reality, knows that there is only one truly significant work to do in life, and that is to love." (Williams, 2003)

There is great consistency among the NDEs of thousands of people from many different religions and cultures. It is this consistency which is the strongest evidence that this dimension is real. It is consistent with the idea that the soul itself, the astral body which is able to leave the physical body during an OBE, also survives death and is at home in this realm. In the next chapter we will review some of the evidence for the reality of the Near-Death experience, and its characteristics. We will see that the descriptions support the tenets of many religions that "heaven" really exists, although it may be somewhat different from what we have been led to expect.

CHAPTER 11 - NEAR-DEATH EXPERIENCES

"NDEers universally report that they are never judged by the beings of light, but feel only love and acceptance in their presence. The only judgment that ever takes place is self-judgment and arises solely out of the NDEer's own feelings of guilt and repentance."
   -- Michael Talbot, *The Holographic Universe* (Talbot, 1991)

"People will say you are 'dead,' but that's not true. 'You' are the 'life,' and you have left. 'You' are not dead. It's your body that's 'dead'."
   -- Harry Hone, Near-Death Experiencer (Hone, 1986)

"You are as DEAD right now as you are ever going to be."
   -- Dannion Brinkley, Near-Death Experiencer (Brinkley, 1994)

DEFINITION-NEAR-DEATH EXPERIENCE or NDE: The Near-Death Experience refers to the experience of individuals who have clinically died, and later been rescucitated. During the experience, they describe an out-of-body experience, watching events from outside their body. They also report visiting the "other side", where they encounter deceased relatives, compassionate "beings of light,", and beautiful cities of light.

More NDE Cases due to New Resuscitation Technology

Thanks to new medical technology, increasing numbers of people who clinically "die" for brief periods have been resuscitated. In many cases they are brought back to life even after being certified dead by a doctor. These patients have no pulse, no brain activity, and have stopped breathing. In some cases, clinical death has lasted more than a half-hour, and in extreme cases more than a day. Conventional medicine maintains that after four to five minutes without breathing, the brain should suffer severe and permanent damage, making recovery impossible. And yet, in many near-death cases, when the person is revived his brain seems to work fine.

The two baffling aspects of these cases for the doctors are:

1. How are they able to live at all since their brain should be dead from lack of oxygen?

2. The experiences they recount while "dead," including their awareness of events around them and encounters with dead relatives and other supernatural experiences, challenge the belief systems of doctors and modern medicine.

Based on the research of Dr. Raymond Moody (Moody, 1975), it has been discovered that almost everyone who dies goes through the same process, a similar sequence of events. Moody has identified seven distinct phases of the near-death experience. Many patients experience only some of the steps, depending on how long they are dead and other factors, but there appears to be a universal system which applies to the death process.

During the NDE, the patient first reports an awareness of floating out of his body. He can look down and see his own body and see the doctors working on it, and see those around him. It is an experience very similar to astral travel, or the "out-of-body" experience discussed in Chapter 10.

Next they see a tunnel forming around them, or approaching them, and are drawn into it. Figure 11.1 is a depiction of this tunnel by the painter Hieronymus Bosch. Although painted in the Middle Ages, it is very similar to descriptions given in the modern day after an NDE. This tunnel often has a twist or a spiral aspect to it. Sometimes in the tunnel they meet spirit guides or departed relatives who have come to greet them.

When they reach the other end of the tunnel, they emerge into a bright, beautiful world of light. They often report meeting departed loved ones here as well. They describe a beautiful being of light who radiates love. Depending on their belief system, they may associate him with Jesus or Buddha, but usually this being has no distinct features.

Figure 11.1. Painting by Hieronymus Bosch, *Ascent into the Empyrean*, depicts ascent into heavenly realm through a dark tunnel with angelic spirit figures. The dark tunnel with light at the far end is frequently described in Near-Death Experiences.

They experience a "life review" in which their entire life is replayed before their eyes in vivid three-dimensional panoramic color. They receive lessons about how they have lived their life. After this they sometimes receive information about the future, or have the opportunity to see part of the realm in that dimension. If they do, they describe pastel landscapes and crystalline cities of light.

When they are revived and recover consciousness, they have often undergone a profound emotional and spiritual change. They often say after coming back that they have been taught profound spiritual lessons, that our real home is "on the other side," and that the most powerful force in the universe is love.

Not everyone has experiences as extensive as these, and some may not fully recall their experiences while "dead," but the remarkable consistency of the sequence of events across hundreds and thousands of cases is persuasive evidence that something very "real" occurs. It is not a fantasy of the brain, because legitimate out-of-body knowledge, and even precognitive knowledge, is often acquired during these experiences.

Near-Death experiencers are often able to describe specific and detailed events which occurred in other parts of the operating room or in other rooms in the hospital while they were "dead". They are often able to describe the appearance of unusual medical apparatus and procedures which they would otherwise have no knowledge of. They are often able to quote dialogues between physicians which took place while they were clinically dead. In some cases they roamed "out of body" through the hospital while their body lay on the table, and they are able to give detailed accounts of events occurring in other rooms or other floors of the building.

They describe their experience on the "other side" during the "life review" as a comprehensive, three-dimensional playback of their life. It is reminiscent of the stories of drowning victims experiencing their entire life flashing before their eyes. But for the near-death experiencer, this life review includes details that far exceed normal recall ability. Even more interesting, they report that, in the life review, they experience events from the point of view of the people they affected. Every hurt and every kindness is experienced from the point of view of the other person. It leaves them with the profound knowledge that we are all connected. What we do unto others in this world, we receive back during the life review, whether it be joy and love, or anger and hate.

Often they receive precognitive information about the future, and when they return to life they often watch as the foreseen events unfold. When they return to the world of the living their psychic ability is often heightened. Their sense of morality and spirituality is deeply altered. Time seems to flow at a different rate on the "other side" so they may return with a wealth of experiences to relate, even if they have been dead for a very short time.

All of these factors reinforce the hypothesis that the NDE is a very "real" phenomenon. It is not simply a biochemical hallucination occurring in the brain. It tells us something important about the multidimensional nature of reality. Based on the testimony of thousands of near-death experiencers, the "other side" is real; spiritual beings are real; and we are all spiritual beings. It will be easiest to appreciate the power of these experiences by recounting of few of them in detail.

Dannion Brinkley

Dannion Brinkley has been clinically dead three times. And yet today he is alive, having been resuscitated by modern medical technology. He is a member of a growing fraternity of people who have visited the other side, have medical documentation to prove they were dead, and yet returned to the land of the living to tell us of their experiences. (Brinkley, 1994, 1995)

He describes himself as a bully as child. He was disliked by his schoolmates because he was always taunting them or beating them up. After high school, he joined the military. His passion for adventure and violence led him, in his twenties, into covert military operations. He describes political assassinations he helped carry out for the U.S. government during this time.

But one day while he was home in South Carolina, he was talking to a friend on the telephone when a late summer thunderstorm came up. He heard the crackling on the line and could hear the approaching thunder. He tried to get off the phone. His buddy on the other end made fun of the "tough guy" for being afraid of a little lightning. This taunt kept Dannion from hanging up the phone. A moment later a searing pain shot through his body as a bolt of lightning passed through the phone wire, into his body, and out of his shoes into the floor. The nails of his shoes became welded to the nails in the wooden floor, but Dannion's body was thrown ten feet.

Frantic attempts by his wife, who had just completed a CPR course, and his buddy, a former Marine Corpsman, failed to revive him. When the ambulance arrived the medics used every modern technique to save him, but to no avail. When his body arrived at the Emergency Ward, there were further efforts by the hospital staff to revive him. CPR, heart massage, defibrillator, adrenaline injection into the heart, all were tried. The doctor told his distraught wife and friend the news: "We've lost him."

Meanwhile, Dannion was somewhere else. He found himself floating in the room after the lighting strike. He looked down at his battered, lifeless body on the bed. He said "the surprising thing was, I thought I was better looking than that."

He floated out-of-body and followed the ambulance as it raced to the hospital. He watched inside the ambulance as the medics exerted every effort to save him. He commented on the beautiful lights around the rescue workers as they worked on him. These lights were the auras of the men, their subtle energy fields which he had never seen before. He noticed how much they loved their work, and what joy they experienced when trying to save someone.

And then he noticed, toward the front of the ambulance, just over his head, a small black spot. It began growing and moving toward him. It was a tunnel. He thought, "That looks like an interesting place to explore," and immediately he found himself surrounded by the tunnel and moving into a realm of beautiful white light.

He said it was the most beautiful, brightest light he had ever seen. But it didn't hurt his eyes. He felt enormous love and peace. And then he saw a being made of light coming toward him. It projected enveloping love. No face or features could be seen. He looked "like a bagful of diamonds." And there was no judgment, only love.

Figure 11.2. Dannion Brinkley was declared clinically dead on three occasions. The first time, he was on his way to the morgue, covered by a sheet, after being dead without pulse, brain waves or breath for more than twenty-eight minutes, when he suddenly found himself back in his body and "alive." He was able to describe in detail events which happened while he was dead.

The being led Dannion to re-experience his entire life in an instant. But, instead of experiencing it from his point of view, he experienced the feelings that he had caused in others. He experienced the sadness and pain he had inflicted. Of men whose death he had caused, he experienced their puzzlement and sadness when they died, and the longing and loneliness of their families they left behind.

His first life review was painful. But the Light Being was not judgmental. He projected only love. He taught Dannion that we who incarnate on Earth are "powerful spiritual beings embarking on a great adventure." It takes courage to come here, but the attraction is that it is possible to learn so much so fast while here. Dannion learned that <u>it is each act of kindness which we do while here that helps us to grow</u> and allows us to experience the pleasure of the recipient after we die.

During his time on the other side, Dannion described a meeting with thirteen beings of light. Each being radiated a different color. Besides the principal being who led him through his life review, there were twelve others. "Each one of them represented a different emotional and psychological characteristic that all humans have. For example, one of these beings was intense and passionate, while another was artistic and emotional. One was bold and energetic, another was possessive and loyal. In human terms, it was as though each one represented a different sign of the zodiac." (Brinkley, 1994)

This observation may be very important in terms of developing a theory for the subtle energies, which seem to be at the heart of psychic phenomena. Acupuncturists have noted that there are twelve primary acupuncture meridians or subtle energy transport systems in the body. Each person comes into this life with problems in one of them. There seems to be a relationship between emotional qualities, astrological symbols, and acupuncture meridians.

As we will see in Volume II, Astrology is also built upon a system of 12 "qualities." Each quality is related to a particular form of subtle energy and a particular emotional characteristic. Some of the mathematics of this system has begun to be decoded in the work of Dr. Manfred Clynes (Clynes, 1967, 1989), who finds that the ability of music to evoke emotion also stems from this same underlying relationship. He has discovered that these elements make up a "language" of the emotions. They represent a universal system, a "language," which is key to understanding the emotional makeup of human beings and the nature of subtle energy.

Figure 11.3. Dannion Brinkley and the thirteen beings of light. At one point in his life review, Brinkley was confronted with thirteen beings, from whom he received "boxes of knowledge," visions of events in the future.

Each of these emotional elements corresponds to a unique form of subtle energy. The acupuncture meridian system controls and regulates these energies within the body, resulting in the "aura." As the emotions change, the aura changes. Brinkley's observation of twelve distinct emotional qualities may be a fundamental clue to understanding subtle energy and how it relates to acupuncture, astrology and the human emotional make-up.

The doctor in the hospital had pronounced Dannion dead many minutes earlier. His body was covered with a sheet and was being sent to the morgue. While waiting in the hospital hallway, his spirit left the realm of the light beings and re-entered his body. He suddenly felt the searing pain of his injuries. He was unable to move. He tried desperately to do something to let them know he was alive. He did the only thing he could: he blew on the sheet. An intern saw it and he was taken back to intensive care.

Brinkley has experienced clinical death two more times since that day. Each time he experienced a full life review. All of the bad memories from his early years are still just as bad when he re-experiences them. The life review for the early part of his life is identical to what it was the first time. But he now looks forward to the experiences which come later. Since the first NDE he has devoted his life to helping others. He spends his time comforting the sick and dying and has founded a national hospice organization, "Compassion In Action," so no one need die alone. And he has worked to create a new healing center based on principles he learned while on the other side.

Like so many others, he reports profound changes caused by the NDE. He is no longer afraid of death. He knows that love is the most powerful force in the universe. He knows that we are not physical beings trying to have a spiritual experience, but "great, magnificent and powerful spiritual beings trying to have a human experience." In the process, Dannion has provided an invaluable glimpse for all of us into what awaits us after death, and helps open our eyes to the higher dimensions which exist beyond our narrow three-dimensional physical reality.

Joe McMoneagle's Near-Death Experience

Joe McMoneagle was a career soldier. He had spent his life in Army intelligence, including a tour in Vietnam. There he displayed an uncanny intuition for when attacks were about to occur. Other soldiers began watching him and imitating his actions. He had had a few unusual psychic experiences in his life, but nothing to prepare him for that day in 1970 when he walked out of a restaurant and died from a heart attack.

When he was revived later at the hospital, he was a changed man. His Near-Death Experience left him with heightened psychic abilities. He was able to go "out-of-body" easily after that. He became one of the first, and most highly rated, of the remote viewers when the military program began.

Joe's unusual abilities stem, at least in part, from that fatal heart attack. He describes it in his book, *Mind Trek* (McMoneagle, 1993). He was in the Army stationed in Austria. He began feeling uncomfortable in a restaurant and headed outside to "get some fresh air." As he passed through the doorway, he noticed that time seemed to slow down. He told his arm to move but it seemed to take forever for the signal to reach his hand. His body collapsed just outside the restaurant. He remembers falling and expecting to feel his face hit the pavement.

But the next moment, he found himself standing out in the street, feeling very light and calm. He described it as waking up and finding that you are already doing something, like a sleepwalker must feel. He was now outside of his body, but it felt so natural it took quite a while for him to realize it. He noticed that it was raining but he wasn't getting wet. He could feel the tiny raindrops hitting his arm, but then they would slide <u>through</u> his arm and fall on the street. At about the same time he realized he couldn't see his feet. Then he noticed that he was drifting, not walking. Slowly it began to dawn on him that something was very strange.

The amazing thing about the Near-Death experience is how natural it feels to those experiencing it. One is still within one's normal consciousness, still perceiving the world in much the same way as in normal physical life. There is still the same sense of being alive, of being conscious, of being aware. The world looks very similar, as well. But one important difference, as Joe McMoneagle found out, is that you can now look on your old physical body from the outside, like a bystander:

"After recognizing that it was my body in my friends lap, and assuming that I was either dead or dying, a lot of things quickly began to happen. My friend, I observed, was jamming his finger down my throat, and, while I could watch it being done, I couldn't feel it...I could even see the blue forming around my lips and beneath my eyes." (McMoneagle, 1993)

184

Joe described the attempts by his friend to revive his body: "He began to violently strike me in the chest, cursing me to breathe with each punch...The interesting thing I experienced through all of this was that, every time he stuck me in the center of the chest, I would feel a click and find myself looking up through my physical eyes at his. This would immediately be followed by another distinct click, and once more I would be out of my body looking down at him from above. After ten minutes of this I was beginning to feel like a yo-yo. Click-pain, click-no pain...and so forth."

Each time he was momentarily revived, he popped back into his body and heard a click, and immediately experienced the pain of the body. Then he would go out of body again and feel no pain. He describes his out-of-body state as feeling like a kid again. He loved the feeling of no restraints. He could fly, just by willing it. He rose up in the air for a better view, and floating in the air, he followed the car into which his body had been loaded to be returned to Germany.

He raced along behind the car, ducking under electrical wires and occasionally dipping down to look in its windows as it raced toward the hospital. On arrival there, he watched as his friend kicked the hospital doors in frustration, not being aware then that hospitals in Germany lock their doors by 7:00 or 8:00 PM.

Like so many others, Joe, in his near-death state, then entered a tunnel, falling through it as he accelerated. He then found himself enveloped by a being of light, which filled him with peace and love. He says it exceeded the definition of good, then great, then glorious. He coined the phrase "exceedingly-outrageously-fantastic" to describe the feeling. These feelings came in response to his inner question of what God is like. Joe was encountering a Being of Light on the other side of the tunnel. He did not know it then, but his description closely matches those of the many thousands of others who have shared the experience of dying and coming back to physical life.

He then went through a life review. He saw his shortcomings, and how poorly he measured up to the Being of Light. His wasted time, misjudgments, and failings he was able to see clearly for the first time. Yet there was no judgment, except that which he applied to himself. From the Being of Light he felt only immense warmth and love. He describes it as a "giving or unconditional sharing, ... an in-love feeling."

The Being of Light then told Joe that he had to go back, that he could not remain on the other side just yet. He resisted this. He argued with the being. The spirit side was so peaceful and full of love, and the physical earth has so much struggle and pain. Joe did not want to return. But the Being told him he must, and the next thing he knew he was sitting bolt upright in his bed in the hospital in Germany (McMoneagle, 1993).

Harry Hone

Harry Hone went into cardiac arrest in Newport Hospital, and was "dead" for only a few minutes (Hone, 1986). He had been admitted the night before with severe chest pains and indications of heart attack. He was already in the cardiac care unit of the hospital when it happened. He suddenly found himself in a realm which was darker than dark, and yet somehow he was able to see. The experience of dying was unlike fainting. He just felt like he was going "somewhere else."

He still felt that he had his own identity, his own consciousness, but without the weight and inertia of his body. He was aware that he had left his body behind. He turned around and looked at it from above. It appeared inert and lifeless. He saw the doctors and nurses feverishly working on his body. His attitude was one of detachment. They worked feverishly, but he, looking on in his out-of-body state, was calm.

Then he felt pulled away and began traveling at lightning speed. He felt no desire to resist. The new force moving him was "delightfully persuasive." He felt a gentle, pulsating power that drew him into a dark tunnel, and yet he could see. At the far end of the tunnel he saw a bright light.

Like so many others who have traveled to the "other side," it was beautifully peaceful. He sensed that light was from an "indescribable, effulgently pure white world of 'light'." He developed a love for this place. As with so many others, he was reluctant to leave that side and come back to the world of the living. In his brief near-death experience, his perspective was forever changed. He realized that it is in this physical world that we fight the unending battles. On the other side we find the "peace that passeth all understanding." (Hone, 1986).

He concluded from his experience that the "real Harry Hone" consisted of a "tiny speck or spark of light," and upon death that spark of light has left its physical house. He realized that his own tiny spark of light, his own identity or soul, was an integral part of the immense world of bright white light which he encountered at the other end of the tunnel.

He remembers a life review, in which his entire life flashed by in the blink of an eye. It was just like an instant replay on television, flashing across his vision and going from birth to death in an instant. He saw certain moments in his life when he increased his share of the "light," and other times when he diminished it.

So much happened to Hone during his brief time of death that it makes apparent how time can flow at very different rates in the two realms. After his recovery he found that his psychic ability had been enhanced. Hone received several prophetic visions which were very detailed and which came true shortly afterwards. One was the collapse of the Toccoa Dam in Georgia; the second was the religious scandals of the 1980s; a third was a prophecy of the meeting in Egypt and the peace treaty signed between Sadat and Begin.

In addition to these remarkable events, something else happened during his NDE which was even more wonderful. When he was dead he was told exactly where he would find his long-lost sister. He had been separated from her for thirty-four years. They had been children in England together, but World War II had separated them. He had completely lost touch with her. While on the "other side" he was told by a voice the exact location where he would find her. She was living half way around the world from him, but using the paranormal information he received, he found her easily after his recovery.

"If this is what happens when people die, they have absolutely nothing to be afraid of," he said. Like so many others who have experienced NDEs, he found that on the "other side" was no "heaven" or "hell" in the conventional sense. The only heavens and hells to be found are in the belief systems we take with us to the other side. "We build our own heavens and hells right here in our own lives," he said.

Of his near death experience, Hone's most profound revelation is that he, Harry Hone, is <u>not</u> his physical body. "People will say you are 'dead,' but that's not true. 'You' are the 'life,' and you have left. 'You' are not dead. It's your body that's 'dead'." He learned that the power of visualization and imagination can be used to bring into being that which we desire: "All power resides in imagination." Like so many other near-death experiencers, he emerged from it with no fear of death, and with a profoundly enriched spiritual perspective. "When you know that you ARE THE LIGHT—you can find your own way to "heaven" and you'll never be in the dark again." (Hone, 1986)

Dr. Melvin Morse

Dr. Morse is a medical doctor. He did not always believe that Near-Death Experiences were real. When he first heard of them, he thought they were just hallucinations caused by lack of oxygen to the brain or by the medications the patient had been given. Like most doctors, he believed such experiences were some sort of psychological defense mechanism which the patient uses to counter his fear of dying. During his practice, Dr. Morse helped many patients narrowly avert death. Many of them may have had near-death experiences. He does not know because he did not ask.

Then one day he encountered Katie, a shy seven-year old who had drowned and then been revived. She had been clinically dead for nineteen minutes. She related to him in a straightforward manner what happened to her. When she saw the alarmed look on his face, she said "Don't worry, Dr. Morse. You'll see, heaven is fun!" (Morse, 1992)

The fact that Katie was alive at all was a miracle. She had drowned in the swimming pool at the YWCA. She was found floating face down in the water, and brought to the hospital. Dr. Morse resuscitated her in the Emergency Room of the Hospital several hours later. Her CAT scan showed massive brain swelling. She showed no gag reflex. Morse estimated she had only a ten percent chance of surviving. He described how her family formed a prayer circle around her bed and prayed out loud during the catheterization he had to perform. Three days later she made a full recovery. One can never prove that prayer did it, but Dr. Morse acknowledges that he never expected her to survive, and yet she did (Morse, 1990).

After her recovery he talked to Katie about the accident. She was able to recount for him details of the sequence of events which occurred while she had been unconscious. She described the other doctors who had been present, and the procedures they had administered to her, including putting a tube up her nose while she was completely unconscious. Then she described what happened next. She was in darkness first, and then a lady named Elizabeth appeared and guided her up a tunnel, where she met her late grandfather and several other people. Among the new friends she met in the tunnel were two boys, Andy and Mark, with whom she played for a while. They were souls waiting to be born.

While in the tunnel, she was allowed to view her home. She could see her brothers and sisters playing, and could see her father in the living room staring blankly ahead. She felt he was worrying about her. Later, when she described these scenes to her parents in detail, they were astonished at their accuracy. Then Elizabeth, who seemed to be a guardian angel for her, took her to meet, as she described it, The Heavenly Father and Jesus. She was asked if she wanted to go home and she said yes. The next moment, she was awake in the hospital bed. The nurses said that the first words out of her mouth were "Where are Mark and Andy?"

Dr. Morse researched Katie's religious background (she was a Mormon) and found that none of her young education would cause her to believe in spirit guides, nor that Heaven is a place you get to through a tunnel. Like so many thousands of other Near-Death Experiencers, Katie reported spirit guides and a Being of Light which is sometimes identified with Jesus, sometimes not. Katie met dead friends and relatives, and passed through a tunnel to get there.

Dr. Morse became very interested in the scientific side of the NDE. One question he asked was whether the patients "really" went out-of-body or just "thought" they did. One of the doctors who investigated this was Dr. Sabom, an Atlanta cardiologist who studied 32 patients who had undergone near-death experiences from heart attacks. He asked them to answer a series of questionnaires involving minute details of the procedures employed when their doctor tried to get their hearts started again.

Since they were "dead" at the time, they could not know about the details unless they had really been hovering above their bodies watching, as they claimed. These were patients with no medical training and therefore unlikely to know the answers unless they had actually witnessed the event. He also posed the same questions to a group of twenty-five medically knowledgeable patients who had not had near-death experiences. He found that twenty-three out of twenty five in the latter group made major mistakes in describing the process, while <u>every</u> member of the NDE group described the process correctly (Morse, 1990)! Research of this type has proven over and over again that in the near-death experience, the patient really <u>does</u> go out of his body.

As a physician, Dr. Morse has encountered many other patients who have had near-death experiences. In some cases, he was the physician who revived them. The consistency of their stories, together with verifiable information which was independently checked, and coupled with the profound changes wrought in them by their experiences, convinced him that these experiences are real and tell us something important about the realms beyond death. Here is how he put it:

> *"Then one day I read a long article in a medical journal that tried to explain NDEs as being various tricks of the brain. By then I had studied NDEs extensively and none of the explanations that this researcher listed made sense. It was finally clear to me that he had missed the most obvious explanation of all— NDEs are real. He had missed the possibility that the soul really does travel!"* (Moody, 1988) [quoted in Talbot, 1991, p. 243]

Dr. Morse has summarized his research and findings in two deeply moving books, *Closer to the Light* and *Transformed by the Light* (Morse, 1990, 1992).

Dr. Raymond Moody's Research

When Raymond Moody was an undergraduate at the University of Virginia, he met a professor in the School of Medicine who had been clinically dead on two occasions. The Professor gave "a most fantastic account" of what had happened to him while dead. As the years went by, Moody heard similar stories from others who had died or come very close to death. The stories came from people with different religious backgrounds and different circumstances, but they all sounded remarkably similar.

By that time, Moody had received a Ph.D. in Philosophy, taught for several years, and had entered Medical School to become a doctor. But his interest was aroused by these stories surrounding death. He began collecting them:

> *"What has amazed me since the beginning of my interest are the great similarities in the reports, despite the fact that they come from people of highly varied religious, social, and educational backgrounds." (Moody, 1975)*

By the time he wrote his first book, *Life After Life*, he had collected more than 150 such cases. They involved three different circumstances: (1) clinical death with subsequent revival; (2) extreme illness; and (3) actual death where the dying person related his experiences during the death process to a third party. Dr. Moody found similar patterns in virtually all of them, including a series of steps or stages that the dying person goes through.

There were differences from case to case, and very few subjects experienced all of the steps. The number of steps experienced and the richness of the experience depended on whether clinical death actually occurred, and how long the person was clinically dead. "How far into the hypothetical complete experience a dying person gets seems to depend on whether or not the person actually underwent a clinical death, and if so, on how long he was in this state." (Moody, 1975)

Moody's findings (Moody, 1975, 1978) have been supported by other researchers, such as Dr. Kenneth Ring (Ring, 1985a, 1985b) and Dr. Michael Sabom (Sabom, 1985), who have conducted in-depth scientific studies into the near-death process. There are numerous first-person accounts available (Eadie, 1992; Farr, 1993;

Ritchie, 1978), and accounts by hospice workers at the death-bed (Kubler-Ross, 1997). Other researchers have used hypnotic past-life regression to retrieve memories of previous deaths and the "between life" period after past deaths and before the present life (Fiore, 1978; Newton, 1995; Weiss, 1991, 1996, 2000). In these cases, as the hypnotic subject describes the events immediately following his death, the same sequence of events found by Dr. Moody often appears.

According to Dr. Moody's research, there are seven stages of a Near-Death Experience (NDE). These occur roughly in sequence. Most experiencers return after only two or three stages in this process. A few have gone through the entire process before returning. But what is remarkable is that the descriptions are so similar. Despite religious and cultural variations in the accounts, Dr. Moody says "there is a system." Here are the main stages which have been documented:

(1) Floating out of the body in an OBE, and often looking back at the body
(2) Seeing tunnel form, and then being drawn into it
(3) Meeting spirit guides and departed relatives
(4) Emerging into beautiful world of light and love
(5) Meeting a dazzling "Being of Light" and love, sometimes identified with Jesus or Buddha
(6) Experiencing a "panoramic life review" from the viewpoint of those affected, judging oneself.
(7) Receiving lessons on how they lived their lives

Some experiencers are allowed to see more on the "other side" including crystal cathedrals made of light and beautiful pastel countrysides. Everywhere there is a feeling of great love. When the experiencer is told he must return to his body, he usually objects. They always want to stay on the other side, so great is the joy, peace and love there.

The consistency in the accounts of near-death experiences is one aspect which gives them credibility. These accounts come from people of all ages, cultures, and religions. Although there are some cultural differences in the accounts, they usually include an out-of-body phase, a tunnel, and the passage over to the "other side," often described as a realm of brilliant white light where they are met by a being of light projecting great love. Sometimes there are prophetic messages which, when confirmed, serve as validation of the experience.

The light in this realm is extraordinary. It is often described as "all-loving" or "all-forgiving." Here they often meet departed loved ones and family members. They experience a "panoramic life review" in which every event and deed of their life is relived and experienced from the perspective of the people they affected. Often it is the need of someone back on earth among the living, or unfinished obligations, which brings them back.

The message they return with is that Love is the most powerful force in the universe. They learn that we are not mere physical beings, but something much greater and more wonderful. They say we come here, to the physical plane, to learn, and then we return to the other side. There is an evolutionary growth process involved.

The great message for Western man is that the physical world is not all there is. It is only a playground on which we can meet and learn and grow. As the Hindus would say, the so-called "real world" is illusion. It is "maya". It is the higher dimensions, on which the soul and consciousness exist, that are more lasting and more important.

Based on the evidence of Near-Death studies, as well as other research, this is how our universe seems to work. The Near-Death experience and the "light beings" are part of it. Our science must broaden its assumptions in order to understand how these invisible consciousnesses and other realms can exist. The various religions of the world can perhaps begin to resolve their differences and end their theological debates when they realize that there is a seemingly "objective" reality. There are ways of finding out the truth of what happens when we die, and our true relationship to these other dimensions. The amazing accounts of Near-Death Experiencers provide one window into this larger world.

The "Dark Side" of the Near-Death Experience

Although the majority of Near-Death Experiences are filled with light and love, a significant minority of experiencers report something quite different. According to P. M. H. Atwater, (Atwater, 1994) who has experienced clinical death three times and also conducted research into others' NDEs, about one out of seven NDEs are quite negative and frightening. After traveling through the tunnel to the "other side," one woman encountered "a landscape of barren rolling hills filled to overflowing with nude, zombie-like people standing elbow to elbow doing nothing but staring straight at her." She had been in the hospital clinically dead during this experience. When she was revived, she came back screaming and declared death a nightmare.

Atwater recounts other cases from her research to support the conclusion that not all NDEs are purely positive and wonderful. This point of view was well-expressed in the movie *What Dreams May Come*, with Robin Williams, which depicts experiences on the "other side" during an NDE. There were wonderful and glorious landscapes in some places. There were also hellish regions with souls seemingly trapped in despair. The movie makes the point that Atwater and some Near-Death researchers have made: one's expectations and emotions, and especially one's feelings of guilt, exert a strong effect on the NDE. For the "other side," also called the "astral dimension," is strongly affected by emotions and beliefs. We are learning that emotions are real, substantial forces. In the astral domain, they can often be instantly translated into an apparent reality. Williams' movie makes this point. So does Atwater's research:

> *"I have noticed that: Deeply rooted belief systems and regionalisms can color an individual's description and interpretation of his or her [NDE] experience."* *(Atwater, 1994)*

Atwater also recounts the various stages of the Near-Death Experience as it is described in the *Tibetan Book of the Dead*. Its description is consistent with her findings. There are stages within the NDE. It is, in this sense, truly a "system" as Raymond Moody and Dannion Brinkley have described. But there are more stages to it than is generally recognized. Most people reporting NDEs are "dead" for a short time and then revived. Because of this, they experience only part of the process. To the Tibetans, Death was an important journey with many stages. It was important to do it right. This could greatly shorten the number of reincarnations one must endure. The *Tibetan Book of the Dead* is a guidebook to help in this process.

According to this book, the heavenly visions most often described occur during the first week after death. During the second week there are hellish visions. During the third week are opportunities to judge one's life. This process continues for twenty-eight to forty-nine days after death. The heavenly visions in the *Tibetan Book of the Dead* are very similar to the positive NDEs most frequently described: full of light and love. The hellish visions and the opportunities for self-judgment are similar to the negative NDE accounts.

In trying to understand this complex system which exists on the other side, the *Tibetan Book of the Dead* states, according to Atwater:

"...all postmortem visions, regardless of type, are actually projections from the mind of the participant. This implies that the next world may be structured by the subconscious mind, that mental imagery somehow determines what is met after death. Also implied is that both heavenly and hellish scenarios might well represent part of the natural course of the subconscious as it shifts from one state of awareness to another, and through numerous levels of existence. Oddly, the realness of the near-death experience is not diminished by this claim, or others like it. The phenomenon instead becomes subjected to psychic rather than physical laws, which I believe accounts for the variation of details and descriptions from culture to culture, group to group."(Atwater, 1996)

This reference to "psychic, rather than physical laws" is very significant. The astral domain is often said to be a realm in which the laws of physics are different from those in our three-dimensional physical world. They are governed by emotions, desires, and by all the deep parts of us that are familiar to the subconscious mind. This may be "why" the subconscious mind is so receptive to psychic information, while the conscious, logical mind is oblivious. Perhaps psychic information travels and is transmitted in the astral realm. The laws of physics for this realm are unexplored by our science. But the similarity of structure of NDEs for so many people is evidence that this astral realm is "real" in some sense, and does have laws which govern it. They provide a challenge and a wonderful mystery to explore further.

The Science of the Soul

Although the phenomenon of the "near-death experience" may seem to be a modern discovery, with which we in the West are just becoming familiar, in many traditional societies it is very ancient knowledge, and has been integrated into language, ritual, and religion. In Tibet, for example, a great deal is known about the steps one goes through when dying, and after death, and about the processes which occur between lives leading to another incarnation. This is evidenced by *The Bardo Thodol*, or *Tibetan Book of the Dead*, mentioned above. It is an ancient text meant to be "read aloud to the dying and to the newly dead" (Cockell, 1996). It describes the various steps one will go through during and after death, and is meant to guide them in the death process and the afterlife, so they will not have to be reincarnated. The description of the early stages in this process are remarkably similar to modern accounts of the NDE.

In Chapter 10 on the out-of-body experience and in the present chapter on the near-death experience, we have encountered abundant evidence that an energy form exists which is the center of consciousness, which can travel outside the body, and which survives death. This energy form has a remarkably similar appearance in cases of remote viewing, out-of-body travel, and at the moment of death. The simplest conclusion is that this energy form serves as the seat of consciousness of the body, and can leave the body during OBEs and at death. The same type of energy form has been photographed by "ghost hunters" in haunted areas (see Figure 10.12) and may represent the consciousness of those spirits who are trapped in such places.

Thus a unified picture is emerging. This energy form, which we have often referred to as the "astral body," may be the key to understanding ghosts, remote viewing, and the out-of-body and near-death experiences. It has measureable physical properties under some circumstances: It has been photographed, and it registers on electromagnetic and strain sensors. At the same time it is capable of defying the limitations of space, time and gravity, breaking many of the rules of conventional science in the process.

191

It may be that this energy form is the human soul or some aspect of it. Many OBE and NDE cases imply that this energy form serves as a window into other dimensions and times. Identifying these small spheres with some aspect of the soul is a long way from understanding the soul. Nevertheless, it is an important step forward. The spiritual realm, the realm of the other side where we go at death, was described by one small boy who had an NDE as follows: "It's sort of like if you went through another passageway…you walked right through a wall to another galaxy or something" (Morse, 1990). The "other side" is often described as coexisting with normal physical reality, in the same space but in another dimension.

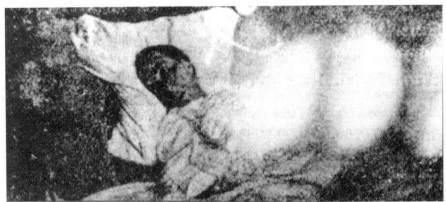

Figure 11.4. Photograph taken by French psychical researcher Hippolyte Baraduc at the moment of his wife's death. The cloudlike formations in the photograph were believed by Baraduc to be the departing astral form of his wife, possibly accompanied by her young son, who had died several months earlier, and whom she described as being "present" shortly before her death. Although skeptics will ascribe such features to imperfections in the film, similar glowing orbs have been observed by many people at the time of death. (BPCC, Aldus Archive, London)

The "science of the soul" is in its infancy. Near-death studies support the reality of its existence, and of other, higher dimensions which co-exist with our own. These provide profound challenges for modern science. If science can get over its denial of these phenomena, and begin studying them with open-minded objectivity, great strides can be made.

The new science which emerges from these studies will not be in conflict with spirituality. There is a common ground on which both may meet. It is the common ground of Truth. Science claims that it has the responsibility of describing how the universe works. It appears that the soul and spiritual beings and higher dimensional realities may very well be objectively real, and therefore are an integral part of this universe. The evidence in favor of this is mounting. It is time for a new, broader physical theory which addresses these phenomena. New technology may assist us as we learn how to measure and observe, and perhaps communicate. It will require new paradigms and new models of the universe, especially involving the higher dimensions.

Current physics theory teaches that there are 10 or 11 dimensions, but that only the four of space-time are directly accessible to us. Perhaps these other dimensions are accessible in ways we don't understand right now. It may be that the veil between our dimensions and other higher dimensions are only pierced occasionally, notably at the time of death. One hundred years ago the director of the Patent Office wanted to close it because he thought all the science had been discovered. The later revolutions which occurred in science were impossible for him to imagine. A similar revolution awaits us as we begin to develop the science of spirit.

As we come to understand these other realms, it may also change the conventional teachings of some established religions. But it will also place many of their articles of faith on firmer ground. The reality of the soul and the survival of death will no longer be conjecture. It will become a proven scientific fact apparent to everyone. When this happens, the age-old rift between science and spirituality will begin to heal. It will be the beginning of a more mature physics and a more mature religion. The universe for the first time will be understood from a single unified perspective.

Summary

The scientific study of the Near-Death Experience is beginning to provide answers to some of the deepest questions which plague mankind: "Is there life after death?" "What happens when we die?" "Is there a heaven or a hell?" and "What is the soul?" In the past these questions have been solely the domain of religion and philosophy. There has been no known scientific means of studying these questions. But with the large number of people who have been revived after clinical death, this is no longer true. The consistency of their accounts cannot be ignored.

It is also important that many of the great spiritual leaders who have founded religions have reported out-of-body or near-death experiences. It seems likely that their unique insights into the spiritual world arose from those experiences. In other words, their knowledge of heaven and the spirit world was not based on fancy, but on direct experience. They had been there. This may account for the underlying similarity of the basic tenets of many of the world's religions.

As Dannion Brinkley, who has been clinically dead three times, says, "There is a system…" The simplest explanation is that there is a parallel dimension to our own, one that few can see or hear when alive, and yet which is present and coexists with our own. In the Hindu religion of India, this other dimension is called the "astral," and it is made up of a form of energy which is quite different from the solid matter we know. Yet, as those who return from NDEs report, this realm is quite real.

A reasonable hypothesis is that if we understand the form of energy which makes up the astral body, we will also begin to understand this other realm, which we call the "other side."

In this other realm, time takes on unfamiliar properties. In our familiar three-dimensional world, time is linear. It trudges forward, one second at a "time." But in the astral realm described in NDEs, time seems to be much more fluid. Beings in this realm seem able to easily move forward and backward in time. When Dannion Brinkley came back from his NDE, he came back with knowledge of the future. There were 117 specific predictions he was given while "dead."

They were in the form of visions resembling a TV film clip. In most cases, he did not understand the meaning or the significance of these visions. Dr. Raymond Moody recorded them at the time, and has provided independent verification of their accuracy. One such "vision" was the nuclear reactor explosion at Chernobyl. This occurred almost ten years into the future from the time Brinkley received the vision during his NDE. But it occurred exactly as he was shown. Almost all of the other visions have since come true as well.

How is it that such precise knowledge of the future is available on the "other side"? It seems that "over there" time is not the limiting factor it is in our material reality. Movement forward and backward in time seems easy there, based on many accounts. This realm closely resembles the realm in which remote viewers move when their consciousness travels in time. Our science does not understand how such "time travel" is possible. Our science does not understand how such precise predictions of the distant future can be made. And yet we have a great deal of evidence. How can this be reconciled with the concept of "free will?" In the next chapter we will address these extremely important questions.

CHAPTER 12-TIME AND PROPHECY

"Can you see the future?," I asked. "She looked slightly uncomfortable. 'Oh, that,' she said. 'Who told you?'"
-- Melvin Morse, M. D. (Morse, 1992)

"Positive time intervals denote perceptions dictated precognitively by the indicated number of hours. Negative times denote data acquired retrocognitively, where the percipient dictated his perception after the target had been visited. Again, over the interval range of several days covered by these experiments, there is no statistically significant dependence on these time intervals."
--Robert Jahn and Brenda Dunne, *Margins of Reality* (Jahn, 1987)

"A most striking feature of psi effects is the violation of the causality principle. Causality, in the meaning in which I am using this term, concerns the time order between cause and effect, with the cause always preceding the effect."
-- Helmut Schmidt, (Schmidt, 1993)

"Everything is determined, the beginning as well as the end, by forces over which we have no control. It is determined for the insect as well as the star. Human beings, vegetables, our cosmic dust, all dance to a mysterious tune intoned in the distance by an invisible player."
-- Albert Einstein, (quoted in Quigley, 1990)

DEFINITION-PROPHECY: Statements about the future, based on knowledge or visions of events to occur in the future; a prediction.

DEFINITION-PRECOGNITION: Knowledge of events in the future.

The Arrow of Time

Deeply imbedded in today's physics is the concept of time. Cause must always precede effect. This principle is called "causality" in physics. It implies that time has a specific direction, flowing from the past toward the future. Paranormal phenomena often break this rule. To quote physicist and parapsychologist Dr. Helmut Schmidt:

"Through the results of psi research it became apparent that quantum theory has flaws in a very practical sense. Applied to systems that include human subjects the predictions of quantum theory were seen to be sometimes incorrect."
(Schmidt, 1993)

Another of the most deeply cherished principles in physics is the Second Law of Thermodynamics, which says that entropy can never decrease in a closed system. Entropy is the level of randomness in the system. The more organized and orderly a system, the less randomness is present. The Second Law of Thermodynamics says that, in any physical process, entropy must either remain constant or increase. Therefore, over time the randomness of the universe is expected to increase. It is this increase of entropy, of randomness, which determines the direction of time.

In recent years this basic "law" has come into question. Dr. Ilya Prigogine received the Nobel Prize for showing how, in some physical systems, entropy can behave in surprising ways. In some cases, systems can become more ordered, rather than decay into randomness. Gravity, for example, will act on dispersed cosmic dust and pull it together in organized clumps, eventually creating planets. In this way it creates order out of chaos, and may break this law of entropy. Prigogine states the matter succinctly:

"Important problems still remain unsolved. We do not yet know if the second law applies to gravitational interactions." (Prigogine, 1980)

As physics advances, it is discovering more and more systems which may break the old rules. Order can seemingly grow out of chaos in such situations. The Belousov-Zhaboutinsky chemical reaction can begin with two well-mixed chemical components and produce a separation of components into beautiful ordered geometric structures which were not present to begin with. The photographs below, in Figure 12.1, were all taken of the same shallow dish separated by time intervals of fractions of a second, as the chemical reaction proceeded. Once again, order has seemingly been produced from disorder.

Figure 12.1. The Belousov-Zhabotinsky Reaction may be an example in which order grows out of chaos. Biological, living systems also appear to extract order from chaos. Photographed by Fritz Goro in Arthur T. Winfree's laboratory (Prigogine, 1980).

These examples challenge our fundamental notion that time always flows in a single direction, namely the direction in which entropy or randomness increases. Other challenges to the conventional wisdom have been offered by biological systems.

Can Order be Collected Again?

Entropy is expected to increase when a physical process produces heat or radiation. These are two forms of energy which tend to spread. The energy radiates out into the vast blackness of space, where it is presumably absorbed by distant matter. Heat spreads as it moves from hotter to colder regions. Both methods appear to spread out the energy, which means entropy has increased. It is supposed to be impossible to reverse these processes. But there may be ways, such as gravity and nonlinearities, which reverse this outward flow of energy, and bring back the order and the energy to the local region from which it originated.

One example of this was discovered by the Nobel Prize winning physicist Enrico Fermi. In a now famous computer experiment called the "Fermi-Pasta-Ulam" problem, his team built a computer model of a crystal, in which the atoms interacted via fairly realistic "non-linear" springs which imitate the forces between real atoms in a crystal. They started the computer calculation by dumping some energy, basically a "hot spot," into one region of the crystal. This is illustrated in Figure 12.2, first panel. As the computer model crunched away, they were expecting it to show the heat spreading out through the crystal, so eventually it would be evenly distributed. This is what the "Second Law of Thermodynamics" predicts, and is illustrated in the second panel of the figure.

But to the shock of Fermi and the other team members, as the computer model progressed, the energy began to collect back in another "hot spot" at later time! This is illustrated in the third panel. This is <u>not</u> what was expected by the laws of entropy.

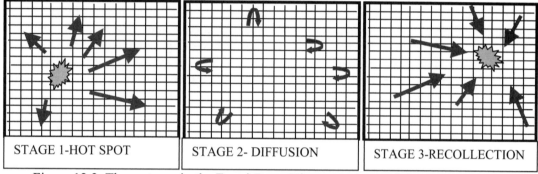

Figure 12.2. Three stages in the Fermi-Pasta-Ulam experiment. It is a computer model of a non-linear crystal. Energy is deposited initially as a "hot spot." After diffusing through the crystal as expected, the energy begins to re-focus and form another hotspot later in the process (Stage 3). This is not expected by the Second Law of Thermodynamics, which predicts that the energy will become evenly distributed throughout the crystal.

The model universe they built was refocusing its energy, collecting it into a new, localized lump. Out of chaos had come order! It turned out that the non-linear component in the spring model caused this effect. It resulted in what is called a "soliton." But such non-linear effects occur all the time in nature. This may give us a hint of how the universe really treats time and entropy. Things may appear to initially spread out and decay according to the Second Law of Thermodynamics, but this may be too simplistic. There may be processes which can refocus the energy again, creating order out of chaos.

This mathematical example illustrates the possibility that, even though physical phenomena appear to increase entropy, as radiation and heat spread out into the universe, there might be subtle non-linear mechanisms which cause this very same energy to "double back" to collect again and reconcentrate itself over time.

This question becomes even more important when living systems are considered. Living systems specialize in creating order out of disorder. Put a tiny acorn into the ground with some dispersed nutrients, and it filters and organizes the nutrients into a huge oak tree over time. It seems to have created order out of disorder. Does it violate the Second Law?

According the Russian scientist Alexander Dubrov, it does indeed:

"It is a fact, as investigations on biological thermodynamics have shown (Trincher, 1964), that in the metabolizing cell performing internal work, heat is not generated and hence entropy does not increase. This is due to the fact that the cell has a unique mechanism of heat removal involving continuous microphasic transitions of intracellular water and proteins from the liquid to the crystalline state. Their close interaction and the interdependent "liquid-crystal" or "disordered-superordered state" transitions constitute a unique mechanism for the creation of negentropy [negative entropy] in living material."(Dubrov, 1977)

Dubrov and others have discovered that, when there are outside sources of energy at a particular frequency which can drive the system, then it need not decay into randomness. It may develop stable ordered structures in such situations. This is one of the keys by which biological systems are believed to produce "negentropy" (see next chapter).

Recent Russian research into the science of "torsion" appears to shed light on this question. Astrophysicist Nikolai Kozyrev has proposed that, in any process in which entropy increases, there is an additional form of radiation called "torsion" which carries away information exactly balancing the entropy, so overall within the universe the total amount of entropy remains fixed. It implies a form of radiation which carries negative entropy, also called "negentropy" or "syntropy." This radiation plays a crucial role in life processes, and is the central focus of Volume II of this series.

The Second Law, which mandates increase of entropy, applies to the entropy of the total system. Therefore, all of the energy put into the oak tree from sunshine must be included. All of the rain, all of the wind, the reflected heat and the energy of the fertilizers and chemicals in the soil must be taken into account. This is a complex and difficult process.

The physicist Erwin Schroedinger noted that one of the remarkable distinguishing characteristics of living organisms is their capability of "drinking orderliness from a suitable environment" (Schroedinger, 1967). It is a question at the forefront of scientific research today, whether living systems violate the Second Law of Thermodynamics. The importance for this chapter is that, if they can reverse entropy, then maybe they can reverse time.

Laboratory Research Into Precognition

Future knowledge poses one of the greatest challenges to conventional science. The future, according to the present quantum-mechanical view, is unknowable, and only exists as a set of probabilities. At every instant of time the probable events multiply, so there are virtually an infinite number of possible futures even one day into the future. Therefore the probability of obtaining accurate information about a future event should be minuscule. In other words, there are so many possibilities that prophecy should be impossible.

The uncertainties of quantum mechanics are added to the recent science of "chaos," which has proven that very small changes in conditions can lead to very large differences in end results. An example is the "butterfly effect," discovered by Edward Lorenz of M.I.T. (Lorenz, 1963). He was trying to understand the weather. He built a simple equation approximating how the atmosphere behaves. It was a very simple equation, but it contained some "nonlinear terms," i.e. terms like the product of two weather parameters.

He found it behaved like the weather all right…too much like the weather. It was a chaotic system. A very small change in starting conditions led to big changes in his predictions a couple of days ahead. He described it as the "butterfly effect": a butterfly flapping its wings in Brazil will alter the weather in Boston a few days later! This sensitivity to very small changes in initial conditions makes future prediction even more difficult.

And yet, cases of successful psychic precognition do occur. When a vision of the future occurs it may be in a dream, a meditation, a prayer, or sometimes in an altered state like a near-death experience. These visions are so clear and detailed that it seems as if the experiencer is really there. It is as if one has jumped forward in time and come into direct contact with future events. The myriad possible alternative futures do not enter into such a vision.

If such seemingly prophetic experiences cannot be explained away as coincidence or random chance, then they pose a serious problem to conventional physics. If physics says a billion alternative futures are equally likely, and the psychic is able to identify the correct future which will occur, then somehow the psychic knows more about the future than does the physicist. There must be additional information which determines the future which physics knows nothing about.

This brings back the old debate between the two great physicists, Albert Einstein and Neils Bohr, which took place in the early years of the twentieth century. Bohr maintained that Quantum Mechanics describes all we can know about the universe. It describes a future in which there are many possible outcomes, and beyond the probabilities of the various paths, it can say nothing. Einstein believed that there must be additional information hidden deeper in physics which could select among these myriad possible futures. He did not believe that selecting among future time lines was simply a matter of chance based upon the odds of the various alternatives. "God does not play dice with the universe," was Einstein's rejoinder. If we knew the hidden, missing information we could, in principle, know the future path with much greater exactness.

The data acquired in remote viewing experiments supports this position. Remote viewers are able to view future events with no difficulty. The accuracy of precognitive sessions is just as high as for contemporaneous targets or past targets. For trained remote viewers it can be well above 60% in all cases (McMoneagle, 1999), and is no worse for the precognitive targets.

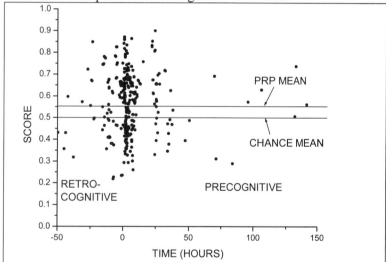

Figure 12.3. These data, from the extensive laboratory research of the Princeton PEAR Lab, show that remote viewing is equally accurate whether the targets are in the future, the present or the past. There is a definite ability to see future targets accurately (Jahn, 1987b).

One of the most prolific scientific laboratories studying the paranormal is that headed by Dr. Robert Jahn, Professor Emeritus of the Engineering Department at Princeton University, and founder of the Princeton Engineering Anomalies Laboratory (PEAR). His colleague, Dr. Brenda Dunne, along with Jahn, has directed the research of this laboratory for over two decades, and has overseen the accumulation of an impressive and powerful data set on paranormal phenomena.

Figure 12.3, from their important book *Margins of Reality* (Jahn, 1987a), illustrates the role which time plays in paranormal phenomena. This graph shows, on the vertical axis, the accuracy or success in a certain form of remote viewing involving a sender and a receiver. The horizontal axis shows the time offset between the sending and the receiving of the scene. Most of the data points fall in the middle at about zero time offset. This reflects the conditions of the experiment. Most of the receptions were done at about the same time as the sending.

But when one looks at larger time offsets of many hours, the accuracy is about the same. In other words, based on many experiments, it doesn't matter whether the data are sent BEFORE or AFTER they are received. Either way works! This is very alien to our normal experience: the idea that someone could receive a message from us before we send it. But this happens frequently in ESP experiments.

Dr. Dean Radin conducted a series of experiments to test whether an individual is capable of going into the future to detect what his or her emotion would be at a later time (Radin, 1997a). He devised an experiment where the individual, called the "operator", would be shown a series of pictures. Some of them would be very calming. Others would be arousing, either of a violent or sexual nature. The individual was instrumented with devices to measure physiological responses to these two types of image.

The key part of the experiment was that these images were selected randomly, so the viewer would not know whether the next image would be calming or violent. Yet Radin found that, a few seconds <u>before</u> being shown the next picture, the operator began responding as if he knew what the image would be. He began responding as if he was already viewing it! If the next picture was a calming one, the viewer would begin calming down a couple of seconds before seeing the image. Likewise, if the next picture was going to be arousing, the viewer began reacting appropriately <u>before</u> the picture was shown.

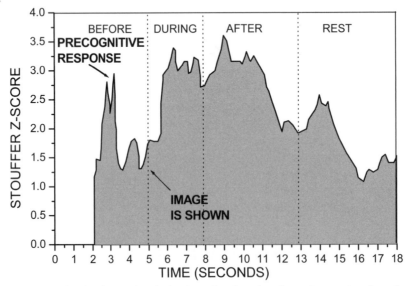

Figure 12.4, The horizontal axis is time for the viewing of a randomly selected image, involving a five-second period before the image is shown, a three second viewing time, a five second response time after the image is shown and another five second period of rest. Note the distinct and strong peak in the emotional response several seconds <u>before</u> the image is selected and shown (Radin, 1997a).

In part of the experiment, a random generator selected the picture at the instant it was shown. Even in these cases, the subject began reacting several seconds <u>before</u> he was shown the image. But <u>at that moment, the image had not yet been selected, even by the computer</u>. Nevertheless, the subject's physiological response was correct for the image. His body reacted as though it knew which picture would be selected, even though the random generator had not selected it yet. Again, we find that the subconscious mind is psychic. It is precognitive. It knows which picture will be selected seconds before the selection actually occurs. Figure 12.4 shows some of Radin's data establishing this effect.

Radin conducted extensive statistical tests to ensure that the data were not biased and could not be explained by coincidence. He found that the probability that coincidence could explain the results was about 8 parts in a thousand. His work was replicated by other researchers (Klintman, 1983, 1984; Bierman, 1997). They concluded that the operators responded precognitively to the images. They responded a couple of seconds <u>before</u> the image was selected. Therefore the "effect", their emotional response, <u>preceded</u> the "cause," which is the photograph.

Dr. Helmut Schmidt carried out experiments in which an effort was made to affect events in the past. This is called "retro-PK." He used animals in some of these experiments. He found that, by using operant conditioning, he could achieve successful PK performance with those animals. However, as in the previous data sets, he found that <u>if the data had been viewed by someone else</u>, even a goldfish, then the subject was subsequently unable to affect the pre-recorded data. In other words, retro-PK only seemed to work for the first viewer of the data.

This result is strongly reminiscent of one of the pillars of quantum mechanics: that all the physically allowed possibilities remain open until an observation is made. The observation is said to trigger the "collapse of the wave function", after which the event is completely determined. This may be what is happening in retro-PK experiments (Schmidt, 1993).

Another candidate explanation for the ability to seemingly influence hard-wired data rests with precognition: if the subject is able to sense the future sequence of numbers, then it is possible for him to select the optimum starting and stopping times which maximize the desired score. This may involve pushing a start and stop button with a timing accuracy of a few milliseconds, which again transcends conscious human ability. So this type of precognitive, instinctive action is one more possible way to understand this type of PK data.

In one set of experiments conducted by Schmidt, he used a computer clock combined with a Geiger counter to generate a truly random sequence of numbers which he recorded. Each number ranged from 1 to 4. Since the numbers were pre-recorded, presumably the option of changing the sequence by PK would be ruled out. Then he asked operators to guess what the next number in the sequence would be. This required that the operator be able to look into the future. Since a truly random quantum mechanical process, radioactive decay, was used to generate the numbers, the next number should unpredictable so each of the four possible values had the same probability, 1 in 4, or 25%. However, systematically, he found that the operators were able to correctly guess the next number with a higher accuracy, ranging between 26% and 27%. (Schmidt, 1993)

All of this research supports the notion that it is possible to look ahead into the future and obtain information, even when such information might violate the laws of Quantum Mechanics. This is a serious and important result. Physics may have to change its ideas about time to accommodate such results.

Speeding Up and Slowing Down Time

When I was a child I used to go to Sunday School at a Methodist Church. I remember a preacher who described a miracle as "a natural thing done in an *unnatural* way." The ability to speed up the flowering of plants and flowers may be one such gift. The journalist Paul Dong has written extensively about the EHF, or "Extra-High Functioning" young people of China. They have demonstrated their abilities repeatedly to visiting dignitaries. One of these abilities is the power seemingly to affect time.

They are able to make a plant bud, which is days or weeks away from flowering, bloom in a few minutes by mental concentration. In some cases, after the seed is held in the hand for a few minutes, it will sprout and grow an amount which should take weeks. In other cases, flower buds open almost instantly on command. There is now enough circumstantial and "anecdotal evidence" from credible witnesses to conclude that this phenomenon is real. The government of mainland China is involved in serious research into these abilities.

Through a nationwide screening program, these children have been located and carefully selected. They demonstrate very strong psychic and paranormal abilities of various kinds. The Chinese government is involved in scientific research to understand how these powers work and how to develop and strengthen them.

Figure 12.5 shows some of these children demonstrating their abilities for visiting dignitaries, in this case U.S. oil executives in 1992, from Paul Dong's book *China's Super Psychics.* (Dong, 1997) This demonstration was held by the Tianjin City Human Body Science Institute as a way of entertaining and honoring the guests by giving them a glimpse of a talent few westerners have been privileged to see.

Figure 12.5. Yao Zheng, in foreground is preparing to "speed up time" by causing the flowers before her to bloom due to her prayer. The photograph was taken in Beijing in 1992 (Dong, 1997). *Courtesy of Paul Dong.*

In the photograph, the child in the foreground, Yao Zheng, appears to be praying next to some flowers which are lying on the table. The oil executives are watching in good lighting and from several different angles. Reportedly the flowers bloomed before their eyes after the girl prayed for about fifteen minutes. Next to her is a girl who is removing pills from a bottle with what the Chinese call her EHF ability. This talent was discussed in the "Teleportation" section of this book (Chapter 7), because it involves causing the pills to be removed from a sealed bottle without opening the bottle. Of course, she is not touching the bottle and remains one or two feet away from it while being carefully watched by a roomful of observers.

To quote Paul Dong:

"There are many people with the ability to open flowers in China, and Yao Zheng is only one example. Of course, there are others whose powers are stronger. On the evening of April 1, 1994, in the Beijing Signal Corps auditorium, Colonel Fu Songshan was able to open all of the flower buds in the hands of an audience of over a thousand people within thirty minutes. (I have a photograph of this event, but cannot reprint it here because of copyright restrictions.) However, Fu Songshan is not the top man. There is one mysterious woman who, facing thousands upon thousands of flower buds, can make them all bloom instantly by saying, 'I want you all to open,' and waving her hand."(Dong, 1997)

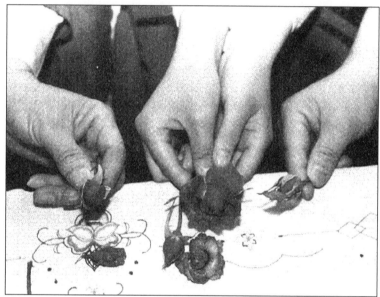

Fig. 12.6-Photographs of flowers which were made to open by Chinese psychic Yao Zheng in the presence of author Paul Dong, whose hand is seen at the left in the photograph (Dong, 1997). *Courtesy of Paul Dong.*

In order to understand "psychic superpowers," the theme of this book, it is first necessary to grasp the point just quoted by Paul Dong. I will repeat for emphasis:

"There are many people with the ability to open flowers in China, and Yao Zheng is only one example. Of course, there are others whose powers are stronger…There is one mysterious woman who, facing thousands upon thousands of flower buds, can make them all bloom instantly by saying, 'I want you all to open,' and waving her hand."

This extraordinary ability, which might be ridiculed in the West and ascribed to trickery, is undergoing serious research in China. It is one of many unusual powers exhibited by the EHF children. Other young people around the world have exhibited similar talents in many areas of psychic phenomena. It is vital for us to recognize the reality of these abilities and begin to work to understand them. They hold the key to the next stage of scientific progress and to a deeper understanding of our true nature as human beings.

Suspended animation is another way in which paranormal abilities are able to seemingly alter the flow of time. Instead of jumping ahead in time, certain gifted individuals appear able to virtually make time stop. They can remain in a state of "suspended animation" for weeks or longer. Tara Bey, a famous fakir who was interviewed by Paul Brunton, was an expert at this, as are some yogis in India (Brunton, 1973; Green, 1977).

Bey explained to Brunton that, in such demonstrations of suspended animation, the fakir must be very careful to seal up all openings in his body to prevent insects from entering. In the case of long interment of weeks or more, it is wise to seal the entire body in soft wax to prevent the entry of other animals. It appears that, when the fakir enters the special trance state, all respiration ceases and the entry of oxygen into the body at such time can actually be harmful. If this is true, then such feats must be examples of true suspended animation. These feats have been demonstrated by both yogis and fakirs on many occasions, lasting for periods as short as an hour and as long as several months.

After 7 minutes or so, the brain of the fakir should be dead from oxygen starvation, and no fakir should ever be able to revive after a few hours of being buried alive without oxygen. Yet they do. Here is Bey's explanation:

"We must begin by recognizing within ourselves the great possibilities which we all possess, and until we do this we must remain bound, hand and foot, to unnecessary limitations that prevent us exploiting our marvelous psychic and material powers. People, when confronted with the phenomena which I can produce, think it either some kind of conjuring or else something entirely supernatural. In both cases they are wrong. They do not seem to grasp the fact that these things are perfectly scientific, obeying the laws of nature herself. It is true that I am using psychic laws which are little understood, but, nevertheless, they are laws. Nothing that I do is arbitrary, supernatural, or against such laws."(Brunton, 1973)

The Uses of Prophecy

Prophets played an important role in ancient societies. In the Book of Genesis, Joseph was released from slavery and elevated to royalty because of his ability to interpret the prophetic meaning of a dream. His king was troubled by a dream, and Joseph correctly interpreted it as a prediction of 7 years of abundant harvest followed by seven years of famine. In the Book of Kings, Elisha was able to warn the king of Israel about the plans of the Syrian army, averting an ambush. In many ancient societies there was a vizier or wise man at the right hand of the king, to advise him. One of the important roles of the wise man has always been prophecy. In the time of Julius Caesar, the seers threw bones, or examined entrails, or meditated over a bowl of water. The advice of such visionaries was valued by rulers, and sometimes played a decisive role in decisions of war and diplomacy.

In modern times, we have the example of President Ronald Reagan, who is now known to have relied upon astrology in scheduling important events. Although he always, prudently, attributed this interest to his wife, we now know he used it to schedule the timing of his acceptance speech at his party convention and the conduct of important international initiatives (Regan, 1988, 1989; Quigley, 1990).

Given his success and popularity as President, we must ask whether perhaps it worked. The historic reliance by rulers upon such "wise men," whether they used astrology, entrails, bones or meditation, leads us to ask whether maybe there is something to it. Perhaps some people some of the time can see the future clearly. If this is the case, then physics needs to be rewritten.

In our present age, we have just passed through the millennium. This is one of the most prophesied and predicted periods in the world's history. There have been dire predictions of pole shifts and earth changes. Some of these were supposed to have already happened and obviously have not occurred. Therefore, is all prophecy thus disproved? Let us examine the record for some of these predictions.

Hopi Prophecies

We began this book with the Hopi prophecies. The Hopi are a Native American tribe who live in Arizona today and have an ancient spiritual tradition. Their prophecies have been held as a sacred part of their religion for hundreds of years, but have recently been made public. (Waters, 1963) These prophecies included predictions of World Wars I and II, as well as a major war still to come, which we will call World War III. They also predicted remarkable changes in the land: the coming of the white man to America, the covered wagons, the introduction of long horn cattle, the overhead telegraph and power lines, transcontinental roads, airplanes, oil spills on the ocean, and other changes in the environment and in society.

The Hopi prophecies speak of "an eagle landing on the moon" which foresaw the Apollo astronauts announcing to the world in 1969, "The Eagle has landed." They predicted that the "blueprint" for life (DNA) would be discovered and that it would be misused. We have now seen human cloning and genetic engineering, which would appear to be a confirmation of that prediction. They predicted a "gourd of ashes" which was said to represent the atomic bomb. The recent births of several white buffalo calves and the appearance of three comets, culminating in comet Hale-Bopp, are considered by the Hopi to be among the last of their prophecies. Up to this point, the Hopi prophecies provide an example of a remarkably accurate series of predictions. (Brown, 1998)

The few remaining Hopi predictions involve apocalyptic events which, we hope, will not come to pass. However, the central place held by prophecy in the culture of the Hopi illustrates the power of prophecy as a guide for action, a focus for religion, and as an arbiter of meaning.

A General Consensus Among Major Prophecies

The Hopi prophecies are similar to others pertaining to the present time. Some of the most famous are the predictions made by Edgar Cayce, the "sleeping prophet." Cayce predicted massive changes in the weather followed by earthquakes and a calamitous "pole shift" around the time of the millennium. It would be accompanied or followed by a war in the Middle East. Yet the earth changes have clearly not happened, which has caused many to become skeptical of all prophecy.

At the same time, there are other, independent sources of prophecy which envision a remarkably similar scenario. The Church of Jesus Christ of the Latter Day Saints, or the Mormons, place great importance on prophecy, and one of the highest officials in the church has the formal title "Prophet." It is his responsibility to make and evaluate predictions and to advise the church hierarchy. (Skousen, 1939) There are also very interesting predictions in Dolores Cannon's *Nostradamus* series, as well as the writings of Dannion Brinkley and those of Mary Summer Rain. These predictions were all made more than fifteen years ago. I have been able to meet and interview these latter three writers, and believe they all operate with integrity and high spiritual intent.

205

Each of these prophecies predicts the following series of events pertaining to the present and near future time period:

(1) Increasingly severe and extreme weather events: droughts, floods, tornadoes, unusual high winds

(2) A world-wide economic collapse. In the U.S.: deflation, stock market collapse and high unemployment

(3) Religious conflict within the U.S.: the rise of Christian fundamentalism and closer involvement between church and government

(4) Major war focused on the Middle East, which will be called World War III (Desert Storm and the recent Iraq war are viewed as only preludes to a world-wide conflict)

(5) Major and severe earth changes: earthquakes, tidal waves, culminating eventually in a pole shift and changes in the land contours of the U.S. and Europe

Prophecies of "No-Eyes" and Mary Summer Rain

Because the five main predictions above are consistent among these prophecies, I will focus on the prophecies of the Native American medicine woman named "No-Eyes," all made before 1983. These are recounted in a series of books written by Mary Summer Rain. (Summer Rain, 1985, 1987) Several prophetic visions of future events were described, predicted to begin around the millennium:

- A general worsening of economic conditions in the United States, caused by the export of manufacturing jobs to third world countries, combined with jobs lost to automation. This would cause an economic decline in the United States, and a weakening of the stock market and financial markets.

- This would be accompanied by massive corporate, or "white collar," crime and corruption. No-Eyes predicted that formerly respectable executives at big corporations would use their position to rob the treasuries of those companies, and this would shatter the faith investors had in corporations.

- A final trigger to a global financial collapse would be the disappearance of international free trade. She predicted a trade war would erupt between countries, and international free trade agreements would break down. A deflationary spiral would result, leading to a collapse in commodity prices and the destruction of the banking system.

- These economic changes would be accompanied by massive changes in climate. The seasons would be "all mixed up," with large temperature fluctuations from day to day. This would be accompanied by increasingly fierce storms. Tornadoes would appear where they had never been seen before. Drought would be widespread, and would be alleviated only by flash flooding, as the weather behaved erratically and went through wild fluctuations.

- The droughts would cause sink-holes to be a spreading problem, swallowing up homes without warning. This would also be a time of rising disease, including biologically engineered diseases, which would kill many.

- Increasingly, religious organizations would become involved in politics, and the politicians would make more laws about religion. The constitutional guarantees of separation of church and state would begin to disappear, and this would lead to protests.

- The United States would increasingly become involved in military operations and wars overseas. We would become involved in many wars in "little countries" and this would bring back the draft. The expense of conducting military operations in so many countries would break the national budget, further damage the economy and lead to burdensome increases in taxes.

- The earth itself would go through extreme changes, with large earthquakes leading to a shift in the earth's poles causing massive tidal waves and destruction. This would be forewarned by several days of "green sky" which suggests auroras and atmospheric electrical activity, perhaps indicating solar activity as the trigger. The shape of the land masses would be different after the resulting massive earth changes.

- There are many predictions she made pertaining to the time following this. A catastrophic war in the Middle East, nuclear weapons detonated by men with "brown skin," and eventual political upheaval in the United States were among her predictions. A long term change in the weather was predicted, leading to a time of dramatically reduced rainfall. A time was predicted in which global average rainfall would shrink to near zero.

The Dolores Cannon/Nostradamus prophecies are consistent with this scenario. They add more detail about a world-wide Arab conspiracy and a Pan-Muslim alliance leading to a major world war. They speak of covert involvement by the Chinese starting in the early 1990's, which has been confirmed to some extent. There was a news report, largely ignored by the major media, to the effect that Chinese advisors were found when Osama Bin Laden's hideout in Afghanistan was raided. Certainly, Al-Caeda sounds exactly like the international group Cannon described in 1989 (Cannon, 1989).

About twelve years after the publication of Cannon's three volumes on Nostradamus, I reviewed the predictions which were to have already occurred. I identified about a dozen such predictions. The rest may or may not come to pass in the future, but these twelve predictions quoted specific times which enabled me to evaluate them. I found that about half had come to pass and half had not. So from what I have seen so far, they are about 50% accurate, very roughly. Given the specific detailed nature of the predictions, I believe this is far higher than would be expected from chance or coincidence. At the same time, they are far from infallible.

What I found fascinating was that, even when a prediction failed, it seemed to describe qualitatively certain trends which have been occurring. The rise of a pan-Muslim confederation, initially established in secret, seems to be one of the biggest successes of this prophecy. The predictions of Chinese involvement, and the description of a "cabal" in America which also favored and promoted this war, seem to be successes based on what we have seen so far. I also noticed that the exact timing of the events was often in error and seemed to be the most likely aspect to go wrong.

This minor exercise in prophecy evaluation led me to the following two conclusions:

(1) Prophecy often seems to capture the large scale or general trend of a time period even if it misses on the specific event.
(2) Time and time ordering seem to be the most likely parts to be in error.

Evaluation of No-Eyes' Predictions

Most of Mary Summer Rain's conversations with "No-Eyes" occurred in 1982, when she received her predictions. Since that time, we have seen the weather go crazy.

Number of Killer Storms & Droughts Increasing Worldwide is the headline of a report from the World Water Forum in Japan (Cosgrove, 2003). The number of world-wide flood disasters has been increasing rapidly, from an average of 6 per decade in the 1950's to 26 per decade in the 1990's (see Figure 12.7).

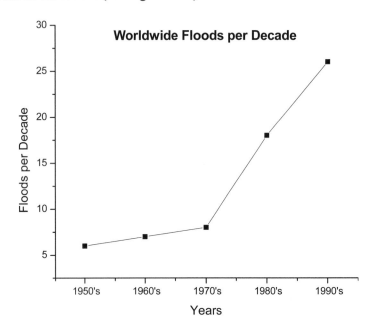

Figure 12.7. The number of major floods worldwide has been rapidly increasing during the last fifty years. (Cosgrove, 2003)

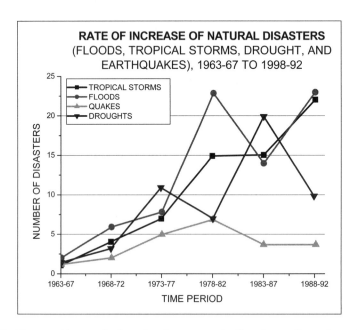

Figure 12.8. Composite graph showing increases in floods, earthquakes, droughts and tropical storms over the last four decades. (McCulloch, 1993)

Other natural disasters, such as droughts and tropical storms, have also been increasing worldwide during the same period (Figure 12.8). The number of tornadoes per year in the United States has undergone a steady increase as well, as shown in Figure 12.9. These graphs confirm that global weather has indeed become more severe, more extreme and more destructive.

**NUMBER OF TORNADOES PER YEAR
IN THE UNITED STATES**

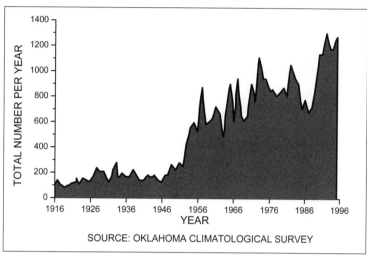

SOURCE: OKLAHOMA CLIMATOLOGICAL SURVEY

Figure 12.9. The number of tornadoes per year in the United States. In the first half of May, 2003, more than 400 tornadoes occurred setting an all-time record, breaking the all-time record set only three years earlier. As No-Eyes predicted, the number of tornadoes has increased over time, and has become a widespread hazard.

Young people today do not realize that our erratic weather is very different from the weather of 1982. The last decade has seen six of the hottest years in history. Although No-Eyes made her predictions in 1982, it was not until 1992 that meteorologists at NASA began warning of "global warming" and the greenhouse effect. It was in those predictions that the scientific community first heard that global warming might bring with it changing patterns of global weather, and this transition would be accompanied by severe and erratic swings in weather. Of course, these early scientists were not heeded by most of the public nor by the media. But more importantly, their announcements came ten years after No-Eyes had made her prediction.

Today, droughts and powerful storms have become the norm. Insurance losses due to storm damage rose dramatically in the 1990s (see Figure 12.10). The number of severe winter storms over the ocean has increased during the same period (see Figure 12.11). Sinkholes in Florida have claimed a number of homes in recent years. Droughts have become so extreme that they now are the underlying cause of huge wildfires which have devastated many areas of the country. The CO_2 released into the atmosphere by such fires is further accelerating the greenhouse effect, which then further exacerbates the extreme weather.

Global warming has gone from a controversial theory announced by a courageous NASA meteorologist in the early 1990s, to a series of unprecedented temperature records. *"Scientists Meeting in France say 2002 was the Second Hottest year on Record,"* announced the BBC News (Bentley, 2003). This comes after the decade of the 1990's in which five of the ten years were the hottest on record worldwide. The accompanying graphs of global temperature, compiled by the U.S. National Oceanic and Atmospheric Administration (NOAA), confirm this ominous trend (Figure 12.12).

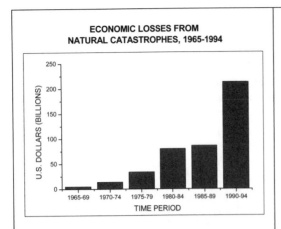

Figure 12.10. Economic losses from natural disasters, in constant 1990 dollars, has increased dramatically over last 40 years (Francis, 1998).

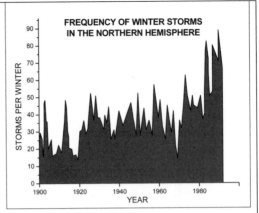

Figure 12.11. Number of severe winter storms in the extratropical Atlantic and Pacific Oceans. Note the rapid increase in the last two decades (Francis, 1998).

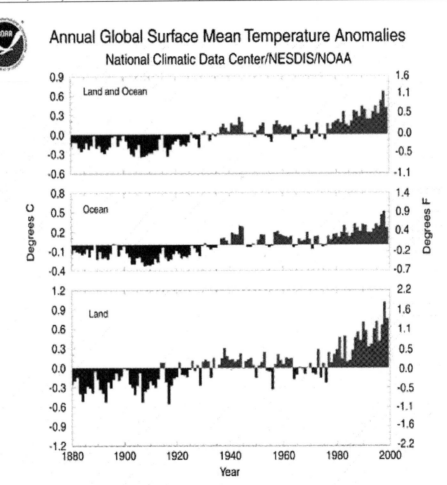

Figure 12.12. Combined global changes in land and sea temperature since 1880. Note the steady rise in both land and sea temperatures in the past two decades, with all time high temperatures reached in 1998, and several records broken in the 1990s. Data is from the U.S. National Oceanic and Atmospheric Administration, National Climatic Data Center, Asheville, NC (Vellinga, 2000).

No-Eyes predicted that eventually these weather changes would lead to a time of no rain. I thought this was a remarkable and strange prediction. Then I began to investigate the weather prediction models to understand what causes rain. I discovered that we get rain because of a delicate balance between the moisture content of the atmosphere, its temperature, and the wind speed. This leads to what are called "fair weather" clouds in the summertime, also known as cumulus clouds. They are caused by updrafts and downdrafts in the lower atmosphere. Meteorologists call them "convection cells": warm air rises carrying moisture. As it rises it cools and becomes heavier. The moisture cools and forms droplets which fall as rain. And the cycle continues.

I discovered that, if there is not sufficient moisture in the atmosphere, or if the winds become too high, then these convection cells cannot form and rain does not fall. I realized that this is exactly what could happen as the weather patterns shift due to global warming. It is the very likely "end state" of a new global weather pattern if something is not done to stop it. It is not a well-known or widely publicized prediction, but it is now a likely prediction from some of the long-range weather models.

The droughts we have been experiencing (Figure 12.8) may only be a prelude. Somehow, the blind medicine woman knew this in 1982, before any scientist had ever uttered the words "global warming." This is one more prediction of hers which appears to be coming true.

Accompanying the extremes in weather is a weakness in the world economy which does not seem to be going away. After the boom years of the 1990s under President Clinton, an economic malaise seems to have settled over the country. The first three years of the new millennium saw a decline in the Dow Jones of over 30% and a decline in the NASDAQ markets of 80%. A partial recovery followed this, but tby 2009 the world economy seemed even more fragile. Will it slide further into the financial abyss predicted by No-Eyes? It is too early to tell. But there are many warning signs.

The export of jobs to low-cost third world countries occurred just as No-Eyes predicted in 1982. This has given rise to that "giant sucking sound" of jobs leaving the country, to use billionaire Presidential candidate Ross Perot's description. Unemployment has risen, and most of the jobs which remain are in the lower-paying service sector, not manufacturing.

Automation in the work place has further reduced the number of jobs in America. While greatly enhancing corporate profits over the last ten years, it has weakened the finances of the average American worker, just as No-Eyes predicted.

She also predicted that an international trade war would erupt between the U.S. and its trading partners, and this would further deepen the economic crisis. While this has not happened yet, there have been numerous trade disputes in the past several years, including boycotts of U.S. goods in some quarters. The war in Iraq has exacerbated anti-American sentiment and seems capable of further damaging international trade. In the fall of 2003 international trade talks on agriculture broke down, prompting predictions by economists of a serious negative impact on commerce. Most recently, U.S. tariffs on imported steel were declared illegal by the European Union. After threatened retaliation, the U.S. backed down on these tariffs. Whether or not the trade war materializes, it certainly has been an important theme in international economics.

The large scale business corruption she predicted is occurring. A recent headline in the *Washington Post* (Tuesday, June 25, 2002) reads: "WorldCom Says its Books are Off by $3.8 Billion." The Justice Department began a criminal probe. Elsewhere in the same paper was news that United Way has admitted to skimming off a very high percentage of its charitable gifts for "operating expenses." It was found to be using illegal accounting practices to conceal this.

211

Enron, the seventh largest corporation in America, collapsed in bankruptcy after its corporate executives skimmed off huge amounts of money into their own private corporations and suspicious off-shore accounts. Its accounting firm, Arthur Andersen, one of the largest and most respected, was convicted of criminal activity for shredding its records of these transactions.

ImClone Systems, Tyco International, and many other large companies have also been involved in high level, large scale corporate corruption. This prediction by No-Eyes has come true in dramatic fashion. An Associated Press headline, "Corporate Scandals Taking Toll on Markets," seems to confirm the other part of her prediction, that these scandals would engender distrust which would contribute to the collapse and eventual destruction of the stock market.

Another prediction is that it would be a <u>deflationary</u> collapse. This means prices would fall during the collapse. For the past seven decades the principle devil of the economy has been inflation. During Jimmy Carter's presidency both inflation and interest rates rose into double digits. Houses have traditionally been considered to be good investments because they are leveraged against inflation. But No-Eyes predicted something quite unusual. She said

"...price of land and houses gonna go way down—it gonna go way down like water through old broken beaver dam....Many people gonna try to sell house and land to get more monies—to live. They not gonna get 'nough even. They gonna still owe plenty monies. Stuff gonna be like big whirlpool circle going down and down, deep and deeper. It gonna go such way down. It not gonna go up—ever."

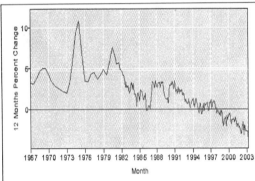

Figure 12.13. Annual percentage change in Consumer Price Index for Department Store inventories. This reflects consumer prices in department stores. Note the prices have been falling for more than five years. Falling prices are known as deflation. (BLS, 2003)

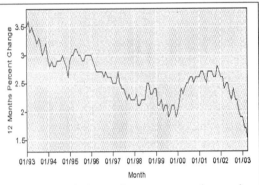

Figure 12.14. Annual percentage change in U.S. Consumer Price Index, less energy and food. Prices, according to this index, are growing at a very small annual rate, and that rate is decreasing rapidly. If this continues, this will further confirm the presence of deflation. (BLS, 2003)

Fortunately, these dire predictions have not come to pass, yet. However, by the end of 2009, we have seen nine years of a deflationary trend, ending with house prices and other commodities falling by record amounts. International trade has become precarious, and there are strong rumors that the dollar may lose its place as the international standard. It has weakened rapidly in value, which seems to portend increased interest rates to defend it. If this comes to pass, the deflationary spiral predicted by No-Eyes may yet come to pass.

The deflation has been aggressively fought by the Federal Reserve, with the lowest interest rates (down to 1%) in the last fifty years. However, constraints from international trade and borrowing may prevent interest rates from staying low. As we

212

pass through the time for which her predictions apply, it is interesting that her prophecies have captured some of the dominant themes of the economy.

The earth changes predicted by No-Eyes have thankfully not yet occurred. However, in late 2009 a flurry of large quakes in the Pacific and Asia reminded us that they are still possible. Ice caps continue to melt and seas continue to rise. No-Eyes predicted that the worst changes would be preceded by several days of unusual "green sky," which indicates auroral activity and resulting atmospheric electricity. In the latter part of 2003 we saw the largest solar flare ever recorded, as the earth experienced an unprecedented series of "direct hits" of massive energy from the sun. These are called "coronal mass ejections" and consist of solar flares which bombard the earth with huge numbers of charged particles. These disrupt the magnetic field of the earth, cause auroras, and can theoretically induce stress on the earth's crust or perhaps even a pole shift.

During this period, the number of strong earthquakes (magnitide greater than 6.0) tripled for several weeks, perhaps warning us of greater earth changes to come. The similarity between the recent spectacular auroras and No-Eyes warnings of "green sky" is uncanny, but thankfully the predicted massive earth changes have not occurred. However as 2012 approaches, geological and solar activity is expected to increase, and presents the most dangerous period for such catastrophes.

On other fronts, No-Eyes predicted "Desert Storm," the first war in Iraq, but according to her it is only a precursor to a coming larger war. It has set the stage for a possible later war by increasing tensions between Muslim states and the United States. Although the U.S. has hopefully stabilized Iraq for the moment, Afghanistan and Pakistan are showing signs of increased instability. The outlines of the next war seem to be forming. In the mean time, nvolvement in many "little wars" threatens to lead to higher taxes and further economic weakness, as she predicted.

Other Prophecies

The Elders of the Church of Jesus Christ of the Latter Day Saints, or Mormons, have received similar prophecies. The Mormons take such prophecies seriously, to the extent that long term underground survival shelters, complete with food and weapons, are maintained in Utah for most church members. They expect to use them.

A set of Mormon prophecies, apparently accepted by the church, predict a sequence of events leading up to what might be called the "end times." The Mormons do not consider these events to be the end of the earth but they do foresee a time of devastating earth changes, including changes in the shape of the North American continent accompanied by huge earthquakes. A breakdown in government control and a rise in anarchy would follow such events. The Mormon Church would be called upon to help bring order to their region of the country. Leading up to this, a global economic collapse and the outbreak of an intense widespread war is predicted (Skousen, 1939).

In the Book of Revelations in the New Testament of the Christian Bible, there are also prophecies of "end times." None of these specifically points to this millennium. Many Christians in the Middle Ages believed it would occur in the year 1,000 AD. In Hungary, the Unitarians in 1600 A.D. believed that the century mark heralded the return of Christ and the "rapture," which would cause them all to ascend to heaven at the stroke of midnight. Many Unitarians climbed to the tops of pine trees in the forest and leaped out at the stroke of midnight on New Year's Eve, expecting to be turned into angels. It did not happen, at least in the way they expected, and many were injured or killed. It led to an overthrow of their dominance in Hungary.

The Book of Revelations is more vague on the details of millennial changes, and therefore is subject to widely varying interpretations. In fact it does not state clearly when these events are to occur. The rich symbolic language leads to ambiguity about the exact form of the events predicted, except that they will be horrible. Today, some Christian ministers have offered their own, more specific, interpretation of the Book of Revelations. They involve a global war, centered in the Middle East, with the United States and Israel on one side, and China, Russia and the Arab states on the other. Catastrophic earth changes are usually predicted to accompany these events.

Despite the differences, it is interesting that many of these prophecies, from very different sources, predict the same basic scenario: global economic collapse, increasing global military strife culminating in a third World War, alignment of America with Israel against a coalition of Islamic states together with China and Russia, and catastrophic global earth changes. An interesting survey which compared a number of prophecies available at the time is *Pole Shift* by John White (White, 1988).

The interesting question, from a scientific point of view, is why are so many of these prophecies so similar? Are they merely copying one another? Are they telepathically picking up the thoughts of others, and mistaking them for future knowledge? Or are they all legitimately glimpsing the future? And if there is truly a single time line for our future, perhaps all the prophecies agree because they are all seeing the real thing?

Some prophets, or would-be prophets, have claimed that the time-line containing these events has changed. They maintain that, although these dire events <u>were</u> in our future, that the future has been altered and we no longer have to go through it.

We will see later that it is possible to change a time line, to change a future. A time line may at one time be the destiny of all to live through. This may be the "most-probable" future. And yet it can be changed, with enough prayer, meditation, awareness and action. We will cite examples here to support the idea that: (1) there is a unique "future" at any given time, and that is what is seen in prophecy, and (2) the seemingly contradictory notion that the future time line can be altered. It is usually necessary to first know the prediction before trying to alter it.

The Apocalypse

The political aspect of prophecy has been highlighted by a recent cover story in *Time Magazine* titled "The Bible and the Apocalypse-Why more Americans are reading and talking about the End of the World." It highlights a series of best-selling novels by a Christian evangelical minister, Tim LaHaye, and a professional novelist, Jerry Jenkins. It portrays events which are supposed to occur in the "end times," presumably just after the millennium, and it begins after a select few Christians miraculously vanish overnight, their bodies having been taken to heaven.

For those who are left behind on the earth, a very unpleasant series of events is predicted, based very loosely on the Book of Revelations. The question about why Christians, or anybody else, would need their physical body in heaven arises immediately. But the most interesting aspect of the Evangelical interpretation of prophecy is that it concludes that the United States should support Israel no matter what it does, thereby abandoning the "even handed" approach which has characterized past U.S. Mideast policy. This point of view has been echoed by many television and radio evangelists, who also seem to base their philosophy on the expectation of the Apocalypse. This policy has angered Muslim states around the world, who total over 1 billion people, thereby exacerbating, rather than calming the situation.

A strong political alliance between President George W. Bush, American Evangelical Christians, and the Likud Party in Israel emerged in the first years of the new millennium. It is reported that several key figures in that administration hold Evangelical views, and this may be a contributing factor in policy making. From the Evangelical viewpoint, the Book of Revelations predicts the "final battle" of Armageddon, and actually seems to look forward to it. As a result, many evangelical Christians are staunch supporters of military spending and military intervention abroad, despite the injunctions of Jesus to love one's enemy.

This is an illustration of one of the uses of prophecy. Its use to influence public opinion by influencing beliefs has undoubtedly gone on since the Druids predicted their first eclipse and frightened the masses into obedience. In this way prophecy can still be powerful today.

Ironically, the beliefs and actions of these groups make it <u>more likely</u> that the prophecies will be fulfilled. Instead of working for a peaceful settlement in the Middle East, these parties prepare for war. It is urgent that people who are expecting an apocalypse understand one thing: The future <u>can</u> be changed.

With the election of Barack Obama, there have been hopes for a lessening of tensions in the Arab world, and a renewal of the peace process. The world may have been presented an opportunity to change the disastrous time line we are on. However, there is also inertia from past policies and old agendas. It may be up to each person to use his own power of prayer and intention to help us through this crucial period of history.

We can use the lessons of prophecy as a valuable guide, which enables us to see our present most probable future. But we also have abundant evidence that knowledge of the future, combined with action and prayer, can CHANGE THE FUTURE. We have innumerable examples of this.

For example, during his first near-death experience, Dannion Brinkley was shown numerous apocalyptic visions similar to the ones just discussed. But he was told:

"If you follow what you have been taught and keep living the same way you have lived the last thirty years, all of this will surely be upon you. If you change, you can avoid the coming war." (Brinkley, 1994)

Again the message comes through: Yes, there is a probable future. If you do not use your knowledge of it, you will surely live it. But IF you use your knowledge of the prophecy in order to avoid it, then mankind need not endure the terrible suffering described in these prophecies.

It is important for Christians, Muslims, Jews and everyone else to understand this important principle. It is vital that everyone uses his or her god-given abilities and work to dampen the war fury. If we all project the future we want, there is abundant evidence that we can alter the future and achieve it. Unfortunately, some who believe in these prophecies are, at the present time, acting in a way to make it <u>more</u> likely that they will come true.

The Place of "No Time" – Prophecy as a Way of Life

Today we find ourselves in the "educated" West debating the existence of prophecy and other psychic abilities. However, in some cultures which we would call primitive, these abilities are an integral and essential part of life. They are taken for granted and used every day for survival. In such cultures, "psychic" ability is the accepted norm. One such culture is that of the Australian aborigine. Living in a desolate land, how do they survive with primitive hunting tools? Visitors who have closely studied the aborigine in the outback have learned that many of them communicate telepathically, and take other psychic phenomena as a matter of course. We Westerners use a cell phone if we want to send a message. They are reported to do it telepathically.

The following story comes from Fay Marvin Clark, who visited the aborigines in the company of a long-time Australian resident who helped him translate. Clark was introduced to a young aboriginal man who was known to have high psychic ability in the village. The young man described to Clark how he, the aborigine, had been interviewed for hours by a visiting American college group studying the paranormal. He told Clark that he met with them for a long time, but he could not communicate with them because they would not accept the "first principles of life." The subtle energies and chakras, which we will discuss in Volume II, were not a matter of conjecture to this young man. He could see them all the time. His sensitivity to the subtle energies and to psychic information was an integral part of his life. He told the following story of how he hunted for food each day:

> *"Yes, I come out of my humpy (shelter) in the morning, knowing my family needs food. I stand silently with my arms at my sides with my eyes closed and slowly turn clockwise three times. This releases the real me from the physical body, and I move upward into the 'No Time'. I see where the wallaby or the kangaroo is, and I also observe where it will be when I take my physical body there. [my emphasis] I return to my body and go where the game will be, and of course it is there. I ask its forgiveness, and then I kill it and we have food." (Clark, 1988)*

This young aboriginal man, according to his own description, routinely traveled out of his body. This is a useful technique to locate game or anything else in the trackless wilderness of Australia. Soldiers dying on the battlefield in Vietnam, later revived, have also recounted near-death experiences in which they went out of their body and floated up high in the air, where they could see the surrounding countryside, thereby getting their bearings and locating a friendly camp. (Alexander, 1980) In aboriginal tribes this skill is taught as a rite of manhood. The rites of passage often include, as in the case of this Australian man, many days of deprivation and suffering during which he must go out of body if he is to pass the test.

The interesting point in this story is that the young man could see more than just the present location of the game. After viewing the game's coincident location, the hunter could pass into the zone of "No Time," where he could see the world as it will be in the future. He used the information thus obtained to guide him to the exact location of the quarry at that future moment. Such a skill is invaluable for a hunter, and Darwin could certainly explain how such a skill would enhance our own survival.

Conventional science normally disposes of such examples by dismissing them. If we deny the evidence then there is no problem with contemporary science. But the fact is that this young man does catch game. He doesn't starve to death. And he feeds his village year after year in this way. Millions of people from traditional societies have described a similar way of living.

We saw the example given by Douchan Gersi of how the Tuareg peoples normally communicate telepathically across hundreds of miles. They have no cell phones. Yet they are able to coordinate movements and rendezvous in what to us is a trackless desert. In the same way the aborigines of Australia, whom we call "primitive," have adapted their psychic ability for survival. To them it is a natural part of everyday life. Even looking into the future to find game is part of normal life. If psychic abilities are real, and the preponderance of scientific evidence shows that it is, then it would be natural that certain groups would evolve using these abilities for survival. In such groups these abilities would be highly developed.

Examples of Precognitive Messages

Precognitive and prophetic messages often come during near-death experiences. In one example, related by Dr. Melvin Morse, M.D., a patient of his, a young woman named June, had a near-death experience as a child which she often talked about. (Morse,

1990) It was a beautiful experience which removed all fear of death for her. It happened at the age of five during an open-heart operation to repair her leaky heart valve and install a pacemaker. During this experience, she found herself floating above the table observing the doctors working, then traveled down a tunnel to a region of light and love. This experience removed all fear of death for the rest of her life.

Although she knew that pacemakers could fail at any moment, she lived without fear. Yet one day, as she was sitting at her kitchen table drinking a cup of coffee, her sister, who had been dead for many years, appeared before her. Her sister, in ghostly form, sat down and appeared to drink a cup of coffee, as well. Her sister told her it was time to go. In other words, it was June's time to die. June knew that her husband would not be able to handle this information, so she did not tell him. But she told several family members including her aunt and uncle who had raised her, and her two brothers. She told them that she just wanted to say goodbye, and she told them what happened. That night, in her sleep, her pacemaker stopped working and she died.

This simple, well-documented, story illustrates a fact which recurs in cases of precognition. We, the living, enmeshed in material bodies who take time for granted, have difficulty looking into the future. But often, beings on "the other side," such as the ghost of June's sister, have full and accurate knowledge of future events. This pattern frequently appears in paranormal phenomena. It seems that in the spirit realm, time does not exist. For beings on the other side, it is possible to acquire reliable knowledge about the future.

Sometimes these prophetic messages come in the form of imagination, and it may be that the recipient does not even realize that he is tapping into the future time line. A possible example of this is the author Hector Bywater, who in a series of books and articles written before 1925 foresaw and described the Japanese war in the Pacific which began in 1941. Bywater was a correspondent for the *New York Herald*, the Baltimore *Sun*, and later for *The New York Times*. He wrote two books on the subject of the future war: *Sea Power in the Pacific* and *The Great Pacific War* (Bywater, 1921, 1925). The peculiar accuracy of his vision, and the events which unfolded around his writings, are described in *Visions of Infamy-The Untold Plans of How Journalist Hector C. Bywater Devised the Plans that Led to Pearl Harbor*, by William H. Honan (Honan, 1991).

The first of Bywater's two books was written in 1921 and the second in 1925. The second book in particular was written as a "history" even though it described events more than a decade in the future. Bywater foresaw the specific movements and phases of the Japanese war in the Pacific, including the correct sequence of events and the overall strategy. One could argue that the Japanese studied Bywater's writings, as we know they did, and just copied his ideas and used them in their Pacific naval campaign.

However, the remarkably accurate, detailed and vivid manner in which he described future events conveys the impression that perhaps he truly did have a vision. Perhaps he truly was given prophetic insight into the conduct of the Pacific war. This notion is strengthened by the accuracy of his description, and by the peculiar perspective he chose. As the title suggests, he felt he was writing a <u>history of events that had already occurred</u>, not a projection or a guess about the future.

This notion is further strengthened by the commentary of military writers of the time. When war did break out, his book was reissued with a forward by Hanson Baldwin, entitled: *The Great Pacific War: A Historic Prophecy Now Being Fulfilled* (Bywater, 1942). These aspects make his prophetic vision all the more remarkable. One sad footnote to this story is that Bywater was mysteriously murdered under strange circumstances a year before the Japanese attacked Pearl Harbor.

Figure 12.15. Japanese attack on Pearl Harbor, December 7, 1941. *Courtesy of Naval Historical Society, National Archives*

Another famous case of precognition with far-reaching political consequences involved President Abraham Lincoln. It concerns the events leading up to his assassination. These events were related by his close friend and biographer, Ward Hill Lamon. Lincoln had a precognitive dream on several successive nights before his assassination. He found himself wandering through the White House in his dream. He found a body draped in black and lying in state. He heard weeping. When he asked who had died, the mourners told him "The President. He was shot by an assassin." Lamon had written about these events <u>five days before the assassination</u>, so this precognitive dream of Lincoln's is very solidly documented.

What is not so widely known is that General Grant's wife, Julia, also had a strong premonition of this event. It occurred on April 14, 1865, the day after a great celebration in Washington. Her husband Ulysses S. Grant had accepted General Lee's surrender at Appomatox, and the Civil War was over. But on April 14 she awoke with a feeling of profound dread. She felt that she, her husband and child, must leave the city of Washington immediately.

They were scheduled to accompany the Lincolns to Ford's Theatre that evening. When the messenger came from the White House to make theatre arrangements, she sent him away saying that the Grants were leaving the city and would not be joining the President that evening. She felt a growing sense that something tragic would occur if she did not leave immediately. She succeeded in persuading her husband, General Grant, to leave that afternoon for Philadelphia. When they arrived there they learned of Lincoln's assassination. Later they learned that General Grant's name was also on the list of those scheduled to be assassinated at the theatre that evening (*Time-Life Books*, 1987).

This story is an example of how precognition can be useful for survival. It warns us of impending danger. It enables us to make preparations while there is still time. However it is only helpful if we trust our intuition enough to listen to it.

218

Throughout history there have been famous prophets and psychics who predicted the future. Among the most remarkable of these was Ursula Sondheil, known today as Mother Shipton. Born in 1488 in Yorkshire, England, she was deformed at birth but became famous in her time for her psychic ability and accurate prophecies. Some of her prophecies dealt with a time in the far future when technology would surpass anything that could be imagined in her day.

In that age she predicted *"Carriages without horses shall go, And accidents shall fill the world with woe."* She seemed to predict the invention of television and the telephone when she said *"Around the world thoughts shall fly, In the twinkling of an eye."* She seemed to predict the opening of the New World and the import from America of tobacco and the potato by Sir Walter Raleigh when she said *"Over a wild and stormy sea shall a noble sail, who to find will not fail a new and fair country, from whence he shall bring an herb and a root."* And modern steel ships and submarines may have been foreseen when she predicted *"Men shall walk over rivers and under rivers. Iron in the water shall float."*

The accuracy of a prophet can only be determined after the fact. There is always the issue of selective memory and exclusion of data. It is natural that the most successful predictions are remembered and recalled while the failed ones are forgotten. This is called the "file drawer effect" among psychic researchers. It is the tendency not to publish data unless it shows something new and interesting. If we dream of an event and it comes true a few days later, we will remember it and be deeply impressed by it. If it does not come true, we think nothing of it and soon forget it.

This phenomenon of data selection is always important in assessing paranormal effects. The other aspect of prophecy is that some predictions come true in remarkable detail which defies mere coincidence, and yet other predictions do not come true at all. It brings up the issue of whether the future is firmly fixed, or whether it is mutable. If it is mutable, then prophecy involves a trip into the future down a time line of a "probable future," but that time line may not actually come to pass. We will see examples later of prophecies which begin to come true, and then are changed by making use of precognitive knowledge of the event.

The Gift of Prophecy and the Near-Death Experience

An example of the detail which accompanies a prophetic vision comes from Dr. Raymond Moody in his monumental book *Life After Life*. During a Near-Death Experience, a woman while "dead" was shown a photograph of Dr. Moody, and was told his full name (Moody, 1975). This occurred in 1971, before Moody had begun his research into near-death studies. He was unknown to the public, so the photograph meant nothing to the woman. However, four years later Moody "coincidentally" moved to the same street the woman lived on. His young son went "Trick-or-Treating" to the lady's house on Halloween. On hearing that the boy's name was Moody, she realized this must be the man she had been told about. She told the young boy that she needed to talk to his father. In this way Moody learned of her amazing experience.

If one were to assess the probability of such a sequence of events it would be extremely small. There were many seemingly "free-will" choices made along the way. Were such events pre-ordained on a higher lever, or did some higher beings interfere by providing "guidance" to ensure that this event would transpire four years after the NDE? We cannot know the part played by predestination and the part played by spiritual guidance. But in the case of Dannion Brinkley, whom Dr. Moody began studying in 1975, the knowledge of future events included many world events over which he had no influence. And yet they have come true with remarkable accuracy as well.

When Dannion Brinkley was "dead" the first time, he was given 117 "boxes of knowledge" which described events in the future (Brinkley, 1994). When he met Dr. Raymond Moody in 1975 he recounted the events he had been shown, and Moody carefully recorded each one. At that time neither of these men understood the significance of these visions. They did not know that they were precognitive.

Of the 117 visions which Dannion had been given in 1975, 95 had come to pass by 1994 (Brinkley, 1994). In one vision from 1975, he found himself in a cool, wooded area next to a river. He saw a massive, square cement structure nearby. He sensed fear and foreboding but did not know why. Then he felt the earth shake and he saw the top of the structure explode. He sensed that the explosion was nuclear. He knew that hundreds of people were dying around him. Through telepathy he received the year 1986 and the word *wormwood*. It was not until a decade later, in 1986, when the Chernobyl nuclear plant exploded in the Ukraine, that he realized the meaning of his vision. The word *Chernobyl* means <u>wormwood</u> in Russian! In this vision he sensed the nuclear pollution which spread across Europe, and the subsequent death and illness of many people from the accident.

In another vision from 1975, he was shown "images of warfare in the desert, a massive show of military might." He saw armies racing toward one another, hundreds of tanks and vast clouds of dust. He saw cannon fire and explosions, and afterward the ruins of an army spread over many acres. He was given the date 1990. Fifteen years later he was to discover that his vision was of "Desert Storm."

He was shown cartoons of a future President with the initials "RR", having the image of a cowboy and a background as an actor. He could never get a look at this President's face, so he could only guess who it might be. When he was asked by Dr. Raymond Moody in 1975 who he thought "RR" stood for, he guessed Robert Redford. Of course, the cowboy-actor President turned out to be Ronald Reagan, a fact that Raymond Moody has kidded him about for years. But still, the information was quite accurate.

In another vision, he saw older women marching through the streets of a European city. They wore black shawls covering their heads. He was told in the vision that many of the future events might be changed by wise action. But if this vision of the women in black protesting and marching came to pass, then many of the later darker visions would also occur. Several years ago, he was watching the television evening news showing a protest by Muslim women in Sarajevo. He realized this was exactly the same vision he had seen in 1975. This confirmation would seem to indicate that more of his prophecies are destined to come true in the next few years.

Brinkley's visions included the fall of the Egyptian government, which probably occurred when Sadat was assassinated. He foresaw the rise of biological warfare and an alliance between China and the Islamic states. This may have happened but it has not been publicized. He also predicted a future conflict between Russia and China, and a coming economic collapse in the United States. These events were also predicted, quite independently, in the Dolores Cannon/*Nostradamus* material.

As of the present day, more than twenty-five years later, the great majority (over 95%) of Brinkley's predictions have come true. A few appear to be wrong, while others may yet come true in the future. This ability to "predict" the future in such great detail, with cinematic accuracy and vividness, violates our current scientific understanding of the predictability of the world. The "uncertainty principle" in physics would suggest that the future is not determined, and that many outcomes are possible. Because there are so many possibilities, predicting the future with the detail found in Brinkley's prophecies should be impossible. Something important is missing from our present understanding of physics.

In order for such prophecies to occur, the future must already "exist" in some sense. It must already be laid out before us like a destination on some higher dimensional plane. In view of this, we must ask the question, "Can the future be changed, and if so, how?"

Changing the Future

After Dannion Brinkley's near-death experience, he was flooded with prophetic visions. They would come at unpredictable times. On one occasion he met two strangers at a bar. He suddenly had a vision of a 1976 Camaro following another car along a dark wet road at night. The car in front came to a bridge and then just disappeared. Then the Camaro followed and went into the river as well. The bridge had collapsed. Dannion sensed this vision applied to one of the men there. It turned out that one of them did indeed own a 1976 Camaro. Dannion was even able to sketch the strange little wooden bridge which was on their way home. He persuaded them to stay there and not to drive that night. The next morning they learned that the little bridge had collapsed during the night, and two cars had driven off it, injuring three people. But by warning the men, he had prevented them from being hurt, and had prevented the Camaro from going off the bridge.

In another example, he was walking across a road when he had a vision of a big old yellow Chrysler coming around the curve and hitting two girls. It was driven by an elderly lady who had lost control. He sensed that this was about to happen. He turned around and saw behind him the same two girls, starting to cross the street. At that moment the yellow Chrysler came around the corner. It was driven by an elderly lady. He raced out into the street and yelled at the girls to get back on the sidewalk. Her car careened and crashed into a parked car, just as he had foreseen. But because of his quick action, no one was injured.

These stories reveal two fundamental truths about prophecy. First, there is validity to it. True prophetic visions do happen. They describe future events in great and precise detail. When the actual event unfolds, there can be little doubt that it was not coincidence. It was foreseen. But the second truth is that these events can be changed. This most often happens because one makes use of the prophetic information to alter the event.

The rule seems to be that if we have no information "outside the timeline" then events will unfold just as foreseen. But if higher dimensional knowledge is used then we can bypass the event. We can change the future. Dannion's precise information about the little bridge, and his knowledge about the yellow Chrysler and the two girls, enabled him to change future events which otherwise appear to have been destined to occur (Brinkley, 1995).

One prophecy from No-Eyes involved a very powerful hurricane which would destroy the Kennedy Space Center at around the millennium. Such a hurricane actually did appear. It was one of the most powerful hurricanes ever to threaten the Florida coast. It was Hurricane Floyd, and on September 15, 1999 it was heading directly toward the Kennedy Space Center, and projected to hit it.

Figure 12.16 shows a GOES Infrared satellite image of the hurricane on that day. Its edge was already impinging on the Kennedy Space Center, and the velocity of its eye was pointed right at the space complex.

The weather service projected that it was likely to hit the Space Center, and NASA officials admitted they could do nothing to protect the tall buildings and rockets from the 175 mile-per-hour winds the storm carried. The buildings were not built to withstand such high winds.

At the last minute, the hurricane turned to the north, sparing the space complex. This hurricane fit the description in No-Eyes' prediction perfectly, and yet at the last minute it turned. Does this mean that No-Eyes' prediction was wrong? I do not know, but I do know there were some powerful psychics who were intensely praying that the storm would turn to the north and not come onshore.

We can never prove that those prayers were responsible for averting this catastrophe, but the exact correspondence between this scenario and No-Eyes' prediction up until September 15, 1999 cannot be easily dismissed.

Figure 12.16. Hurricane Floyd on September 15, 1999 was projected to hit the Kennedy Space Center.

Another area in which prophecy and "time travel" have proven useful is in the development of new inventions. During Dannion Brinkley's NDE, for example, he was shown some future medical technology. Just as some remote viewers have been able to project themselves into the future to see inventions, and then bring back the technology to the present and apply for patents, so Brinkley found himself exposed to technology which does not exist today but will in the future:

"…I was given a tour of the operating room of the future. There were no scalpels or sharp instruments in this operating room. Instead, all healing was done by special lights. Patients were given medications and exposed to these lights, said a Being who was with me, and that changed the vibration of cells within the body. Every part of the body has its own vibratory rate, said the Being. When that rate changes, certain illnesses take place. These lights return a diseased organ to its proper vibratory rate, healing whatever illness was plaguing it." (Brinkley, 1994)

This technology of the future sounds amazingly similar to the breakthroughs being made by Dr. Jacques Benveniste at his laboratory in Clamart, France (Benveniste, 1998, 1999a, b), and replicated by others (Senekowitsch, 1995; Citro, 1995; Endler, 1994; Frey, 1993). He has shown that the action of many medicines and drugs can apparently be duplicated with electromagnetic frequencies. The technology reported by Brinkley is also very reminiscent of the discoveries reported by Royal Raymond Rife in the 1930's, in which he used strong light of a specific color to combat certain microbes (Lynes, 1987). These technological advances, always controversial at the time because they upset the orthodox methodology, may be the forerunner of the advanced medical techniques which Brinkley was shown in his near-death vision.

During the NDE state, or when one is visiting the "other side," knowledge of the future often seems to come. The near-death experience often enhances the psychic and precognitive abilities afterwards, as well. When Dr. Melvin Morse, MD, interviewed one of his patients, Donna, who had survived an NDE, he asked her how it had changed her life. "Can you see the future," he asked her? "She looked slightly uncomfortable. 'Oh, that,' she said. 'Who told you?' Without further prompting, Donna began telling tales of precognitive dreams, ones that warn of events soon to come. In all she could remember four such dreams that fit into the category of 'verifiable psychic experiences,' which means they are dreams she told others about *before* the events in the dream occurred." (Morse, 1992)

There seems to be a definite association between having a near-death experience and acquiring the ability to see the future. The cases of Dannion Brinkley and Joe McMoneagle certainly illustrate this. Over one hundred of Brinkley's prophecies, which were documented by Raymond Moody in 1975, have come true. Joe McMoneagle became a champion remote viewer, and has demonstrated his ability to remote view the future as well as the past and present.

Crossing Points and Critical Points – Toward a Science of Prophecy

In our model of physics, to be outlined in the next chapter, every tiny particle in the universe is in constant interaction with both the past and the future. Even in conventional Quantum Mechanics, particles can go forward and backward in time over small distances. In our proposed model, communication occurs over much larger intervals of space and time. We have seen how some clairvoyants and remote viewers can look into the future with high accuracy. Does this mean that the future is determined? Is it all set in concrete and is Free Will therefore an illusion?

This question is important not only for physics, but is also at the core of religion and philosophy. It affects how we make decisions and go about our daily lives. Here is a possible answer to this question and a solution to the age-old dilemma it poses:

We know that the future is to some extent determined. Our present physics allows us to compute the orbits of planets to high accuracy. We know when eclipses will occur down to the minute. We know the sun will rise tomorrow, or at least we think we know this. With less accuracy, we know the weather two days from now and the Gross National Product for the current year. We are used to the idea of predicting the future, and do it all the time.

Yet we also act as though it is uncertain and can be changed by our actions or our will. But what if our decisions and actions are also predetermined? What if our "free will" is just an illusion, and our every deed is determined by the forces acting upon us? Certainly we have psychology which explains that many of our decisions which feel like free will are really just the "acting out" of some ancient childhood event. Biologists would tell us that our hormones and instincts control much of what we normally think of as "free will". And with this new information about prophecy, it leads to the very valid question: Where does "free will" fit into the science of the future?

The answer can be found in one of two ways. First of all, there are wise people on this planet who are able to enter altered states at will, and for whom these issues are quite familiar. Their answer seems to be that we do indeed have free will. We are able to change the future, but our ability has limitations. Some events seem to be predestined, or have overwhelming likelihood to occur. Other events can go either way, and can be influenced by the exercise of free will.

In Mary Summer Rain's book, *Phoenix Rising* (Summer Rain, 1987), the Native American Medicine Woman "No-Eyes" described an event in which Mary Summer Rain's husband could have been killed. No-Eyes described this event as one of the days on which he could have died. On that occasion, Mary had been with him and used her own abilities to save him from what would have otherwise been certain death. No-Eyes described that event as one of the possible days on which he could have died. Since he had been saved, <u>she then knew the next likely day on which he might die</u>. That day was many years in the future. No-Eyes was aware of the detailed circumstances of the event, just as she knew the details of the earlier near-fatal incident.

No-Eyes explained to Mary that some events are essentially predestined. They have been determined for so long and are so overwhelmingly probable that there is nothing one can do about them. Other events can be changed with an act of will, so the future can be changed to a limited extent.

Remote viewers experience this when viewing a future event, such as the election of the next president. If the viewers are good and performing under favorable circumstances, they will arrive at similar descriptions of the future event. In the advanced remote viewing course I took in 1997, there were four individuals who quite independently provided similar descriptions of events surrounding the next presidential election, for the year 2000. Such agreement would normally be considered a confirmation, and would appear to make such a future event more likely to occur.

Professional remote viewers often experience the same effect. They will view the same future target repeatedly and find that the event is virtually unchanged. Other viewers may concur. All of this is done with "blind targets," of course, so the viewer doesn't know the identity of the target he has been given.

But sometimes a peculiar thing happens. After some point in time, the description of the future event may change. Initially the remote viewers may have described the election of John Smith, let's say, by a landslide. Then, later viewings of the same event yield a different description. After a particular day, all of the viewings of the election describe John Smith as losing by a narrow margin. From the remote viewers' point of view, it is as if the future has changed. It is as if we had been on one time line destined to arrive at one outcome, and suddenly something changed and we find ourselves on a different time line headed toward a different future.

The physics model which describes this sort of universe would look something like Figure 12.17, below. It is modeled after a ball rolling down a hill. On the hill are gullies and arroyos, deep furrows which tend to guide the ball. If it falls into one of these, it tends to stay trapped there unless the gully branches. This picture actually resembles the "random cascade" used by the Princeton PEAR Lab, in which a metal ball falls downward and collides with metal posts. Here, once it is trapped in a certain groove, it is not likely to escape unless the groove crosses another one at a crossing point or "crux point."

This corrugated surface is actually very much like the probability surface which quantum mechanics would predict. The path along the bottom of a gully represents a high probability path. Once the system falls into such a path, its future can be considered determined unless a crux point is reached. Now in reality, there is always the possibility that the ball could jump out of the groove. But the deeper the groove, the higher the probability that the ball will stay trapped in it.

The grooved surface is a "terrain map" in which the ball represents the state of the system. The system can be my life, your life, or the state of the entire universe. This ball can be thought of as the "world point." When released, it rolls downhill. It will follow some path depending on the shape of the terrain. Its motion corresponds to the passing of time. It moves according to its laws of motion.

This "world point" can describe all the states of the universe. The shape of the terrain, the hills and valleys and well-worn paths, determine the "most likely" path of the world point (i.e. of events). This surface can be thought of as a "probability surface." Its shape is determined by all the forces acting upon it, from throughout the universe.

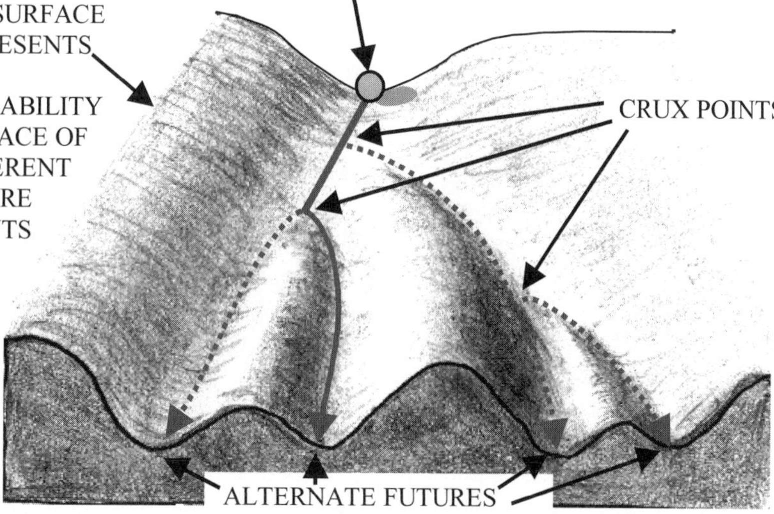

BALL REPRESENTS ANY
PHYSICAL PROCESS

THE SURFACE
REPRESENTS
THE
PROBABILITY
SURFACE OF
DIFFERENT
FUTURE
EVENTS

CRUX POINTS

ALTERNATE FUTURES

Figure 12.17. Causality and determinism are affected most strongly by "crux" points at which future paths divide. The effect of prayer, visualization and will power have greatest effect at such crux points (after Sheldrake, 1995).

When the world point is rolling in a deep valley with steep sides, it is very difficult and unlikely for it to get out, and it travels along this deep valley until it reaches a flattened out area, a "saddle point," where several paths meet. At these junctures the rolling ball must select a path. But in these flattened out areas, a very small change in the terrain can cause the ball to select a different path. These are the "crucial points," the turning points, of history. A very small shift at such a point will mean that the ball will select a different path from there on downhill.

Here is the key hypothesis: the map above is like a terrain map of the future. As we move through time we are like the little ball in the picture, rolling down the rutted hill. We can only see the path in our immediate vicinity. But in the altered state, the psychic can rise above the terrain and see the path leading ahead.

The remote viewer is also able to move around in this terrain, moving backward into the past or forward into the future. This model offers an explanation for why many prophets and remote viewers see exactly the same future. It suggests that the future line of maximum probability lies before us like a well-worn path. It is our "destiny." But we can also change our destiny. With determination, and especially with knowledge of the existing terrain, we can say with Michael J. Fox in *Back to the Future*: "History is going to change."

Visualization, meditation, prayer and intent can cause the terrain map to change its shape. This has been shown by the millions of PK experiments conducted at the Princeton PEAR Lab. It has also been shown by the worldwide group prayer sessions and group meditations which have been analyzed by the Consciousness Research Laboratory and the Global Consciousness Project (Nelson, 2003).

Attempts to change the shape of the terrain, thereby altering the future, may be in opposition to other powerful forces which are imposing a different path. These forces need not be from living beings. The mighty force of planets and stars also exerts influence on the system. It would take a powerful act of prayer or meditation, for

225

example, to perceptably change the orbits of the planets. Therefore certain future events are highly probable, and prayer is not likely to change them.

If we wish to change the future, then clearly <u>it is best to focus on the crux points, the crossing points</u>. It is clear that they are the easiest points to change. At these points there are several different paths which are almost equally likely. The terrain in their vicinity is almost flat. Relatively little psychokinetic force, i.e. prayer, meditation, or visualization, is needed to introduce a change in the preferred path in such an area. Prayer and visualization can change the tilt of the probability surface at such points. It is easy to see that a small tilt in the terrain at a crux point can be enough to change the path of the ball.

In one of the prophecies which Dannion Brinkley brought back from his NDE, he was told "if you see this, then all the rest of the prophecies will come true as you have been shown." In other words, even in these prophecies, it was implied that the future has crux points, and that alternative futures are possible. However, after a certain point in the unfolding timeline, when certain events have occurred, it implies that the crux point has passed and that a further sequence of events is unavoidable.

Prophecy and Knowledge of the Future

To change the future, it is most effective to focus on these "crux points", the saddle points, of the world path. These are areas where the terrain is flattest, and the smallest change in slope may cause events to take a new path. Concentrated prayer and visualization at these points should be the most efficacious.

If you notice how great prophets talk about prophecy, this model seems to be implied. Free will exists, and we can affect on our future, yet at the same time some events are so large and have so much momentum behind them that in their broad outlines they are inevitable. In the picture proposed here, the world point is traveling in a deep valley with steep sides, and the amount of prayer and visualization required to change its path in those regions is very unlikely to be available. Therefore, once events pass a certain point, they become virtually inevitable, until the next "crossing point" is reached.

This example illustrates the way prophecy appears to work, based on interviews with many remote viewers and psychics. The graphs shown are "space-time" graphs in which time is the vertical axis. The horizontal axis, labeled "space" represents all of the other dimensions in the system. This can be many more than the three ordinary space dimensions. It represents the "state" of reality, so a single dot on the graph represents the state of the universe at a moment in time. The shaded dot represents the present state of the universe (we are omitting complications due to relativity right now) As time passes, the dot moves upward which means it is moving forward in time to a later time. The line it follows represents the "state" of the universe at some future time. This line is called the "worldline." The most probable worldline is printed heavier in the figure.

Therefore, starting in 1990, as represented by the small shaded dot, if we were to remote view a future date, say 2012 AD, from that point in time, we would see a particular future state of the universe. This would be the state on the "most probable" worldline. The remote viewing session would involve primarily exchange of data with this point on the future time line at the date 2012. At a later time, say 1995, a second remote viewing session can be done, also looking at events in the year 2012. If we assume the most probable future line has not changed, then in the remote viewing session we see the same "most probable" future. This is illustrated by the diagram on the left side of Figure 12.18. The future hasn't changed. In cases like this, prophecy can be of great value, and can be accurate.

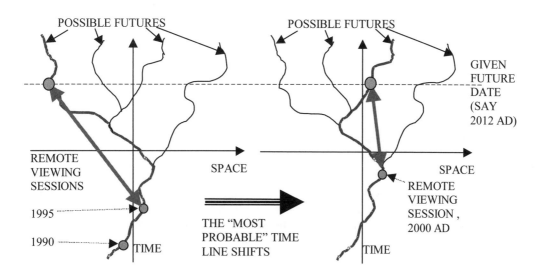

Figure 12.18. This figure illustrates how prophecy can affect the future time line. The graphs show time on the vertical axis, and represent how events unfold. The horizontal axis can be thought of as representing the possible states of the system, i.e. the possible different future events which may occur. This graph is really just like an overhead, aerial view of the furrowed probability surface of Figure 12.17. Since the ball only moves along the bottom of a furrow in that figure, we can represent each path by a line, as we do here. When a crux point is reached, the lines branch. As time passes, the ball moves up the tree-like graph. It represents the state of the universe at a given moment. The branch points shown here are exactly the same as the crux points illustrated in Figure 12.17.

However, suppose that, at some time later, say in 1997, something happened to shift the most probable future. This might be an influence from outside the system. This could be the action coming in from a parallel dimension, a parallel reality, which causes phase shifts in the local phase-locked system. This would change the way events evolve. At the critical branching points or crux points, the probabilities will have changed slightly. A slight change coming from outside the system can shift the most probable time line, especially at a crux point. We assume this happens, causing a shift in the time line after this point. Therefore, a remote viewing session conducted after 1997 will see a different future for the year 2012. This is illustrated in the right hand graph in Figure 12.18.

The model which most closely conforms to the description of clairvoyants is that, at any one moment, there is a most probable future time line. This time line extends far into the future. In principle, on a given day, if many remote viewers try to view a distant event they will all see the same thing. And experiments of this kind have reportedly been done. Therefore at that moment, there is a "most probable" future and that is what is seen.

At a later time, if they were to all to remote view the same future event again, they should still see the same thing. However, if some outside event or higher dimensional event has occurred, or perhaps a major act of free will or a mass prayer or meditation, it may shift the probabilities and shift the time line to a nearby trajectory. These shifts will occur at branch points where history bifurcates. The points at which this happens are called "critical points."

At a critical point, several future time lines have very nearly equal probability. A slight shift one way or the other can cause the time line to shift from one path to a different path. If one wishes to change history, it is most easily done by influencing events at such critical points.

Since world-line trajectories are controlled by the interference of phases from the many particles in the system, a slight shift in phase of some components can cause the most probable world line to shift at such points. Influences from other "dimensions" (parallel universe phase systems) and influence from prayer (phase-cohering process) can be most effective at such critical junctures in history.

The beauty of this model is that it explains how there can be laws of physics, and there can be determinism, and <u>at the same time there can be free will.</u> The free will is limited in a sense, because it competes with the free will of others and against the forces of nature, which can be very powerful. For example, I might make a free will decision to levitate my body. But in attempting to do so, I will be struggling against the force of gravity, the attraction of all the atoms of the earth which are working to hold me down. We have seen earlier evidence that some individuals may have learned how to do this, but it is very rare.

In this view, free will can affect the future, but only to a limited degree. It is limited by the strength of the will itself. It is most effective at the crux points, and these are limited in number. This serves to limit the number of future possibilities. Because there are only a limited number of likely futures, and one is most likely of all, therefore prophecy is possible. Prophecy sees the most likely future time line. But free will can change this time line. The odds are best when its action is focused on the crux points. Then, like a railroad switch shifting the tracks for an oncoming locomotive, the path traveled can be altered between a limited number of future possibilities.

Therefore we need not believe the skeptics who say it is impossible. We need not believe the prophets of Doom, who say we are destined for more bloody war ending in some sort of apocalypse. The future CAN BE CHANGED. This is one of the great lessons. It is a graduation exercise, in a very real sense. If we are to inherit a future world of peace, prosperity and enlightenment, then we must help to create it by using these lessons in the right way.

Summary

In this chapter we have dealt with some of the deepest and most difficult issues in science. What is the nature of time? Is there free will? And if there is, how is it affected or limited by the rules of science, by determinism? And what of prophecy? Can one truly see the future? And if that is possible, how can there also be free will, since the future is already determined?

In seeking answers to these questions we have used the best sources available. First of all, we have shown scientific evidence, from the Princeton PEAR Lab and other laboratories, that knowledge of the future is obtainable. It is possible to access information from the future. This has been proven in careful laboratory experiments with hundreds of thousands of runs. We have seen that certain gifted individuals are able to access the future with great accuracy, although not perfectly. There are many examples where events in the future were seen with such clarity and detail that it could not be due to chance. And certain remote viewers such as Joe McMoneagle have been rated at over 65% accuracy when viewing future targets. Therefore, the data shows that prophecy is possible.

The "butterfly effect" of Edward Lorenz, combined with the uncertainties inherent in quantum predictions, indicate that accuracy in viewing the future contradicts the known laws of science. It is simply impossible, based on known physics, to predict detailed events days or weeks or years into the future. Examples such as Dannion Brinkley's vision of the 1976 Camaro going over a small bridge at night , or his vision of the Chernobyl disaster, or the one hundred other prophecies from his near-death experience which have since come true, are predictions of the future that defy known science. Joe McMoneagle's vision that he would leave Vietnam in a yellow airplane is another example of an absurd prediction, made months or years before the fact, which later came true.

Such events, when taken as a whole, prove beyond reasonable doubt that the future already exists in some sense. Prophecy then consists of accessing that realm. We have proposed that the realm may involve what remote viewers call the "subspace," and Hindu yogis call the "astral." It is a dimension in which time does not exist, and therefore one is able to move forward into the future or backward into the past. Western science knows very little about such dimensions and domains, but in order to understand the paranormal, it will be necessary to study them in detail.

We have also encountered cases in which the future has been foreseen, and then altered. In those cases, events began unfolding exactly as in the prophecy. This confirms that the prophecies were initially accurate and valid. However, because the participants were alert to the outcome of the event, they were able to take action to change that outcome. Meditation and prayer, as well as action, can be effective in doing this.

In view of evidence from many sources, it appears that prophecy is possible, and therefore it is possible to acquire direct knowledge of future events with much greater accuracy than would be expected from mere chance or from the predictions of present physics. At the same time it appears that free will exists. There are many examples of the future being changed, either by using knowledge from the prophecy, or by prayer and visualization.

To resolve these seemingly contradictory conclusions, we propose the "crossing point" hypothesis. Most of the time, events unfold following paths of high probability. It is very difficult to change future events during such periods. It is like a ball in a deep rut rolling down a hill. It is very unlikely that it will jump out of the rut.

However, every so often it reaches a cross-over point where several ruts intersect. This corresponds to points where probabilities of several different futures are nearly equal. At these points it is easiest for meditation, prayer, and "psychic forces," as well as action, to alter the slope of the terrain. The slope is very nearly flat at such points. If we focus our mental efforts there it is easiest to alter the "probability surface", i.e. the rutted hillside, and shunt the ball into a different furrow. In doing so we have changed the future. There is abundant evidence that this occurs. It is up to us to become familiar with this process, and to learn to use it wisely.

In the next chapter we present the beginnings of a scientific model which may explain the strange phenomena discussed in this book. Of course it must also be consistent with known science. The model, which we call the "Synchronized Universe Model" or "SUM," offers a scientific explanation for the power of prayer, meditation, PK and ESP, and offers insights into teleportatation, levitation and the subtle energies. It explains how higher dimensions and parallel universes can exist, and how paranormal effects may involve the interconnection and communication between such parallel realms.

The presentation emphasizes some of the big concepts, the major ideas, and leaves out details which will be presented in later volumes. If someday someone disproves it, just remember that all the data and experiments presented in the previous chapters are still valid. A wrong theory has no effect on the validity of the experiments. They still show that a new, deeper theory of physics is needed. However, there are many good and exciting ideas in the Synchronized Universe Model. It offers a possible scientific explanation for much that is currently unexplained. It may be the road map to a far-reaching and deeper understanding of the universe.

CHAPTER 13 -BEGINNINGS OF A THEORY

"Through the results of psi research it became apparent that quantum theory has flaws in a very practical sense. Applied to systems that include human subjects the predictions of quantum theory were seen to be sometimes incorrect."
   -Dr. Helmut Schmidt (Schmidt, 1993)

"Conditions, thoughts, activities of men in every clime are things; as thoughts are things. They make their impression upon the skein of time and space. Thus, as they make for their activity, they become as records that may be read by those in accord or attuned to such a condition...For thoughts are things."
   -- Edgar Cayce, (Cayce, 1971)

"Whoever undertakes to set himself up as a judge in the field of Truth and Knowledge is shipwrecked by the laughter of the Gods.
   -- Albert Einstein (quoted in Cannon, 1996)

"If we knew what we were doing, it would not be called research, would it?"
   -- Albert Einstein

Can Present Science Explain the Paranormal?

Modern science has given us technological marvels, and enhanced our standard of living in a thousand ways. It has provided tools to understand the atomic nucleus, crystals and metals, electricity, magnetism, and chemical reactions. It has provided useful and accurate tools for explaining and predicting the behavior of the physical world. But the important message, which is lost on students of science, is that all of this expertise applies only in certain limited areas, only for certain topics.

I often wonder how my physics education would have been different if, instead of conducting experiments on radioactivity and superconductivity, for which physics has very good theories, if I had taken the same equipment and gone to a haunted house! Or measured the energy fields around healers as they worked. Then, instead of confirming the science of the textbooks, I would have measured things that defy the textbooks. Unfortunately, my curriculum did not include such adventures, and it was twenty years later before I got around to those more unconventional pursuits.

But it is an important lesson for all scientists. Our educational curriculum is designed to convince the students that the theories in the book are true. There are no organized curricula in physics departments which encourage the student to seek out the strange places and events that break the rules.

Science has no clue about what consciousness is, for example. There is no adequate physical theory of it, and yet each one of us has one (it?). It is familiar but inexplicable. In this book we have reviewed other subjects which science cannot explain: the out-of-body experience, remote viewing, ESP, prophecy (knowledge of the future), the effects of group consciousness, "primary communication" a la Cleve Backster, and psychokinesis (PK), to name a few. These have been proven repeatedly in laboratory experiments over decades, within the rules of scientific statistics and controls. By any objective measure, they are real phenomena.

We have also encountered strong anecdotal evidence for additional phenomena: levitation, teleportation, and the near-death experience. In many of these cases, there is indication that systematic experiments are being conducted, such as in the case of the Chinese military with teleportation, and there is testimony from top U.S. scientists that such phenomena have also been validated in the laboratory. There is a large and impressive literature on the effects of energy healers, which will be reviewed in Volume II. Chinese physicists have conducted experiments in which energy healers have altered the decay rate of radioactive substances from thousands of miles away, under controlled conditions. Machines which can store and manipulate this strange new energy will also be described in Volume II.

The unavoidable conclusion from all of this research is that present science cannot explain these results. A few scientists working on the frontier are attempting to do so. They realize these effects are real, and are testing the limits of present scientific theory to attempt to determine just how much of this data can be explained by conventional science.

Most of the effort in this area focuses on quantum effects in living beings. Quantum mechanics has some strange features. One of the strangest is the idea that simply making a measurement can affect the experiment. This has been interpreted as meaning that the consciousness of the experimenter interacts with the experiment itself. In fact, the experiments of Schmidt (Schmidt, 1993) seem to support this, which indicates that quantum theory holds at least one of the keys to the mystery of consciousness.

This idea originated with one of the inventors of quantum theory, Erwin Schroedinger, who proposed that the quantum mechanical wave function serves as a "field of consciousness" (Schroedinger, 1964). He felt that ESP could be explained by realizing that the quantum wave function extends over the entire planet, and our minds are all immersed in it. He proposed that this may be the origin of some "group mind" effects as well as telepathy.

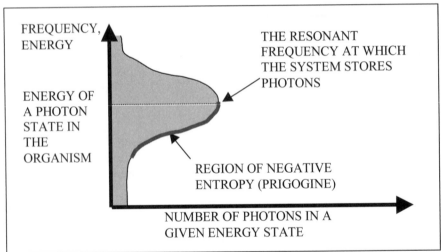

Figure 13.1. Biological systems store coherent photons. This is just like hitting a tuning fork to keep it humming, or continuously pumping a laser so it is always ready to fire. The energy is stored as photons which oscillate in step with one another, i.e. are "coherent." This makes the entire living system phase coherent, and introduces important quantum effects which help to explain life processes, and perhaps even some paranormal phenomena.

Recent research in Germany, Russia and China has uncovered the possibility that macroscopic, "large scale," quantum states may exist in all living things. This work is based on the discovery of the "biophoton," which is coherent, laser-like light emitted by all living cells (Frohlich, 1968, 1980; Popp, 1979, 1989). Researchers have discovered that many molecular and cellular structures generate, conduct and store this light within their cells. DNA, for example, absorbs and emits coherent light at dozens of frequencies. It uses this coherent energy to create "force fields" around it which help maneuver other molecules into place for replication and nucleosynthesis. Other biomolecules, such as enzymes, use this coherent energy in similar ways (Letokhov, 1974; Frohlich, 1968, 1980; Popp, 1979, 1989, 2003).

Light is coherent when all of the photons vibrate in step with one another. This is the secret of the laser, in which these photons are all in the same quantum state. This leads to the notion that coherent, large scale quantum states permeate every living creature, and enables them to carry on essential life processes such as protein synthesis so efficiently (Ho, 1997).

The Nobel Prize-winning physicist Dr. Ilya Prigogine has pointed out the advantage of such a system. By having a store of high energy, coherent photons, the energy state of a living organism resembles the graph in Figure 13.1, above. The peak in the graph represents the energy or the frequency of the coherent photons, which energize the system.

Prigogine pointed out that in such systems, the region on the bottom side of the bulge, where the density of states is increasing, is a negentropic region. This means (roughly) that processes can be carried out using photons from this band which actually decrease entropy, and therefore are very efficient. Entropy measures the randomness in a system. It represents energy which can longer be used, and therefore it also measures the inefficiency of the system. When biological systems operate in the region highlighted on the bottom of the bulge (Figure 13.1), they operate in a very efficient region in which entropy does not increase. This was part of Prigogine's Nobel Prize winning work, showing how systems which operate in this way can achieve efficiencies much greater than previously expected by the Second Law of Thermodynamics.

These large-scale, coherent, resonant processes, where trillions of molecules in the body are in communication with one another and can function in resonance, bring up a new possibility: Maybe the body is a macroscopic quantum system, with a set of coherent quantum states all vibrating in step? If so, then some of the weird phenomena we have called "paranormal" might really be just quantum mechanics working its strange magic on the large scale of every day life. This point of view has been beautifully expressed by one of the leading researchers, Dr. Mae Wan Ho, in her book *The Rainbow and the Worm* (Ho, 1998), which is highly recommended by those wishing to explore this more deeply. However, even she does not argue that quantum mechanics in its present form has all the answers:

"A coherent space-time structure theoretically enables 'instantaneous communications to occur over a range of time scales and spatial extents. What this implies in practice is a vast, unexplored area, as the notion of non-linear structured time this entails is alien to the conventional, western scientific framework..."(Ho, 1998)

Other important research in this area has been conducted by the eminent mathematical physicist Roger Penrose (Penrose, 1989, 1994, 1995; Hameroff. 1994), who, together with Stuart Hameroff, has examined "microtubules" and other biological structures which might carry and store quantum states within the body. There are quantum properties of neurons in the brain for example. Every synapse, which is where two nerves come together and do their "decision making," is really a quantum system. It is a tunneling junction, which is a quantum structure. Therefore, it seems very likely that quantum mechanical phenomena take place in the body and the brain, and play an important part in life processes.

As a physicist, the possibility that quantum mechanics can explain the paranormal must be examined seriously. It is the difference between chucking the present physical laws, saying "OK, they don't work. How do we fix them?" and saying "Oh, my goodness, we CAN explain paranormal effects if we just allow for the possibility that humans, and all life forms, are permeated by macroscopic quantum states." So the question is: "Can quantum mechanics on a large scale explain some of the weird phenomena we have described thus far?"

For example, researchers such as Richard Dobrin, following earlier work in Russia, has used sensitive photomultiplier tubes to measure the biophotons emitted by humans (Dobrin, 1977). It amounted to between 50 and 220 photons per second per square centimeter. He found that certain individuals were able to consciously increase their photon output by as much as 67 percent. This is similar to the process which "energy healers" use. Dobrin confirmed experimentally that the increased photon output occurred when the subject began consciously attempting to increase his "energy field." Can this be the explanation for the human "aura" that psychics see?

Researchers have found that cells are in communication all the time. The DNA molecule, for example, radiates and absorbs in the millimeter wave band. Can this be the source of the "Backster Effect," of cell-to-cell communication? It has been proven now that a "sick" cell radiates something, and when a healthy cell receives this radiation, it becomes sick (Kaznachayev, 1967, 1981,1982). And vice versa, sick cells can be brought back to health with radiation from healthy cells. Can this explain "energy healing?"

Shortcomings of Present Model

Before we get our hopes up too much that conventional science can explain the anomalies of the foregoing chapters, let us keep in mind some of the data we have seen so far. It may be possible, for example, that some form of quantum electromagnetic radiation from cells may cause a "healing" effect, based on the work of Kaznachayev. But those photons cannot reach half-way around the world to explain distant healing or healing inside closed, shielded rooms hundreds of miles away (Yan, 1988, 2000, 2002). Radiation transmission and absorption between cells may play a role in cell-to-cell communication, and this may be a component of the "Backster Effect." But remember that many of those experiments, too, work over distances of many hundreds of miles and through sealed rooms and Faraday cages. What is more, the Backster effect did not weaken with distance, which argues against any normal form of radiation, such as photons, as the explanation.

Therefore it is unlikely that quantum mechanics will explain away all of the paranormal puzzles of the previous chapters. A more fundamental reason can be seen in the way paranormal effects manifest themselves. The best "detector" of paranormal forces in use today is the REG, the "Random Event Generator." This in itself is usually based on a quantum process. It makes use of the electron noise in a resistor, or radioactive decay of a small sample of a radioactive element.

Quantum mechanics states that in these physical processes, this random noise measured by the REGs can only be described by probabilities. Once this has been calculated, nothing more can be said about the event. Quantum mechanics does not describe the nature of the noise, nor offer means for changing it. And yet this is exactly what paranormal phenomena do.

In most of the experiments described in this book, the results can be summarized in the following statement: "Paranormal effects are able to alter the structure of 'random' or 'quantum' noise, thereby altering the probability of events." Although quantum mechanics does provide equations which make it possible to calculate and predict the level of quantum noise, it offers no mechanism by which consciousness could alter this noise. One of the shortcomings of quantum mechanics in the minds of many people, including Einstein, was that there was no underlying explanation of the nature of this noise. It is left as a mystery in quantum mechanics.

Einstein and many others since him, felt that quantum mechanics was a superficial theory, that although it works brilliantly on a certain level, it glosses over a deeper layer of truth. He felt it describes the universe on the average, but there must be "hidden variables" which it neglects, and which are evidenced by the random and unpredictable nature of the theory. Such deeper models are called "hidden variables theories" and they have been proposed by eminent physicists such as David Bohm (Bohm, 1951).

Some physicists believe that such "hidden variable theories" have been ruled out by experiments. This is not true. A famous set of experiments called the EPR experiments, after physicists Einstein, Podolsky and Rosen (Einstein, 1935), ruled out one kind of hidden variable theory, so-called "local hidden variable theories" (Clauser, 1974; d'Espagnat, 1974, 1978). However, "non-local" hidden variable theories, in which particle motion is coupled over great distances, are not ruled out by these experiments (e.g. Cramer, 1980). This is precisely the type of theory we are proposing.

It would appear that paranormal phenomena do affect this deeper layer of physics. In psychokinesis and group prayer experiments, the level of quantum noise was actually found to DECREASE. This has NO explanation in conventional quantum theory. It requires a theory which addresses the nature of quantum noise and describes the forces which can affect it and alter it.

This is just the minimal argument for a deeper theory. Quantum theory also offers no explanation for teleportation through walls, for example. Mainstream science explains the repulsion between atoms based on quantum theory. But there is no mechanism in the theory which would show us how to turn OFF that force. Yet in teleportation experiments, seemingly that is what occurs sometimes.

This is just one of many reasons why paranormal phenomena cannot be explained away by the application of quantum mechanics. Another salient one is the time effect. The ability to affect events IN THE PAST is not part of mainstream physics, quantum or otherwise. And yet, the results of the Princeton PEAR Lab (Jahn, 1987a, 1987b), Radin (Radin, 1997, 1997a) and Schmidt (Schmidt, 1981, 1989, 1993) among others, have demonstrated that this is a real phenomenon.

One of the common aspects of paranormal phenomena is the effect on the random processes and quantum noise. In many ESP and PK experiments, the level of randomness is decreased, as measured on the REG devices. In other cases, the randomness is altered in a specific way to cause the outcome of a random process to turn out systematically "high" or "low". The common element in all of these experiments is that the quantum randomness is being altered. This can be explained if we assume that the zero-point energy of space is being altered.

The zero point energy is the random energy of space which is predicted to be there even by quantum mechanics. It is a direct result of the Uncertainty Principle. But after predicting it, it is ignored in many modern theories. It is assumed to have very little effect, and treated only as a small perturbation. An alternative view, more consistent with the concerns of Einstein, has postulated that this zero-point energy provides this deeper level understanding of quantum mechanics (Boyer, 1969, 1973, 1975, 1984; Puthoff, 1975, 1989a, 1989b). By attempting to develop a theory of the zero-point energy, allowing quantum theory to emerge as an average of this more profound picture, seems to offer much promise if we are to understand the way paranormal phenomena seemingly alter the zero point energy structure of space.

For these reasons, I believe that a "non-local hidden variables theory" which treats the zero point energy explicitly, is the only answer. Physicists who study such things know that the only possible form of this theory is that it must be "non-local," that is, it must involve the interactions of particles over long distances. The theory to be described next has all the right properties. It is only a "sketch" of such a theory, a beginning, and we describe only the concepts (no equations). It shows that many of the strange anomalous events which occur in the paranormal can be fit naturally into such a physical theory. The quantum aspects of living beings mesh very naturally with this theory. It may be the coupling together of the quantized biophoton model with the "Synchronized Universe Model," to be described next, which offers a more comprehensive explanation of a wide range of paranormal phenomena.

Beginnings of a Theory

When I was a freshman in college at M.I.T. I used to daydream about the electron. Einstein used to say that if we could just fully understand the electron, it would probably unlock the mysteries of all the elementary particles. The electron, of course, is familiar to everyone to some extent. It is one of the smallest of the elementary particles, the building blocks of matter. It is the particle that orbits around the nucleus of atoms, giving the atom its size and shape. It is the particle that moves through wires and crystals to make our walkman work, to make our

235

computer function, to generate TV signals. It is at the heart of most of the electronic wonders of the last 100 years.

But as a budding physicist, I wanted to understand it at a deeper level. I had discovered a series of books by the famous physicist Richard Feynman, who unraveled many of the mysteries of the electron. After reading his books, I used to daydream, close my eyes and use my imagination to try to understand what was going on at the deepest level of the electron. The picture he drew, and the picture I saw, was of a small particle zipping around at high speed in space and time.

Feynman explained how the electron probably has no mass, no weight, if we could peer deep inside it. Probably the mass it has is due to the trapped energy of the electric fields around it. He explained that, at very small distances, an electron moves at nearly the speed of light, and can zip back and forth in space as well as in time. This was amazing and exciting to me. The electron was a time traveler, at least on the very small scale!

There is the concept in physics called the "drunkard's walk" or the "random walk." You can imagine a very drunk man trying to walk in one direction. But his balance is so impaired that he keeps veering off in different directions in a random pattern. He may walk many steps but he doesn't get very far. This is a random walk. In the nineteenth century scientists peering through early microscopes saw pollen grains moving in water. These tiny grains also moved in a random pattern. It turned out they were so small, the random kicks they received from water molecules caused them to bounce around in different directions. They also did the random walk. This zig-zag behavior was named "Brownian motion" after its discoverer. This random zig-zag pattern of motion is found many places in nature. And it seems the electron also moves in this way at the smallest scales. But most fascinating to me, it did the random walk in <u>time</u>, going forward and backward in time, as well as in space.

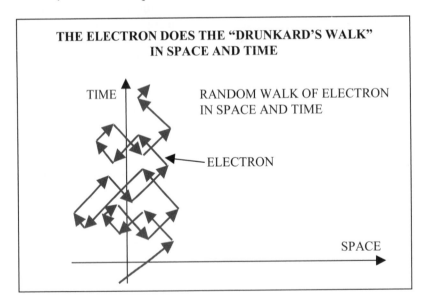

Figure 13.2 The electron zips around, moving rapidly back and forth in space and time. It has a negative electric charge, so it is repelled from other electrons, which also have negative charge. For electricity, like repels like and opposites attract. It is attracted to the positive nucleus of the atom, which is what holds atoms together. It also spins like a tiny top or a miniature planet as it zips about in a random motion.

I spent many hours trying to develop a "feel" for the electron. I did not know then that what I was doing would probably today be called remote viewing. I was just trying to understand the universe from the point of view of the electron. I was trying to see things from its perspective. This intuitive approach has a long and illustrious history in physics. Einstein got his first ideas for Relativity after trying to see the universe from the point of view of a photon, a particle of light. He imagined he was riding the light beam (see Figure 13.3), moving at the speed of light, and he struggled with the notion that time would have to stop in the outside world from that point of view. It led him to Relativity theory and a revolution in physics.

THOUGHT EXPERIMENT:

EINSTEIN RIDING A LIGHT BEAM

Figure 13.3. Einstein discovered the Theory of Relativity while doing a "thought experiment," which is similar to day-dreaming. He imagined he was riding a beam of light, and imagined what the world outside would look like from this frame of reference.

Einstein of course was a hero of mine, but even more so was Feynman. His physics books had a picture of him on the inside cover. His sleeves were rolled up and he was playing the bongo drums. He had gone to M.I.T., where I was going. He was full of practical jokes. He had worked on the Manhattan bomb project as a grad student at Princeton (where I also went to grad school). When he was at Los Alamos he used to crack the Top Secret safes and leave little notes inside: "Guess Who?" they read. It was said that he climbed the outside of the bell tower at the Princeton Grad college. And of course, he won the Nobel Prize in physics. What a guy!

But what I liked most about him was that he emphasized the importance of physical intuition, of visualizing and getting a feeling for the particles and forces he dealt with. In his Nobel Prize lecture, he recounted the conversation with his father when he told him he was going to Stockholm. His father had encouraged Richard all his life to explore physics. It turned out that part of the reason was that his father wanted to understand nature at a deep level. He interrogated Richard about where the photon comes from when an atom gives off light. Was the photon in the atom before it was emitted? He had many questions. He was not satisfied with a mathematical answer. He wanted to understand at a deep intuitive level. Somewhat sadly, Feynman admitted that he could not answer all of his father's questions. Today's physics has constructed mathematical formulas that describe many aspects of fundamental physics. But it is often missing a deep, satisfying intuitive picture of what is going on, and why the equations are the way they are.

Feynman has said that if all mathematics disappeared it would set physics back exactly one week. So, despite the fact that he was a very gifted mathematician, he always emphasized the importance of a physical picture, of physical intuition. This provides the guide to what ideas, what equations to try. Without it, physicists are just guessing blind, just trying different assumptions in the dark. This often seems to describe some of the papers one sees in physics journals. In this chapter, as in the rest of the book, we stick with the intuitive viewpoint. There are no equations, only pictures. Some of these pictures have been converted to equations (elsewhere), and as this theory matures, it must one day be completely expressible mathematically. That process is not complete yet.

However, some of the concepts offered here are very deep, and they do seem to offer a way to extend current physics theory to understand and explain paranormal phenomena. The main point is that we do not have to relegate such phenomena to hoaxes or bad science. We do not have to label it as "occult" or "supernatural," thereby placing it outside of science. These are real phenomena, carefully and rigorously established.

The difficulty with any new theory in science is that it must also account for all the old data. In physics we have two centuries worth of old data. Any new theory must be consistent with the laws of gravity, the laws of electricity and magnetism, and the laws of nuclear and particle physics as we know it. At the same time, it must extend into other realms to be able to explain the paranormal and anomalous effects recounted in earlier chapters.

One of the keys is that we must go beyond quantum mechanics. Most Americans, and even most physicists, are probably not comfortable with some of its predictions. It bothered Einstein all his life. In his gut he felt quantum mechanics was an approximation. Yes, it worked beautifully at the atomic level. But he felt the randomness that was built into it was covering up our ignorance of some other processes at a deeper level.

The paradox of quantum mechanics can be understood by the "Schroedinger's Cat Paradox" (see Figure 13.4). A cat sits in a sealed box with no windows. Also inside is a pellet of cyanide. If it is released, the cat will die. Its release mechanism is triggered by a Geiger Counter, which measures the radiation from a very weak radioactive source. If it detects radiation from the source, it will release the cyanide and the cat will die.

But radioactive decay is a random process. On the average, physics can predict the probability of a decay occurring. But one can never predict it exactly. Now in quantum mechanics, things are measured in probability. After one hour, let's say, the probability is fifty-fifty that a decay has occurred. But since it is fifty-fifty, quantum mechanics predicts that the cat is half dead and half alive. What it actually predicts is that there is a "wave-function" for a dead cat in there, and one for an alive cat. As long as no one looks in the box, both wave functions must continue to exist inside. It is basically saying there is a live cat and a dead cat both in there.

Then if one peeks in, it "collapses the wave function," which means that now an observer has determined which it is. One cat wave-function will disappear, and the cat will become fully the other one. This situation bothered Einstein to no end. It did not seem natural nor likely. "God does not play dice with the universe," was his response to this Las Vegas-like description of physics. But despite his qualms, predictions of quantum mechanics have held up very well. It may only be in recent years, in the face of remote viewing and ESP data, that it is coming under a serious challenge.

In these experiments we have discovered that consciousness can actually CHANGE the rate of radioactive decay. If we had enough people visualizing, we could keep the cat alive much longer! This is no longer speculation. This is established fact as we saw in Chapters 3 and 5. It indicates that the probability of radioactive decay is not just some constant of nature. There is some physical mechanism which is affected by conscious intention, and it can slow down (or speed up) the decay. Therefore there must be some force or some physical connection between the mechanism of radioactive decay and the conscious mind.

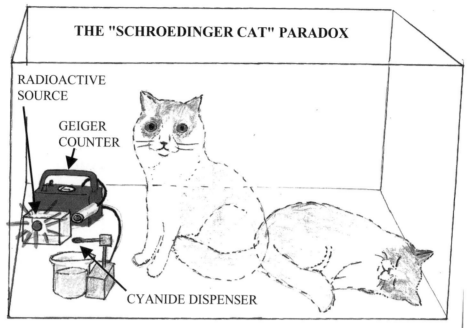

THE "SCHROEDINGER CAT" PARADOX

RADIOACTIVE
SOURCE

GEIGER
COUNTER

CYANIDE DISPENSER

Figure 13.4. The "Schroedinger Cat" Paradox. At any given time the cat must be partially in two very different quantum states. It must be partially in the "dead" state and partially in the "alive" state. When someone peeks in, all of the possible states vanish ("collapse") except one. This is the view of real events through the lens of quantum mechanics. Among other things, it neglects to take into account that the cat is also an observer. The cat knows whether it is alive or not. The intuitive conflict is a challenge to both science and theology.

It is no coincidence that some of the leading physicists investigating Zero-Point Energy have a long history of research in the paranormal. One of these men is Dr. Hal Puthoff, whom we met in Chapter One as one of the founders of the Remote Viewing Program. By the early nineteen-eighties, he had amassed so much data about "anomalous phenomena" that he began seriously exploring how to modify physics to account for the paranormal.

He discovered the works of T. H. Boyer (Boyer, 1969, 1973, 1975), who had gone back to basics and developed some of the first fundamental mathematics for a new theory of the vacuum. He took the notion of Zero-Point Energy, as it is predicted by Quantum Mechanics, very seriously. A basic prediction is that, because of the Uncertainty Principle, the so-called vacuum of space is actually filled with fluctuating energy, random photons which zip about in all directions.

On the average, the number of photons moving in any given direction is equal, so no force is detected. But just like the invisible water molecules knocked around the pollen grains, giving rise to Brownian motion, he theorized that this bath of random photons would kick around electrons causing them also to undergo a random walk. This offered a more satisfying model for the randomness of Quantum Mechanics. It offered a more fundamental explanation for why there must be an Uncertainty Principle.

This pioneering effort by Boyer and Puthoff, together with the work of Rueda (Rueda, 1981, 1986, 1998) and Haisch (Haisch, 1997a, 1997b, 1998) has become known as "Statistical Electrodynamics." Whereas the older, establishment theory of the electron was called "QED" for Quantum Electrodynamics, this new alternative approach became known as "SED."

The following sketch illustrates the difference in the assumptions. In Quantum Mechanics, the randomness is built-in, without any physical explanation for its origin. There is randomness, it is given by equations, and the level of this randomness is described by a constant, known as Planck's Constant after Max Planck, the original founder of Quantum Theory. As an electron moves through space and time, it will randomly give off or absorb photons which come from and vanish into the vacuum of space. The overall probability for this to occur depends on its charge, and is predicted by the equations of quantum mechanics (the "wave function"). Beyond that, no explanation is given for why or when these events might happen. It is just a random process, built into the assumptions of the theory (see Figure 13.5 below).

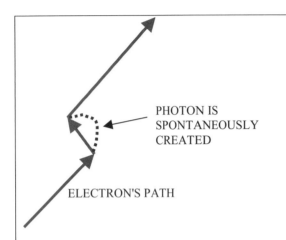

Figure 13.5. QED MODEL-The red arrows represent the electron's path, the blue dotted lines the photons. In QED, the standard model for the electron, photons are spontaneously and randomly created and destroyed, causing the electron to zig and zag in a random walk. This spontaneous creation and destruction of photons (and other particles) gives rise to the Uncertainty Principle.

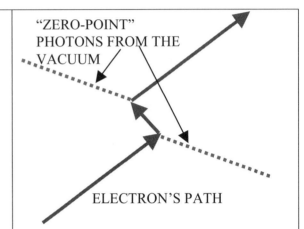

Figure 13.6. SED MODEL-The red arrows represent the electron's path, the blue dotted line the photons. In the SED model, they are present in the vacuum and "hit" the electron causing its random drunkard's walk, and giving rise to the Uncertainty Principle.

SED, on the other hand, developed by Boyer, Puthoff, Rueda and Haisch, offers a deeper explanation of these random events. In their model the vacuum is filled with photons. (see Figure 13.6) This comprises the "Zero-Point energy" of the vacuum. They are real photons, but because they are randomly distributed they do not cause any average force on particles. Their random distribution gives rise to the unpredictability of quantum mechanics. The distribution of the photons is designed so it agrees with the predictions of quantum mechanics. It also, very nicely, is the one distribution which looks the same if you travel at different velocities. Therefore it is consistent with Einstein and Relativity. And, most importantly, it offers a mechanism for the randomness of elementary particles.

Whereas Quantum Theory has no way to explain how meditation can affect radioactive decay rates or electrical noise in a resistor, SED <u>does</u> have a way to explain this: consciousness must affect the Zero-Point energy in the vacuum. It must alter the distribution of the photons zipping through space. Somehow. At least now, we have a mechanism, a handle, on how radioactivity and other quantum processes can be affected. Still missing is any understanding of how the conscious mind might actually CAUSE such a change in the vacuum.

The theory we are presenting in this chapter builds on the SED picture. SED is a big step in the right direction. We have tried to offer the next step. SED suggested that the photons in the vacuum of space are real. We have gone the next step: we assume all those photons in the vacuum <u>originated</u> somewhere. Where? Why, on all the <u>other</u> particles throughout the universe! There are a huge number of charged particles in the universe. All of them are doing the same rapid zig-zag dance. Therefore, they should all be radiating and absorbing photons like crazy. What happened to all the photons which were created by all those electrons in distant stars? Why, THAT IS PRECISELY WHAT MAKES UP THE ZERO-POINT ENERGY OF SPACE! (see Figure 13.7)

Every time a nearby electron makes a zig or a zag, it has just absorbed or emitted a photon. Where did that incoming photon originate? Where does the outgoing photon go? Other electrons (and other charged particles) elsewhere in the universe created the photon that was just absorbed, and will absorb eventually the photon that was just emitted.

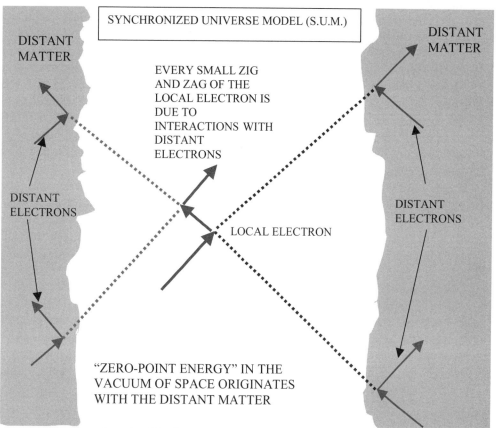

Figure 13.7. The Synchronized Universe Model (S.U.M.) assumes that all the particles in the universe interact with one another. It goes one step further than the SED model. It assumes that the local electrons are tied to the distant matter via photons. The "virtual photons" in space are assumed to be created by the motions of other electrons. Most of them are created by the "distant matter" which contains almost all the matter of the universe. Therefore every zig and zag of a local electron is really a communication between it and the distant matter. This embodies Mach's Principle: the distant matter determines local inertia and local forces.

SO ALL THE ELECTRONS AND OTHER PARTICLES ARE ACTUALLY CONNECTED TO ONE ANOTHER. We call this the "Synchronized Universe Model" or SUM model. The random zig-zag dance they do is actually a dance <u>with one another</u>. Momentum and energy that is created here is absorbed there and vice versa. The local, nearby electron does not dance alone. It is therefore not a random motion that it undergoes. If we could somehow know the motions of the particles at the other end, which are in the distant matter of stars, then we could PREDICT the detailed motions of the local electron as it zigs and zags. Of course, practically speaking this is an impossible task. But the idea that the motions of local particles and distant particles is <u>connected</u> is an important and fundamental insight.

In the history of physics, the first person who had this idea was Ernst Mach, the German scientist and philosopher for whom the Mach Number in high speed flight is named. Mach was convinced that the distant matter of space determined all the important forces locally here on earth. In particular, he noticed that centrifugal force is connected to the motion of stars in the sky. On a starry night one summer as a twelve-year old, I noticed this interesting phenomenon. Look up in the sky and hold your arms out. They want to fall by your side due to gravity. Now spin around. You feel a force lifting your arms and pulling them away from your sides. We call this "centrifugal force." You only feel it when the stars above you are spinning around. When they stop spinning, the force goes away.

Mach noticed this, as well as other considerations, which convinced him that the local forces described by physics have their origin in the <u>distant matter</u> of space. Even though it is very far away from us, there is a great deal of it. The forces from the distant matter should weaken as the square of their distance from us. But the amount of matter <u>increases</u> as the square of the distance away. It turns out there is enough matter out there to account for these forces. There are enough electrons out there to create the vacuum energy we measure, and to absorb all the photons produced by local particles. Therefore this picture actually does make sense. The math to back it up will not be presented in these books. However, we will try to present the intuitive pictures of how we are connected to the distant matter, and how new forces arise from this connection which explain the puzzles of the paranormal.

For when we take Mach's idea seriously, then we find that it is really possible to explain electricity and magnetism as the motions of distant matter. Modern physics always talks about a "force field" nearby, and treats this as a property of space. But we can also explain these "force fields" as being due to the imbalance of charges in the distant matter. When particles in the distant matter are displaced, they exert forces back on the local electron.

The distant matter of the universe can be displaced or disturbed in different patterns, called "modes." They resemble the vibrational modes of a bell when it vibrates after it is struck. These fundamental vibrational modes can be excited and can resonate. We will show in Volume 5 that these modes are responsible for the "subtle energies" as well as the electrical and nuclear forces. These modes have symmetries and interact with geometric shapes. This gives rise to some of the puzzling effects of pyramids and other geometric shapes. It appears likely that Mach's Principle, used in this way, can explain the variety of strange forces in nuclear physics and the subtle energies which are central to paranormal effects.

The "Round-Trip" Photon - How Electrons Interact Across Great Distances

Mach's Principle is troubling to some scientists. They say that any motion of a local charge will send out waves, certainly, but it will take billions of years for that radiation to reach the distant matter. So how can there be any interaction? It just takes too long. The universe is too spread out. Part of the answer came from Feynman and his Ph.D. Thesis advisor John Wheeler, who wrote an important paper about it in 1945 (Wheeler, 1945).

They showed that it is possible for every local, nearby, electron (and any other particle) to interact with the distant matter virtually instantaneously. They showed how radiation can travel <u>backward</u> in time as well as forward. Photons which travel backwards in time are called "advanced waves."

These "backward in time" or "advanced" waves are a perfectly valid solution of Maxwell's Equations, which govern electromagnetism. Evidence for such waves has been found in radiation experiments, where it is called "pre-acceleration." (Feynman, 1970) Photons which travel forward in time, the "normal" direction, are called "retarded waves."

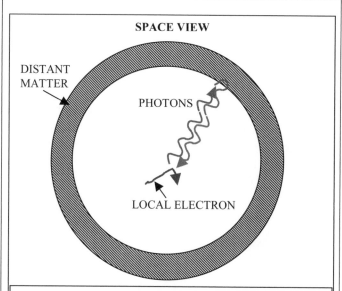

SPACE VIEW

DISTANT MATTER

PHOTONS

LOCAL ELECTRON

WHEN THE LOCAL ELECTRON INTERACTS WITH THE DISTANT MATTER, THE PHOTON MAKES A "ROUND TRIP". THE "BLUE" PHOTON GOES FORWARD IN TIME AND REACHES THE DISTANT MATTER IN THE FAR FUTURE. BUT THE RETURN LEG OF THE JOURNEY (THE "GREEN" ELECTRON) MOVES BACKWARD IN TIME (ACCORDING TO FEYNMAN-WHEELER) , SO THE ROUND TRIP IS ALMOST INSTANTANEOUS.

Figure 13.8. In the Feynman-Wheeler view, all the radiation from a local electron is absorbed and reflected back from the distant matter. It converges upon the electron where it first started, with almost no time delay, giving rise to a force similar to inertia.

According to the Feynman-Wheeler picture, when an electron zigs or zags it creates a photon which radiates away traveling forward in time. At some later time, it is absorbed by electrons in the distant matter. They will accelerate and in turn radiate a photon which will travel BACKWARD in time. It will converge back at the original electron's location. Because it traveled backward in time, it arrives at almost the same moment the first photon was radiated.

Therefore, by combining the two kinds of photons, one type traveling forward in time and one traveling backward in time, they showed how a local electron can be in instantaneous contact with the distant matter. They also showed that this does not lead to contradictions. This is a very important insight. It has recently been further developed by Cramer (Cramer, 1980, 1983, 1986 1988, 1997) and others.

Feynman and Wheeler showed that this concept can explain the origin of the "radiation back reaction," which is an important aspect of the electron. Although this theory has never been formally accepted or integrated into modern physics, Feynman did use the idea of pairing photons, one traveling backwards in time, the other forwards in time, in his later QED model for which he received the Nobel Prize. This became known as the "half-advanced, half-retarded propagator".

So this idea of photons traveling backward in time and equally balanced with those going forward in time is deeply imbedded in the present physics. Even though it sounds contradictory, it really isn't. As we see, it also provides a means for instantly coupling the motions of local particles to distant particles, which is the essence of Mach's Principle.

The "distant matter" and Mach's Principle were also studied extensively by the famous astronomer, Sir Arthur Eddington. He is famous for the experiment which confirmed Einstein's gravity theory by measuring how much the sun bends a beam of light. Eddington referred to the distant matter as the "Uranoid" meaning that it is far away. He saw it as the fundamental reference frame which governs much of our physics. We shall sometimes use his term, the "uranoid," to refer to the distant matter.

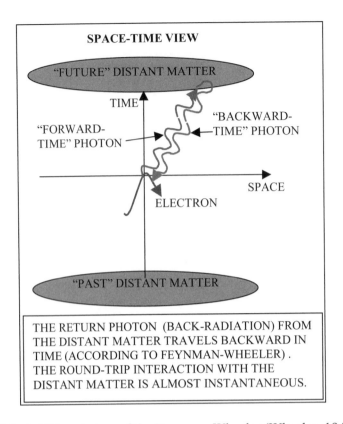

Figure 13.9. A different view of the Feynman-Wheeler (Wheeler, 1945) model. One wavy line shows photons going backward in time, the "advanced" waves. The other wavy line represents photons going forward in time, the "retarded" waves. The arrows show time direction.

We also interchangeably will use the term "celestial sphere," which comes from ancient times when the sky was believed to be a giant dome, and the stars were tiny holes through which light leaked in. It conveys the idea that the distant stars behave as though they are on a sphere far away. Mathematically, this is quite sufficient for most considerations.

This is especially true because the important reactions involve "round trip" photons. If we project all the distant matter onto a sphere having the radius of the universe (about 14 billion light years) this is not a bad first approximation.

The Feynman-Wheeler picture explains how electrons can interact instantaneously with the distant matter, despite the enormous distance. However, they assumed all the electrons moved at slow speed ("non-relativistic"). But if we peer into the smallest scale motions of the electron, we find it is moving at very high speed. So it is necessary to take the Feynman-Wheeler picture into that domain.

We assume the electrons at that scale are basically massless. This means they move at very near the speed of light. An interesting thing happens at this speed. Every time a photon is emitted, it travels straight ahead in a very narrow, focused beam, like a headlight beam from a motorcycle. It points in the direction of the electron's velocity at the moment it was emitted. The closer the electron's speed is to that of light, the narrower and more intense is the photon emitted by it.

This has been proven in huge machines called "synchrotrons" which speed electrons up to near the speed of light. The light emitted is always in a very narrow forward beam, aimed in the direction the electron is moving when it radiates. This is called "synchrotron radiation." It is a consequence of Einstein's relativity theory.

In order for two such electrons to interact, their velocities must point <u>toward</u> one another to a very high accuracy. Otherwise they don't "see" each other and there is no interaction at all.

This is very important: If their velocities point <u>toward one another</u>, there can be an interaction. Since the forward beams of energy are extremely narrow and intense, this enables them to interact over huge distances. If these beams of energy do not point at each other, because the velocities are not aligned, there will no interaction. They will not see one another at all. It is as though the electron has "tunnel vision" and can only see straight ahead!

At these scales we have assumed the electron is massless and therefore has no inertia: it can "turn on a dime," and make extremely sharp turns. But the sharper its turn, the greater the strength of its radiation. Can it turn infinitely sharply? No, because there will be a reaction from the other electron receiving the photon at the other end. Every emission and absorption of a photon involves at least two electrons, one at each end, one emitting and one absorbing the photon.

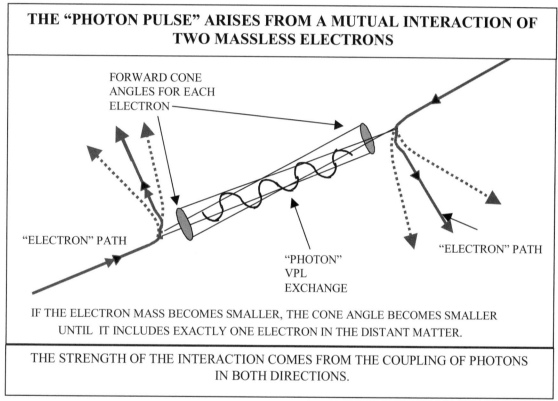

THE "PHOTON PULSE" ARISES FROM A MUTUAL INTERACTION OF TWO MASSLESS ELECTRONS

FORWARD CONE ANGLES FOR EACH ELECTRON

"ELECTRON" PATH

"PHOTON" VPL EXCHANGE

"ELECTRON" PATH

IF THE ELECTRON MASS BECOMES SMALLER, THE CONE ANGLE BECOMES SMALLER UNTIL IT INCLUDES EXACTLY ONE ELECTRON IN THE DISTANT MATTER.

THE STRENGTH OF THE INTERACTION COMES FROM THE COUPLING OF PHOTONS IN BOTH DIRECTIONS.

Figure 13.10. This figure illustrates how the effective mass of the electrons is determined at the very smallest scales by the strength of the two-way interaction. The force from each photon pushes the other electron backwards. The mutual interaction leads to a finite exchange of energy and momentum in the form of a very sharply spiked photon. We call this a photon "pulse." It is these photons which make up the "zero-point energy" of space.

The photons sent and received by the two electrons are <u>coupled together</u>. When the first electron radiates a photon outward, it almost simultaneously receives a photon coming BACKWARD IN TIME from the second electron. The interaction that results can be thought of as a consensus between the two electrons. It is a balance between turning too sharply and not turning sharply enough. The resulting photon is a combination of the advanced photon and the retarded photon. It is a very sharp, short narrow pulse and is probably a soliton. We call it a "photon pulse." It is the basic currency of exchange between electrons. Every interaction between electrons consists of one or more photon pulses.

The process is a little more complicated than this, because the energy from a photon is not always completely absorbed by the first receiving electron. Part of it may be absorbed and part may continue on in the same direction, where it is absorbed by other electrons. We are at a level deeper than the quantum level here, so the energy can split in this way. But the energy that continues along a straight line is absorbed and reflected back by other electrons along the same path. The path of this energy is very narrow and very close to a straight line because of the narrowness of the forward light cone. In our picture we have only shown two electrons for simplicity. There may be many more along the straight-line path which become involved in the formation of the photon "pulse." But because there is an advanced as well as a retarded component to this pulse, all the electrons contribute. Therefore the pulse produced is very likely to be a soliton, and it will have the desired half-advanced, half-retarded" character specified by quantum theory.

The picture we have painted so far applies only at the very smallest scales of motion of the electron, where we can isolate, at least in our minds, the interaction with one photon and one or two other electrons. These interactions occur at an unimaginably fast pace, and at extremely small scales. Physicists have a name for this scale of time and distance. It is called the "Planck scale." It is the scale at which the space-time structure of the universe starts to break up. Smaller distances become meaningless. In existing efforts at quantum gravity, this scale is assumed to be determined by the uncertainty principle, the quantum fluctuations of space-time. In our model, the viewpoint is slightly different but the implications are similar. At smaller scales than this, inertia and position are meaningless.

THE "PHOTON PULSE" IS THE ELEMENTARY INTERACTION BETWEEN ELECTRONS. IT IS A VERY SHORT, VERY SHARP SPIKE OF ELECTROMAGNETIC ENERGY:

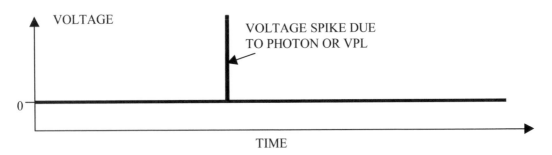

Figure 13.11. The smallest unit of energy exchange in the S.U.M. model is the photon "pulse." It is extremely short and sharp. It occurs when a pair of electrons interact. Other electrons which are in a straight line with the pulse may also take part in the interaction.

Conventional "photons" which are familiar in Quantum Mechanics, and which comprise light, are made up of many, many of these "photon pulses." Because they occur over very short times, they are not truly photons. Russian research indicates that these fundamental exchanges of momentum, which can travel backward and forward in time, actually do exist and make up the fundamental fabric of space-time. They call them "phitons" or torsion waves. This aspect will be discussed much more fully in Volume II. For the moment we will refer to them as "photon pulses."

The synchronization in the SUM model (to be described next) insures that the phases of these pulses will be just right so they add up to the "wave train" which is the conventional quantum photon. An example of such a "quantum wave train" is shown below in Figure 13.12. The conventional quantum description is of a "wave-packet" which is comprised of waves which

246

have a finite length. The energy carried in this packet satisfies the rules of quantum mechanics. In the SUM model this is NOT the deepest description. At a deeper level these quantized packets are actually made up of many photon pulses, which are elementary exchanges between electrons. This is illustrated in Figure 13.12, below.

This subject is deep and important. For this reason it may also be a little confusing. The reader may feel that the detailed private life of an electron, or a photon, is a far cry from ESP and psychokinesis. But notice what the two electrons are doing: They are communicating forward and backward in TIME. And they are sending and receiving signals across the entire breadth of the universe, essentially instantly. Doesn't this sound a little bit familiar? Isn't this what is so puzzling about psychic phenomena, that it travels with ease across great distances, not weakening with distance? And the signals are transmitted backward in time, like some of the Princeton PEAR Lab experiments. It is my belief that these interactions between electrons across great distances and backward in time, are essential in understanding these puzzles.

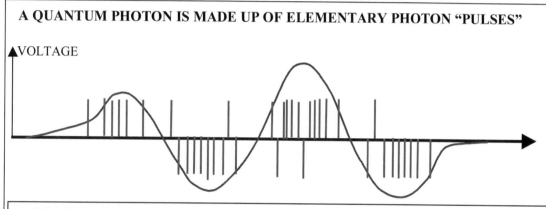

A QUANTUM PHOTON IS MADE UP OF ELEMENTARY PHOTON "PULSES"

A QUANTUM PHOTON IS A "WAVE TRAIN" LIKE THE WIGGLY RED LINE IN THE GRAPH. IT IS THE BASIC AND SMALLEST AMOUNT OF ENERGY EXCHANGE IN QUANTUM MECHANICS. IT IS AN AVERAGE. AT A DEEPER LEVEL ARE THE VIRTUAL PHOTON "PULSES" SHOWN IN BLUE, WHICH ARE ELEMENTARY, SINGLE EXCHANGES OF ENERGY BETWEEN TWO ELECTRONS. THEY COMPRISE THE ZERO-POINT ENERGY OF THE VACUUM AND A DEEPER LEVEL OF REALITY.

Figure 13.12. The conventional quantum "wave packet" of quantum mechanics is shown by the wavy line in the diagram. The energy in such a packet is quantized, and this makes up the "photon" of conventional physics. The SUM model predicts that there is a deeper layer of reality, described by the individual photon "pulses." Each quantum photon is actually made up of many of these pulses. They also comprise the so-called "Zero-Point Energy" of the vacuum of space.

In the next section we will talk about one of the most important concepts of the SUM model: the idea that, because electrons can communicate across the vast distance of the universe, their motions become coupled together. This leads to a very powerful effect which can explain both quantum mechanics and the existence of other dimensions.

The Synchronizing Principle
There are a very large number of electrons in the universe. In the known, visible universe there are about 10^{80} of them. That's written as 1 and 80 zeros after it! There are also other charged particles, and they are all interacting. At the smallest scales, they travel at the speed of light and basically look straight ahead with extreme tunnel vision. Because they have a charge, and are massless and move at the speed of light, something very interesting happens.

They become coupled together and begin moving in a collective motion, forming small orbits around their average positions. The orbits will be in phase with one another so the motions of the electrons at the smallest scale becomes synchronized.

This is what our model predicts. It is called a "collective effect." The electrons undergo a "phase transition." Instead of each electron moving randomly and independently, they begin moving in tiny little orbits which are <u>all synchronized to one another</u>. They are synchronized precisely because they only interact when their velocities point to one another. This only occurs at certain places in their orbits, and therefore only at certain times. There will still be random motions, but they will be superimposed upon the synchronized motions.

We will not prove this here, but it is a well-recognized phenomenon which occurs in many-particle systems. To quote physics Nobel prize-winner Dr. Ilya Prigogine:

"One might first think it would be easier to obtain a coherent oscillating process with a few particles, say 50, than with as many as, say Avogadro's number, 10^{23}, which are generally involved in macroscopic experiments. But computer experiments show that it is just the opposite. It is only in the limit of particles $N \rightarrow \infty$ that we tend to "long range" temporal order." (Prigogine, 1980)

Therefore in the case where all the electrons in the universe, 10^{80} of them, are interacting strongly at the very small scales, it is extremely likely that a collective oscillation occurs, which Prigogine calls "long range temporal order." The resulting motion of the electrons is illustrated in Figure 13.13.

THE SYNCHRONIZING PRINCIPLE

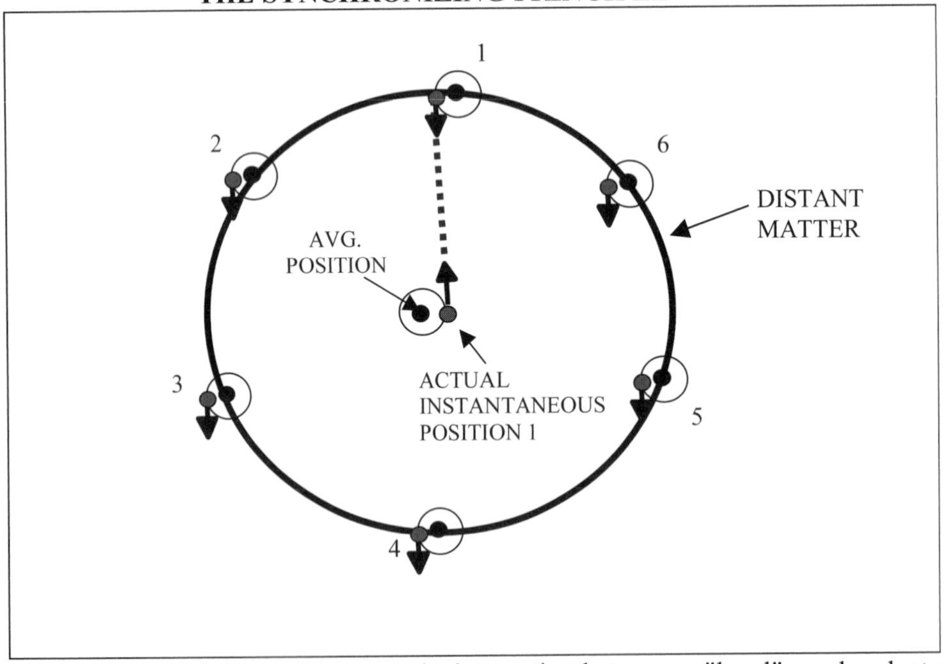

Figure 13.13. This figure illustrates the interaction between a "local" nearby electron and the huge number of distant electrons, represented schematically by the six electrons on the outer circle.

We have sketched a "local" electron in the center of a small circle. It represents a particle which is "nearby." The large circle represents the distant matter in the universe, where the vast majority of particles are to be found. The radius of this circle really represents the radius

248

of the universe, about 10 billion light years. But because the electrons are all massless at the scale of their motions, they can still interact with one another. This is because their radiation is concentrated in a very narrow forward light cone when they travel very near the speed of light.

Figure 13.13 illustrates how the synchronization between the electrons occurs. (Real electrons do not move in simple circles, and the random walk they make further complicates their paths. For simplicity this is neglected in the figure.) All the electrons in the "distant matter" are depicted as being on a sphere at the radius of the universe. Because they all travel at the speed of light, they only interact with other electrons when their velocities point toward one another. At the moment depicted in the figure, the velocity of the local electron, in the center, points toward the distant electron #1, and its velocity points back toward the local electron. Therefore they interact, and the interaction is such as to keep each electron turning in its circular orbit.

If the electrons in the distant matter also move in similar orbits, and with phase 180 degrees out of phase with the local electron, then this circular motion of the local electron will be maintained. But EACH electron is local in its own frame, surrounded by distant electrons in the same picture. We find from this that there is a self-consistent motion, a collective effect, in which all the electrons can interact with one another resulting in this "phase locked" circular motion.

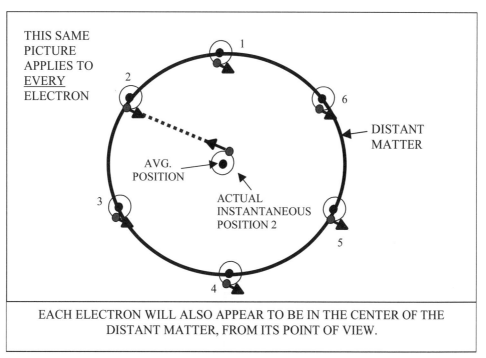

Figure 13.14. This figure depicts the electron positions a short time later. The central electron has progressed part way around the circle so its velocity points to electron #2. Because of the synchronization of the motions, the velocity of electron 2 at this moment points toward the local electron so they interact. This interaction, or energy and momentum exchange, continues to turn each electron in its self-orbit. Note that all the phases of the distant electrons are the same. They are all at the same point in their circular orbits. The central, local, electron, orbits in the opposite direction and is 180 degrees out of phase with the electron it interacts with. This condition can be shown to lead to one of the deepest principles of quantum mechanics, the exclusion principle, which applies to electrons. It is another example of how the SUM theory can offer an intuitive, physical explanation for some of the assumptions of quantum theory.

A moment later, (see Fig. 13.14) the velocity of the central electron has rotated a small amount, and is aiming at electron 2. At this point the velocity of electron 2 must be pointing at the center for a stable coherent oscillation to occur. This is a "synchronized system," where the interactions of all electrons are in phase and reinforce one another. Actual orbits are more complex than just the circles we sketch here.

All the electrons in this synchronized system will interact. Electrons out of phase with this motion will not be in this "universe." They will not interact with this coupled system except randomly, as "noise." These pictures apply for every electron in the system. Each electron is a local, central electron from its point of view, and the other electrons are far away, on the average.

In this model, each particle will see itself in the center, surrounded by the distant matter. The electron in the center only "sees" an electron out at the edge when their velocities line up and this only occurs when they are "in sync." This is the key. They are said to be "in phase" or "in sync" when their periodic motions remain in step with each other.

Therefore, as the central electron orbits around in a circle, the electrons on the periphery must do the same. In fact, they must all orbit at the same speed to keep together. This is called "synchronization," or phase-locking. When this happens, all the electrons in the coupled system orbit around their average position at the same frequency. This is the birth of quantum mechanics.

The frequency they orbit at is their "self energy frequency" in quantum mechanics. It is the frequency which corresponds to the effective mass of the electron. Particles with very small mass and very little energy have low frequencies. Particles with more mass and more energy have more interactions per second, and higher fundamental frequencies for their orbits.

Even though they are massless, and are zipping around at the speed of light, the synchronized forces cause them to orbit around fixed points, which represent their average positions. This average position only changes slowly with time. Hence the electron looks to the outsider as having a mass and moving slowly. He does not see the inner workings, but only the "fuzzy ball" of probability on the outside.

The phase to which all the electrons become locked is a very important phase. It is characteristic and unique to all the particles in this "universe." It is probably related to what physicists call the "Higgs' Phase." It is a choice of a single phase from all possible phases. Before the electrons become synchronized, it does not matter where they are in their orbit. But once they become phase-locked they give up this degree of freedom. This is called "dynamical symmetry breaking." Once a phase is chosen, all the particles in "the universe" are locked to it. It gives rise to the masses of the particles. This is true for the Higgs' phase and also true for the present model.

This picture is reminiscent of a very ancient picture, propounded at the very birth of physics. Giordano Bruno, a contemporary of Galileo, proposed that the stars in the sky were similar to our own sun, and were encircled by planets similar to those in our solar system. From the point of view of each particle, it would seem to be the center of the universe. He even proposed that matter has an active "conscious" nature, and that it interacts with all other matter. In his words:

"We can assert with certainty that the Universe is all center, or that the center of the Universe is everywhere and the circumference nowhere."--Giordano Bruno (Mendoza, 1995)

His cosmology is reminiscent of present cosmology. He envisioned an infinite universe with no boundaries, not very different from the modern view. For his insights, he was burned at the stake by the Catholic Inquisition, which illustrates again that new ideas, no matter how correct, are not always welcomed by the prevailing intellectual establishment.

We have omitted from this discussion an important point, which is the time delay between sending and receiving a signal. The presence of advanced AND retarded waves allows one electron to interact mutually with another one far away. But still they exist and move at different times, so there is a phase difference and a time difference for the different electrons.

When this is combined with the "synchronized principle" described above, it leads to the requirement of the quantization of space. The phase conditions for stable orbits will only be right at certain spots, and not at others. The places at which stable orbits can occur will form a regular array resembling a "crystal structure" at very small scales in space, so electrons actually "jump" from one such point to another. This is actually a desirable feature, but for the sake of brevity this will be described in Volume II.

Figure 13.15 illustrates how one synchronized "universe" relates to the others. Each set of electrons which becomes phase-locked or "in sync" acts as one complete, self-interacting system. It is represented in the figure by one sheet of paper in a stack of paper. Consider "universe #1" on the bottom of the stack. It is really a four-dimensional system, based on space-time, but it also has a fifth dimension, phase, which distinguishes it from the other sheets of paper in the stack. They represent other "universes" which have different phases.

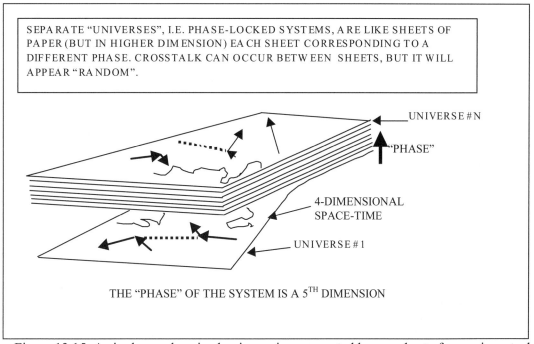

THE "PHASE" OF THE SYSTEM IS A 5TH DIMENSION

Figure 13.15. A single synchronized universe is represented by one sheet of paper in a stack. Each sheet has its own unique frequency and/or phase which characterizes the synchronized motion of the electrons in that system. Other sheets represent "parallel realities" or other "parallel dimensions" which may cohabit the same space and time and yet be unaware of one another. The model suggests how one can cross between such dimensions, by altering the phase of one "universe" to allow coupling and cross-over to another one.

For each sheet of paper, any particle on the sheet is phase-locked to the other particles on the sheet. Therefore it interacts with them in the synchronized manner we have described. "Phase" acts like a fifth dimension which distinguishes one parallel reality, one "universe," from another. It is clear from this model that particles which are phase locked and therefore on the same "sheet" interact in a synchronized manner and exert significant forces upon one another. Particles which are on different sheets have different phases, and only interact sporadically and by chance. They contribute to the random quantum noise of adjacent sheets, but do not exert a consistent repetitive influence on the dynamics of other sheets.

In quantum mechanics each particle has a "self-frequency." It is just given as a rule, based on the mass of the particle: Take the energy corresponding to the electron's mass, and convert it to a frequency using Planck's constant. That is how energy is equivalent to frequency in quantum mechanics. But there is never any explanation for what this frequency means, or its origin. In the SUM model, we see that frequency has a very definite physical meaning. It is the rate at which the electrons (and any other particles) orbit their center of mass location.

The electrons which are all in perfect phase with one another will keep each other in line, so they all continue to move in periodic orbits. But what about some other electron that happens to be in the wrong phase, the wrong point in its cycle when the electrons all become coupled? Such an electron is never pointing in the right direction at the right time. Therefore, it will not exert dependable, regular forces on the other electrons. It will only exert a force at random, when its velocity by coincidence happens to line up with another electron. Because it does not interact regularly with the other electrons, it becomes invisible to them.

Consequently the universe divides up into electrons which are in phase, and therefore can "see" and interact with each other, and all the other electrons in the universe, which are out of phase and therefore invisible.

However, there can be a great many such electrons. There can be enough that they become coupled among themselves and become phase-locked at their own frequency and phase. This frequency and phase will be different from the first system. Therefore the electrons of one such phase-locked system will not interact regularly with electrons from a different phase-locked system, even if the electrons from the two sets are very near each other.

The electrons and the other particles of one phase-locked system act as a universe unto themselves. They are all "in sync" with one another, and therefore interact and exert forces on one another. They "see" each other and would say to the other electrons phase-locked to them: "You are in MY universe." Likewise the particles in the second phase-locked system interact among themselves in the same way. The forces between particles in such a system do not seem to be sporadic, but regular and dependable. But since, at the fine scale, electrons in one system never "see" the particles of the other system, except through random chance, the two systems are oblivious to one another. They do not exert forces on one another, except as random noise. This is the origin of parallel universes and parallel realities. Figures 13.16 and 13.17 illustrate this further.

If the strobe flash and the fan blade rotation are synchronized, or "in phase," then the blades seem to be stationary and "solid." Every time the strobe flashes, another blade has moved into the place of a previous one, and the fan blades seem to be standing still. This is true even if the fan is actually turning rapidly. In that case we see the fan blades and they appear solid and "real." If the flash rate of the strobe is not synchronized with the fan blade rotation, then the blades disappear in a blur. They become invisible and, just from the appearance, we would say they are not there.

In the same way, particles only see one another if their orbits are synchronized so their velocities are in the same direction at the same time in their orbits. In this way, particles which are synchronized "see" each other and say "you are part of my universe." They are able to exert forces upon each other. Particles that are not synchronized exchange forces only rarely and by chance. This appears to be source of "quantum noise." Thus, other nearby parallel dimensions normally only interact with ours through quantum noise.

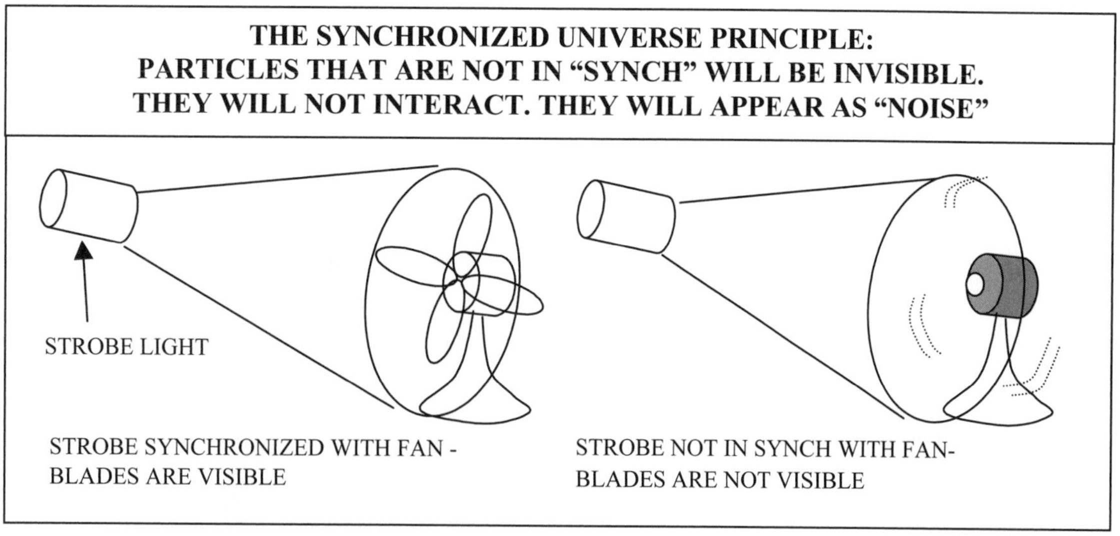

THE SYNCHRONIZED UNIVERSE PRINCIPLE:
PARTICLES THAT ARE NOT IN "SYNCH" WILL BE INVISIBLE.
THEY WILL NOT INTERACT. THEY WILL APPEAR AS "NOISE"

STROBE LIGHT

STROBE SYNCHRONIZED WITH FAN - BLADES ARE VISIBLE

STROBE NOT IN SYNCH WITH FAN- BLADES ARE NOT VISIBLE

Figure 13.16. The Synchronized Universe concept works just like a strobe light shining on a rotating fan blade. When the strobe light is "in sync" with the fan blade motion, then the blades appear to stand still. They appear solid, because every time the strobe fires, another blade has taken up the position of the last one. When the blades are out of with the flashes, they blur and disappear, because they are in different positions on every flash. The strobe light is analogous to the emission of a photon by one electron as it goes around in its orbit. If there is another electron whose velocity is pointing back along the same line at the same moment, the photons are exchanged. If they are in sync, then every time one electron comes back to that point in its orbit, the second one does too. Therefore they are always "in sync" to exert a force on one another, and it is exactly this force which maintains their orbits. This is analogous to the fan blade being in the same place for every flash.

The implications of parallel realities are illustrated in the next figure. Two such parallel systems are depicted. Each one is a complete universe. It has many particles which interact. They appear to exert precisely the forces which are familiar to our science. Therefore atoms, molecules, planets, suns and even life would be expected to appear in each of these parallel universes. We illustrate this with examples of "universe #1" and "universe #2". Each system is oblivious of the other.

Both realities can coexist in the same region of space-time and still be totally unaware of the other. We have illustrated this by overlaying the two parallel systems. The only expected physical interaction between them is random noise, so-called "quantum noise." However, it may be possible to enter a higher dimensional state in which one's consciousness can be aware of these other parallel systems. This amounts to crossing between the sheets of paper, or straddling several sheets at one time. Many of the "out-of-body" experiences reported by Robert Monroe, founder of the Monroe Institute, suggest that he was indeed in some sort of parallel reality. Obviously our knowledge of these matters is in its infancy.

Consciousness interacts across these parallel dimensions. Thus it can affect and reduce the quantum noise. It can even synchronize motions between parallel realities. In this way higher forces (subtle energy) can be created, and energy can be extracted from these other dimensions.

It is a basic hypothesis of the SUM model that, when particles are synchronized and remain on the physical sheet corresponding to their "universe," they obey the current physics laws to a good approximation. This includes the laws of quantum mechanics. It is when a coherent coupling of motions occurs across sheets, across parallel realities, that the most dramatic paranormal effects are expected.

PARALLEL UNIVERSES
TWO SYSTEMS WITH DIFFERENT SYNCHRONIZATION CAN EXIST SIDE BY SIDE AND BE UNAWARE OF EACH OTHER

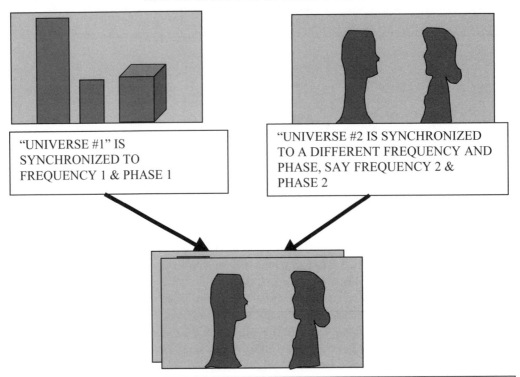

"UNIVERSE #1" IS SYNCHRONIZED TO FREQUENCY 1 & PHASE 1

"UNIVERSE #2 IS SYNCHRONIZED TO A DIFFERENT FREQUENCY AND PHASE, SAY FREQUENCY 2 & PHASE 2

THE ELECTRONS IN UNIVERSE #1 ARE MOVING "OUT OF SYNCH" WITH THE ELECTRONS IN UNIVERSE #2. THEREFORE THEY DO NOT "SEE" EACH OTHER. THE TWO UNIVERSES CAN EXIST IN THE SAME SPACE AND TIME, BUT "OUT OF PHASE." THEY ARE NOT AWARE OF EACH OTHER, EXPERIENCE THE OTHER UNIVERSE ONLY AS "RANDOM NOISE".

Figure 13.17. Illustration of parallel dimensions or parallel realities. Illustration of two physical realities existing in the same space and time. They do not interact normally, and are not aware of one another under normal conditions. The synchronized universe model can explain how these realities can exist. They are separated by a phase or a frequency which is common to all objects in one reality, and different from the synchronization of the other reality.

Subtle energies, for example, may be understood as a coherent structure which crosses several of these parallel realities, and therefore is "higher dimensional." This can be described in a precise mathematical way, and therefore probably leads to a well-defined mathematical description of the various forms of subtle energy. This concept is illustrated in Figure 13.18.

The thick circle passes through several parallel reality sheets. It represents a coherent, stable structure in a higher dimension. It is probably the basic underlying explanation for various forms of subtle energy, as well as coherent, persistent higher dimensional structures. Since it crosses the sheets of parallel realities, each sheet would judge the structure as "non-physical," and yet since it impinges on each structure, it would affect the physics and dynamics in that "universe."

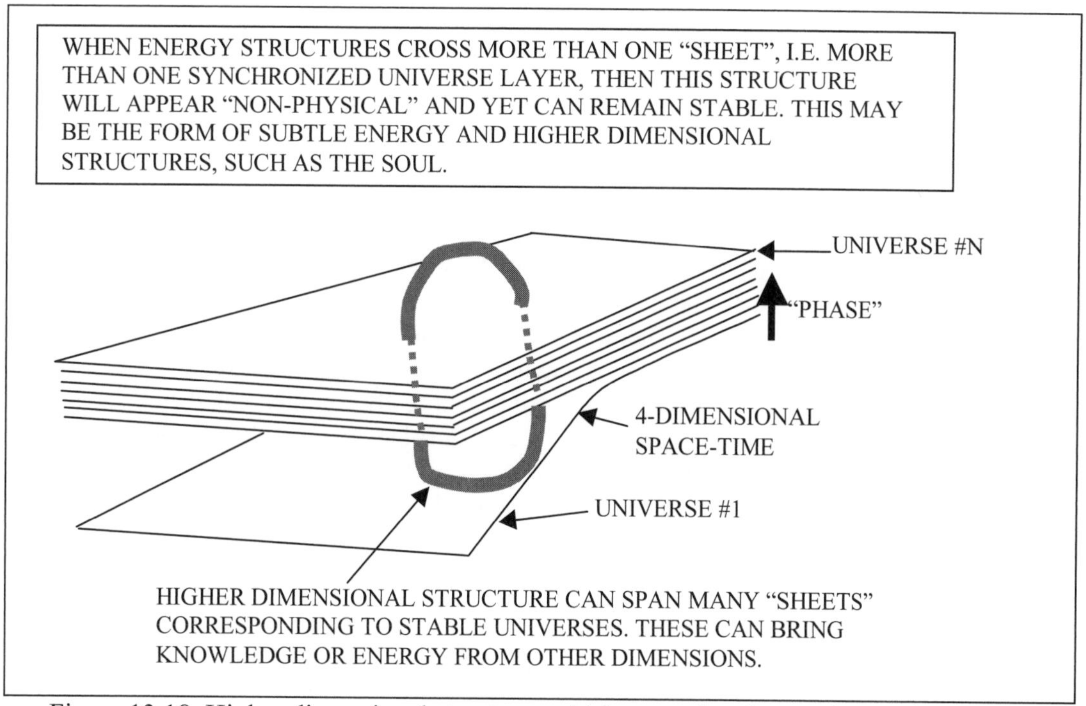

WHEN ENERGY STRUCTURES CROSS MORE THAN ONE "SHEET", I.E. MORE THAN ONE SYNCHRONIZED UNIVERSE LAYER, THEN THIS STRUCTURE WILL APPEAR "NON-PHYSICAL" AND YET CAN REMAIN STABLE. THIS MAY BE THE FORM OF SUBTLE ENERGY AND HIGHER DIMENSIONAL STRUCTURES, SUCH AS THE SOUL.

UNIVERSE #N

"PHASE"

4-DIMENSIONAL SPACE-TIME

UNIVERSE #1

HIGHER DIMENSIONAL STRUCTURE CAN SPAN MANY "SHEETS" CORRESPONDING TO STABLE UNIVERSES. THESE CAN BRING KNOWLEDGE OR ENERGY FROM OTHER DIMENSIONS.

Figure 13.18. Higher dimensional structures which cross the planes of several "universes" may provide a model for some types of paranormal phenomena.

This type of structure, or coherence, may explain what happens in the presence of a powerful spiritual healer or someone able to manifest effects like metal bending or psychokinesis. Such a person brings a lot of coherence into the system, introducing correlations between parallel realities. This has the effect of reducing the observed quantum noise in the system.

The reason for this is that quantum noise, in the SUM model, arises from radiation coming from other parallel realities which are not synchronized with the primary "universe." Because the other systems are not synchronized with it, their radiation appears random as seen in the primary system. Radiation from other systems does not couple consistently with the local electrons in the first system. Consequently it is judged to be quantum noise.

Now when the other parallel realities become partially coupled to the first system, their radiation no longer seems to be random. It may turn into steady, deterministic forces, and will judged a consequence of subtle energy. But the random part decreases since it is now "in sync." For this reason, quantum noise decreases and quantum correlations increase when subtle energy in the system increases. This explains results observed in energy healing, at sacred sites, and many other locations.

It has been shown in many measurements that the noise fluctuations as measured by an REG, for example, are reduced. This figure illustrates how this might occur, because the person is affecting these other parallel universes, or the other systems, by getting a phase-locking between them. This reduces the amount of noise and introduces more cooperation, more coherence, between the parallel sheets, the adjacent universes.

This type of coherence between parallel realities can also be thought of as a hyperdimensional structure which crosses these dimensions. It would be considered non-physical and yet have physical manifestations. Such higher dimensional structures could be designed to be stable due to their shape and topology. Such forms would be possible models for consciousness and the soul.

This model finds a perfect analog in the charming book *Flatland* (Abbott, 1998), a classic tale written for children of all ages, about a land in which everything is two dimensional. All the beings lived on, or in, a two-dimensional plane similar to a sheet of paper. The only objects the Flatlanders knew about were two dimensional, like the square, the rectangle, the line and the circle. They lived in peace, thinking they understood everything about the universe. Then one day a very strange event happened. One of the Flatlanders noticed a single point appear of out nowhere. He went closer to investigate, but as he did to his amazement the point turned into a circle. As he pointed this out to others, the circle unaccountably grew larger. After it reached its maximum size, it grew smaller again, eventually shrinking again to a point and then disappearing completely. This was an "anomalous event" in Flatland, just as strange as ghosts are to us. It appeared from nowhere and disappeared just as easily.

As we wise "three-dimensional" beings can easily comprehend, the explanation is that a sphere had passed through the plane of Flatland! A sphere is three-dimensional, and when it passes into a lower dimensional space such as Flatland, it will appear out of nowhere and can change size in contradiction to all the rules the Flatlanders knew. This is a simple example of how higher dimensional structures can seem contradictory to those existing in a lower dimension. In the same way, it is very likely that "subtle energies" and the other physics of the paranormal involve higher dimensional, or "hyper-dimensional" structures.

It is our proposal that this is exactly the case. These <u>higher dimensional structures are "made" out of the network of phase which permeates the universe.</u>

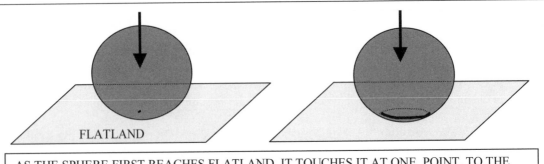

AS THE SPHERE FIRST REACHES FLATLAND, IT TOUCHES IT AT ONE POINT. TO THE FLATLANDERS, IT IS ONLY A POINT OBJECT AT THAT MOMENT. AS THE SPHERE PROCEEDS TO MOVE THROUGH THE PLANE, IT NEXT APPEARS AS A CIRCLE, WHICH INCREASES IN DIAMETER. TO THE FLATLANDERS THIS IS A VERY STRANGE ANOMALY OUTSIDE THE EXPERIENCE OF THEIR SCIENCE.

Figure 13.19. Illustration from *Flatland* of how a higher dimensional structure can break all the familiar rules and defy the "common sense" of a lower dimensional world. Such anomalous experiences could, as they did in Flatland, give rise to occult or supernatural explanations. As we who live in the three-dimensional world can easily see, their anomalous events were simply due to some higher dimensional science that they had not yet conceived of. A *Flatlander* Einstein would be able to see that the event had an easy explanation when viewed from a higher dimensional perspective.

We presume they would have much more complex topological structures than the simple circle or sphere in these illustrations, but the basic principle that they extend across dimensions and are stable, seems to be suggested by the data. Clearly, this science is in its infancy, but these ideas do offer a theoretical and scientific approach to understanding such important subtle phenomena.

The key thing to understand is: WHAT MAKES UP THESE HIGHER DIMENSIONAL GEOMETRICAL STRUCTURES? The answer is that it is the <u>phase variations in the space-time</u>

which make up these structures. Normal space is "in phase" from point to point at this deep level, but it experiences small departures from the common resonant phase of all particles. These departures can become systematic, and when mapped in space -time can form three-dimensional and higher dimensional geometric structures.

These "phase structures" can cross several parallel universes, and become the physical basic for "subtle energy." Each point in space (space-time) has a particular phase associated with it. This phase advances with time so all the points in one universe remain in phase. Forces arise when there are slight differences in phase between different regions. Phase differences cause a net motion of any particle located there. The particle moves to try to stay phase locked with the entire system (the "universe" layer). It is possible to create surfaces in space where the phase is shifted slightly. These surfaces can have geometric shapes (topology) that will influence the motion and behavior of particles which encounter it. This model accounts for electromagnetic forces as well as the "subtle energies." This model will be described in greater detail in Volume II, which deals specifically with the physics of the subtle energies.

Four-Dimensional Holography – Radiation Balance of Past and Future

One of the basic principles of electromagnetism is that a charged particle, like an electron, radiates electromagnetic energy whenever it changes velocity or direction. In physics this is called "acceleration." One of the simplest examples would be the radio waves produced by an antenna. If you have ever used a cell-phone or a cordless phone, you made radio waves. The phone produced tiny electrical currents in its antenna. As the currents flowed back and forth in the antenna, they were changing direction. Therefore they were "accelerating." Each time this happens electromagnetic waves are produced. The waves flow out into space at the speed of light. This is how you communicated with your friend at the other end.

Electrons and every other charged particle do the same thing. Electromagnetic radiation from the countless other particles is hitting them all the time. Because they are very small and lightweight, they accelerate, and in turn will produce electromagnetic waves of their own. These waves will flow out into space and be received and absorbed by other particles far away.

This constant flow of electromagnetic radiation carries with it a <u>force</u>. It causes the particles to move. It is responsible for the forces and motions which occur in our universe. These motions must be in balance. Every time an electromagnetic wave is produced somewhere, sooner or later it must be absorbed somewhere else.

In the SUM model this is the reason that momentum and energy are conserved. In other words, for every action there is a reaction. It is this exchange of electromagnetic energy which carries the momentum and energy and force from place to place in the universe. And we remember that electromagnetic waves are really just a collection of many photons, so when we speak of electromagnetic waves, we are speaking of photons, and vice versa.

One of the basic principles is that energy flowing in must equal energy flowing out. In other words, we can think of an electron as a small box in which there is some energy trapped. This gives it its mass, its weight, its energy. We know the electron's mass doesn't change. Therefore the energy inside the box must stay constant. If energy enters the box, say by the reception of a photon, then equal energy must leave the box. This means the electron must radiate a photon to balance the energy of the one it received.

Thus, if we could see the energy field around the electron, we would see radiation constantly pouring in and flowing out. On the average it must be in balance. There is a very specific pattern to this flow. An electrical engineering professor named Dr. Dale Grimes (Grimes, 1969) discovered that if he just assumed that the radiation was in balance and the electron moved in a random walk, he could derive Quantum Mechanics. In other words, he concluded that the electron moves the way it does, going forward and backward in a seeming random pattern in space and time, in order to balance all the radiation coming in and flowing out. This is a very deep and beautiful insight.

It also fits perfectly with our Synchronized Universe model. The tiny self-orbits in this model serve to balance the incoming and outgoing radiation. Therefore, when we allow the synchronized electrons to have some random motion, which they naturally will, then they will satisfy the equations derived by Professor Grimes. Radiation into and out of the electrons will be in balance.

We can picture this motion as similar to a hologram. In a hologram, there is radiation in and radiation out. Usually the radiation is produced by a laser, which means it is coherent light. The photons are all in phase. The laser light passes through a photographic film which has wavy lines on it. This changes the phase of the photons, so when they are brought together they add up to produce a three-dimensional image.

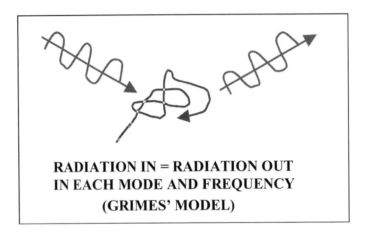

**RADIATION IN = RADIATION OUT
IN EACH MODE AND FREQUENCY
(GRIMES' MODEL)**

Figure 13.20. Radiation in and out must be in balance. This must be true for every frequency, and every radiation pattern (mode).

This is a 3-D picture, a hologram. It really just consists of photons with a specific pattern of phases, passing through a region of space. But to our eyes it generates a 3-D image. It is made from the regions of "constructive" and "destructive" interference. That is, in some places the laser light is in phase, so the photons are all in step and add together. This is called "constructive" interference. The energy in this region will be stronger. In other places, the photons are out of step by 180 degrees. Then they cancel. This is called "destructive" interference.

The 3-D pattern of energy created by these regions of interference is what we see as the image. In the same way the electron, and every quantum particle, is at the center of a pattern of constructive and destructive interference. It is caused by the radiation coming into the particle and being radiated away by the particle. The total interference pattern of energy created by this process is what we call "the particle." What we really interact with and "see" is the radiation pattern formed by the particle. Therefore, in a certain sense we can say the electron, and every particle, is a "hologram." And we see that it is produced as a result of the actions of the electron to preserve the balance of energy.

There is only one problem with such a hologram. It *looks* like a 3-dimensional object. But when you touch it, your hand goes right through it. Then you realize that it is only light. It is not really matter. But suppose you wanted to make a hologram that had more "substance" to it, like the holograms on the "Holo-deck" of *Star Trek*? Is there a way to do that? In the present scientific paradigm the answer would be "no." But there might be a way.

If we look at a hologram and observe the radiation flowing into and out of it, we see that the light is coming from the PAST, flowing through the image and then on out into space where it is absorbed in the FUTURE (see Figure 13.21). This may be a key. The energy only flows one way, from the past to the future. But for electrons and other real particles, we have seen that it flows both ways. As in the old Feynman-Wheeler model, when it is absorbed by distant matter in the future, it is reflected and radiated back in time. These resulting photons flow backwards in time until they reach the present. There they combine with the original photons to create the energy field around a real particle. In the process they also create *inertia*, which is the key to *mass*.

Therefore to make the hologram act as though it is real, as though it <u>has</u> mass, we must include the photons traveling <u>backwards</u> in time from the future. It is the combination of these photons plus the original ones from the past, which may allow the hologram to act as though it is real matter. We call this the 4-Dimensional, or 4-D, hologram. It is an integral aspect of every particle and every real physical object.

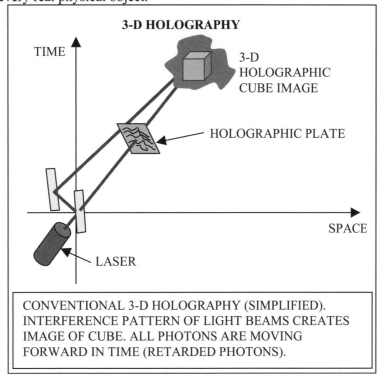

Figure 13.21. A conventional 3-D hologram is created by light waves which pass through a holographic plate. These lines create an interference pattern when they combine with the reference laser beam. They interfere constructively in some locations, and cancel in others, creating a 3-D pattern of light intensity resembling the initial object.

Figure 13.22 below illustrates that the 4-D hologram is an image which involves focusing both the advanced and retarded waves. The advanced waves propagate backwards from the future where they combine with the "retarded" waves traveling forward from the past. They mix together just like normal light waves do, forming the 4-D hologram. In this case the object is an orange cube. It appears to exist at the focal point of the hologram. If the wave fronts are shifted in phase by a small amount, the position of the cube will be shifted in <u>space</u> and in <u>time</u>.

And here is the other exciting aspect of this: If we want to manipulate the particle, the electron or whatever, <u>all we need to do is manipulate its 4-D hologram!</u> It is well-known that a conventional holographic image can be easily moved or shifted. If a holographic image of an apple is hovering in space, simply shift the laser beam, or put it through a lens, or change the phase of the light in some way and instantly, the holographic image will shift. By the same principle, if we shift the phases of the waves making up the 4-D hologram, the position of the corresponding "image" will also shift. But in this case the "image" is a <u>real physical object.</u>

Therefore if we can cause a shift in the phases of the radiation coming in from the past celestial sphere ("retarded uranoid") and from the future matter ("advanced uranoid") then we may be able to cause the particle or the object to instantly move somewhere else! Does this sound like "teleportation"? Does it sound like the "Warp Drive" on *Star Trek*? Yes, it does. That is what it is.

4-D HOLOGRAPHY

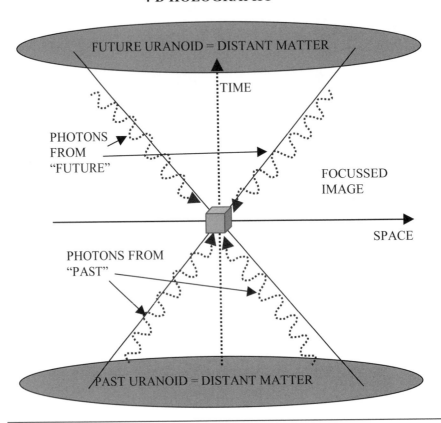

CONVENTIONAL HOLOGRAPHY CREATES 3-D IMAGES USING ONLY PHOTONS FROM PAST. THESE HAVE NO "SUBSTANCE" TO THEM: JUST LIGHT. REAL MATERIAL PARTICLES, LIKE ELECTRONS, ARE 4-D HOLOGRAMS IN WHICH PHOTONS FROM FUTURE ARE ALSO PRESENT.

Figure 13.22. 4-D Holography would involve waves from the "future" (i.e. phase conjugate waves) as well as the past.

The behavior and position of matter is dependent on its radiation field, which keeps it in place, gives it inertia and allows it to interact with the other matter in the universe. If we shift the phases of the radiation coming into the particle and coming out of it from the past and the future, we may be able to shift its position. This appears to be the key to teleportation and to a form of "hyperdrive" that has a chance of really working!

The real difference between this explanation and the common popular models is the difference between a 3-D hologram and a 4-D hologram. Wonderful books like *The Holographic Universe* (Talbot, 1991) have shown that some paranormal phenomena have holographic characteristics. The brain has a holographic structure which might make it an ideal antenna for receiving holographic wave patterns. This may be the key to sending and receiving "thought-balls," for example. These may be holograms which are ideally suited for coupling to the brain's structure. But 3-D holograms only exist for as long as the laser is on. It takes time for the image to be created, and is limited by the speed of light. It can exert no force and therefore cannot mimic matter. Such holograms are also shielded by Faraday cages, while we know that "thought-balls" are not.

By contrast, 4-D holograms can exactly match the radiation patterns of real matter, and therefore can appear like matter, and probably can cause forces and movement of matter. The difference is they involve the advanced, backward time-traveling waves, as well as the normal light waves. Both types of waves must be affected at the same time. To create and manipulate 4-D holograms, it is necessary to create advanced and retarded photons which are coupled together, which are "in synch" with each other. These create interference patterns which shift the 4-D hologram as desired.

We will see later that the DNA molecule, with its double helix, may be perfectly suited for generating waves which can do this. This may explain how ESP can take place in single living cells with the Backster Effect, as we saw in Chapter 4. It should also be mentioned that Dr. William Tiller, former Professor at Stanford University, has been developing a theory of subtle energies and paranormal effects (Tiller, 2001). His model appears to have a number of areas of overlap and agreement with our viewpoint. It suggests that the holographic properties of space are key to understanding the effects of consciousness. This will be discussed further in later volumes.

The Holographic Brain
There is considerable physiological evidence to support the theory that the brain processes information holographically. This tends to support the idea that the brain could be a sender and receiver of holographic signals. Dr. Karl Pribram pioneered this idea, based on extensive research in neurophysiology. He pointed out that the old model of the brain, as a network of neurons hooked up like wiring in a computer, just did not agree with neurological science. He quoted neurophysiologist Karl Lashley: "I sometimes feel, in reviewing the evidence on the localization of the memory trace, that the necessary conclusion is that learning is just not possible at all. Nevertheless, in spite of such evidence against it, learning does sometimes occur" (Pribram, 1969).

Pribram cited experimental evidence in the laboratory: "…rats could remember and could perform complex activities even after major nerve pathways in the brain had been cut, and after as much as 90 percent of the primary visual cortex had been surgically removed…Robert Galambos of the University of California at San Diego has severed up to 98 percent of the optic tract of cats without seriously impairing the cats' ability to perform skillfully on tests requiring them to differentiate between highly similar figures" (Pribram, 1969).

The holographic model of the brain was proposed by Dr. Pribram to attempt to explain how it is that, even without most of the brain, organisms are often able to function almost normally:

"In a hologram the information in a scene is recorded on a photographic plate in the form of a complex interference, or diffraction, pattern that appears meaningless. When the pattern is illuminated by coherent light, however, the original image is reconstructed. What makes the hologram unique as a storage device is that every element in the original image is distributed over the entire photographic plate. The hypothesis is attractive because remembering or recollecting literally implies a reconstructive process…"(Pribram, 1969)

These observations spurred Pribram and others to investigate how memory is stored in the brain and how it is processed. It has been discovered that each memory, in fact each image, is stored over the entire brain, so the recall of a particular memory will involve stimulation and activity of widely distributed neurons. He postulated that, at the synapses where nerves meet, some kind of long lasting change takes place in the proteins and other large molecules. When nerve impulses arrive at a synapse, an electrical response occurs there. Associated with one nerve fiber are dozens if not hundreds of junctions, and the electrical responses can create an electromagnetic standing wave. Pribram postulated that this wave interacts with other similar waves in other overlapping junction systems, to make long-lasting changes in the molecules of the synapse so the memory can be stored and recovered at a later time.

The attractive feature of the model is that it explains how such a memory can be recovered from a brain even after much of it has been destroyed. This is because a small part of a hologram contains the entire image, in this case the entire memory. Of course there is a price. Some of the details of the memory may be lost. But much of the general outlines of the memory will be retained. This holographic model can be extended to explain how the brain can act as a holographic transmitter and receiver so it interacts with the outside world by receiving and transmitting signals of some sort, that can be "stored" and "accessed" through this external system. This may explain some of the extraordinary abilities of brain-damaged individuals, "idiot savants," described in Chapter 9.

In our proposed model, these signals would not be conventional electromagnetic waves, but a 4-dimensional holographic pattern of energy. This is still consistent with the holographic structure of the brain, but allows for explanation of backward-in-time effects and penetration of shielding, as well as the direct and instantaneous communication of images and other anomalies which occurs in paranormal events. This picture will be further elaborated in Volume II, where the Russian discoveries about torsion waves are included. They actually put the synchronized universe model on a firmer empirical footing.

The Synchronized Universe Model Explains Assumptions of Quantum Mechanics

The SUM model predicts that electrons, and all particles in the universe, undergo tiny orbits around their central, average location. All electrons take the same amount of time to make one orbit. This is called the "period" of the orbit. The number of orbits per second is called its "frequency." All electrons will have the same frequency because of the way they interact.

We have assumed the electrons all travel at the speed of light at the very small scales. Therefore, if they go around in a circle at the speed of light, and take a certain amount of time (their period) to do so, this determines how big their circular path must be. It will be the same for every electron. The longer the period of the orbit, the bigger the radius of the orbit. The frequency is just 1 divided by the period, so the bigger the frequency, the smaller the orbit. In quantum mechanics this radius is called (roughly) the "Compton wavelength."

This is illustrated in Figure 13.25a. The electron encounters several photons as it goes around in a circle. Each photon deflects the electron by a certain amount. Therefore these photons must arrive fairly regularly to produce evenly spaced orbits. This will happen because these photons are produced by the synchronized electrons in the distant matter, and they all orbit in step. Therefore the photons they produce will come at regular intervals as shown in the figure. The photons are represented in the figure by the fine dotted lines.

Now consider some other particle, such as the proton, which interacts with other things besides photons. (We use a very simple "proton" here. It has only twice the mass and frequency of the electron. Real ones are 1836 times as massive. For the scientist reading this, it is a highly simplified discussion to put forward the intuitive concepts.) In modern physics, these "other things" are mostly "gluons," which carry the basic forces of the nucleus, like the strong and weak forces. In Figure 13.25b below, these are represented by the dot-dashed lines.

Please remember this is an oversimplified discussion, but it illustrates the main points. If there are as many gluons hitting the central particle as there are photons, then there will be twice as many interactions per second. Half are due to the photons, half to the gluons. The net result of twice as many interactions is that the particle will turn twice as quickly. If it is also traveling at the speed of light, as we assume, then the radius of its orbit will be twice as tight. Its radius will be half as big as the electron. Its frequency will be twice that of the electron.

This is an example where an additional force has been added. The effect of the extra force due to the "gluons" is to cause the particle to orbit more quickly, have a smaller radius and a higher frequency. And each turn or bend counts as an interaction with a force field and therefore raises the total energy of the particle. So we find that when the orbit radius gets smaller, the frequency and energy go up. Since it has just as many lines to photons as the electron did, its <u>charge</u> will still be the same as the electron's. But the other interactions with the gluons have given it extra mass. Along with this comes higher frequency and smaller Compton radius.

This very simple, intuitive model explains, in a natural way, the following basic rules of quantum mechanics:

(1) Each particle has a fundamental frequency.
(3) This frequency is proportional to its mass.
(4) This frequency is inversely proportional to its "Compton radius", the size of its orbit.
(5) Additional forces will raise the mass of the particle and increase its frequency.
(6) Frequency is proportional to energy.
(7) This is true for all particles, not just electrons.
(8) Forces arise when particles are out of phase (Gauge Principle).
(9) Frequencies change due to particle velocity.

In these illustrations we see how the quantum principle arises naturally from the "self-orbit" of the particle, a central hypothesis of the SUM model. The more interactions per second, the tighter the orbit, the smaller the Compton radius, the higher the frequency, the shorter the wavelength, and the greater the mass. In Quantum Mechanics, many of these relationships must be put in as assumptions. In the SUM model they arise naturally from the synchronization and the self-orbit.

Please note that the depiction of the particle orbit as a circle, making a spiral in space-time, is also an <u>oversimplification to illustrate the point</u>. Real particles, like electrons, make circles in FOUR DIMENSIONS, not two. For example, they move forward and backward in TIME as well as going around in circles in space. For the heavy particles like protons, there are three particles in the middle orbiting (quarks) not just one as shown in the figure on the right. In addition, the orbits, instead of being smooth, resemble a random walk in which the paths appear chaotic, so the orbital motions shown only represent the average motion. These and other refinements will be presented in later books. The pictures shown here are to illustrate the intuitive ideas. It turns out that the quarks are very important and deeply connected to some of the paranormal effects, but this will be discussed in later volumes.

The SUM model also has a relationship to Superstrings, because there are internal motions of the electron and other particles which are analogous to the internal dimensions of a Superstring. In that model there are six or seven internal dimensions, which can be described intuitively as giving rise to small "orbits" of the particle on a surface of very small diameter. In conventional QED, the path of an electron is modeled as a line of zero width, shown on the left in the Figure 13.26. It is this vanishing diameter which gives rise to certain mathematical problems.

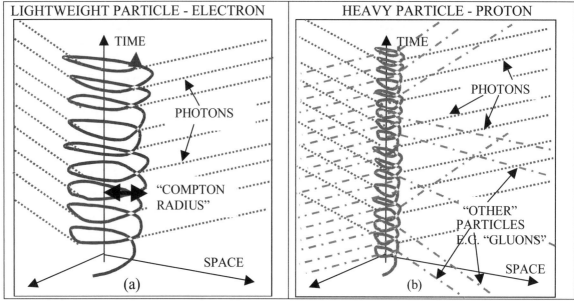

| LIGHTWEIGHT PARTICLE - ELECTRON | HEAVY PARTICLE - PROTON |

Figure 13.23. Some of the basic principles of quantum mechanics arise naturally from the synchronized universe model (simplified illustration). This figure illustrates how the Synchronized Universe Model explains the "size" of particles. In Quantum Mechanics this size is called the Compton wavelength, and is inverse to mass and frequency of the particle.

The superstring model converts this line into a tube of finite radius, as shown in the middle illustration in Figure 13.26. The radius corresponds to the radius of motion of the internal dimensions of the string. The analog for the SUM model is shown on the right in the figure. It also assumes a "particle" of vanishing dimension, but this particle moves in tiny periodic orbits around its central, average position. This is analogous to moving on the surface of the tube as in the superstring theory. The SUM model does predict a number of internal degrees of freedom which will raise the dimensions of the model, and may bring it even closer to the Superstring as the SUM model matures.

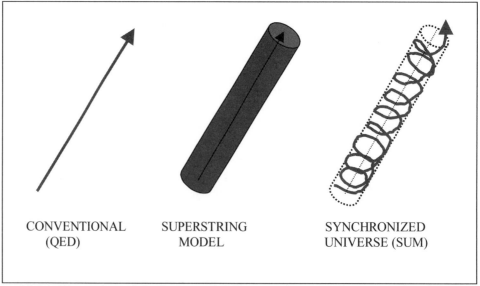

CONVENTIONAL (QED) SUPERSTRING MODEL SYNCHRONIZED UNIVERSE (SUM)

Figure 13.24. Illustration of similarity and differences between the conventional QED model invented by Feynman, the newer "Superstring" model, and the proposed SUM model.

Bose Statistics and the Paranormal

One of the keys to understanding psychokinesis and the power of visualization is something called "Bose Statistics." This is the law of physics which says that photons, which are called "Bose particles" or "bosons," all like to be in the same state. When several photons are in the same state, it increases the probability that other photons will shift into that state as well. Photons have a collectivist mind-set. They like to go along with the crowd.

This is how lasers work. Get a few photons in a certain state, and they will trigger others to join them in the state. This is also called "photon pulling," because photons are "pulled" into the state which is most densely populated.

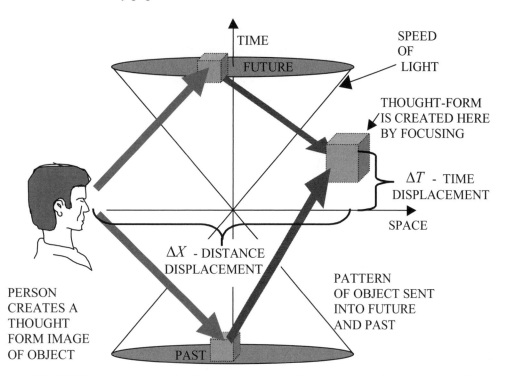

Figure 13.25. 4-D Holographic Projection can cause the focused image to occur virtually anywhere in space-time. Here we show it appearing at a distance ΔX away from the source, and at a time ΔT later. The velocity at which this image "moves" as it is projected from its source would be calculated as distance divided by time, which can be much faster than the speed of light.

Living organisms use this principle. In the cell structure of the body there are membranes which act as conductors of infrared and visible light. Recent research has shown that these structures "store coherent photons." This means they are able to build up a supply of photons, excited vibrations, which are all vibrating in step with each other and can be stored in the cells in this form.

The body is filled with this form of structured and coherent energy. It is one of the keys to how we use chemical energy so efficiently. The scientist Dr. Hans Frohlich (Frohlich, 1983) was one of the early pioneers in this research. He discovered that coherent vibrations and electromagnetism play a fundamental role in life processes, as we briefly sketched earlier. Dr. E. A. Popp at the Max Planck Institute in Germany (Popp, 1979, 1989) has been another leader in this research, which has been beautifully described by scientist Dr. Mae-Wan Ho in a recent popular book (Ho, 1998).

Our bodies use light and coherent vibrations to carry out many of life's processes. Since a store of coherent photons is always available in the body, they can be shaped and controlled to affect external photons and external vibrational patterns. The Bose principle means that, if we create energy within our bodies in a certain pattern and form, this makes it <u>more likely</u> that other photons will join and reinforce this pattern. Because of Bose statistics, these patterns or structures of energy will stimulate other "mirror" structures in the distant matter.

If we energize ourselves before carrying out this process, we will presumably increase the number of coherent photons in the body are carrying carry this visualized pattern. By increasing the density of stored photons carrying this pattern, the probability of affecting other photons increases as the *square* of the number of photons. This may explain why energy healers and those performing PK practice specialized breathing, in which they increase their oxygen intake and presumably increase their stored energy.

If a coherent set of these photons is transmitted both into the past and into the future, then it will refocus at some other location in space-time, forming a 4-D hologram. The background zero point energy at the focal point can be strongly affected. In this way it may be possible to project thought-forms and visual patterns which affect distant events. Figure 13.25, above, illustrates how this may be done.

Because the refocusing of the photons involves both backward and forward time-traveling photons, they can focus to create the image almost anywhere in space AND time. (see Figure 13.26) In other words, we can visualize an event which we see happening YESTERDAY just as easily as an event to occur TOMORROW or RIGHT NOW. This is the key to the unusual time behavior of PK and ESP. The phenomena don't seem to care about time. We can send a psychic message to be received yesterday or tomorrow, and it works just as well as one to be received today.

When personal trainers like Tony Robbins ask us to visualize a future event we would like to happen, this may be the "explanation" of what we are doing. We are modifying the photon background in the space-time vicinity of the event, which has the effect of increasing the probability that the event will occur. In the simplest cases, such as the REG experiments conducted by parapsychologists, the event being influenced is the random motion of electrons in a circuit or the random decay of a radioactive atom. In these simple cases, it has been proven that visualization of the event increases the likelihood that it will happen.

Using this principle, it may be possible to teleport objects, as well as thought-forms, from one place to another. It is simply necessary that the patterns of radiation on the past and future uranoid be modified. These patterns, which hold the object in place, are similar to holographic patterns. Their phases can be altered by the right kind of incident radiation which is coherent on both the past and future uranoids. Therefore, teleportation has much in common with psychokinesis and visualization. Bilocation, by which yogis are reported to have projected their body, or caused a "second body" to appear elsewhere, may also be achievable in this manner.

The mechanism we are describing here may be the key to the physics which connects visualization with manifestation. The human body is able to generate a store of coherent photons. If these photons take up a spatial pattern, then from Bose statistics, it may indeed increase the probability of such a structure appearing. Regardless of the explanation, there is ample experimental evidence that this process works. One of the great lessons to be learned from these discoveries is that we need to pay attention to our thoughts, and especially the thoughts we put energy into. Thoughts, prayers and wishes really do have power to affect reality. Or, as the great American psychic Edgar Cayce said:

"Conditions, thoughts, activities of men in every clime are things; as thoughts are things. They make their impression upon the skein of time and space." (Cayce, 1971)

266

TIME INDEPENDENCE OF ESP AND PK

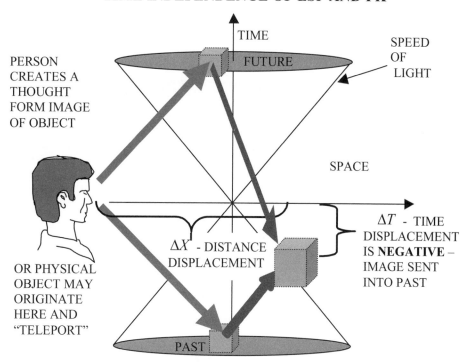

TIME

FUTURE

SPEED
OF
LIGHT

PERSON
CREATES A
THOUGHT
FORM IMAGE
OF OBJECT

SPACE

ΔX - DISTANCE
DISPLACEMENT

ΔT - TIME
DISPLACEMENT
IS **NEGATIVE** –
IMAGE SENT
INTO PAST

OR PHYSICAL
OBJECT MAY
ORIGINATE
HERE AND
"TELEPORT"

PAST

Figure 13.26. The same principle of 4-D Holographic project can be used to send objects, or at least images of objects, into the <u>past</u>. This can be in the form of visualization, such as in the Princeton PEAR Lab experiments when an outcome was affected on a PREVIOUS day. This method also suggested that teleportation may be accomplished into the past under some conditions.

The application of this idea to ESP or telepathy is straightforward. If the sender can cause energy or information to refocus at some other point in space-time using the 4-D holographic principle, then it can be received if a person is there to sense the thought-form. This can be made much more reliable when the receiver also enters the proper, relaxed, meditative state so his conscious mind becomes quiet. In actual ESP experiments, it has been found that the best results occur when the sender and receiver's bio-rhythms become coupled together, that is, synchronized. Heart beat and brain wave pattern, as well as breathing, show synchronization between sender and receiver when telepathy is most effective. Of course, the participants may be thousands of miles apart, so the only way they can get into the same rhythm is if their bodies are already in telepathic contact at the autonomic level. This further supports the notion that synchronized processes are key to understanding ESP and other psi phenomena. This is illustrated in Figure 13.26.

Teleportation
The concepts just described illustrate how a force can be applied to an object, even at a distance, and how random processes can be affected by affecting the distribution of photons making up the "Zero Point" energy of space. But in teleportation experiments, objects are sometimes made to pass <u>through</u> walls, as in the case of Zhang Baosheng in China (see Chapter 7). How can our proposed theory explain that?

Actually, it's very easy. In the Synchronized Universe Model, every electron rotates on a very small scale so that its motion is in phase with all the others in "its" universe. It only exchanges force, i.e. photons, with other electrons when their velocities line up in just the right way on every cycle. Otherwise, there is no force exchanged. The narrow forward light cone, which limits the direction of interaction, just will not line up properly if the electron's motion is too much out of phase.

MODEL OF TELEPORTATION

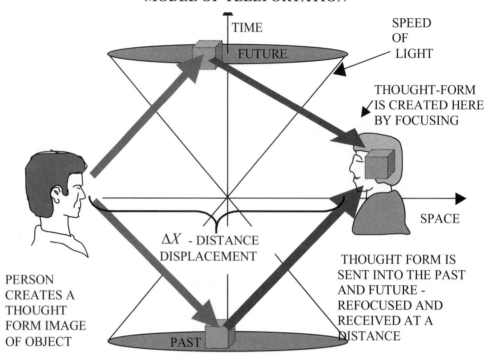

Figure 13.27. This figure further illustrates the process of ESP, in which a "receiver" and a "sender" communicate by "4-dimensional holography" using "advanced" and "retarded" photons. The convergence of the two patterns at a distant point in space-time makes it possible to send information which arrives at either an earlier or later time than it was sent. When a receiver is present, the path of the waves is "reciprocal" meaning that the receiver and the sender are actually in resonance with one another. This explains observations in Prof. I. M. Kogan's laboratory in Russia that the heart rate and brain patterns of sender and receiver become coupled together during telepathy. Given the large separation distances and the presence of shielding, it is difficult to explain this effect in any other way.

So, walking through walls is easy. Just apply a strong, high frequency electromagnetic field to the particles which shifts their phase or their frequency in their orbits. An oscillating electromagnetic field of a high frequency will cause their orbital frequency and phase to begin to shift. It is just like the strobe light and the fan. Let the strobe light pulse rate begin to differ from the fan blade rotation, and suddenly the fan blades disappear! In the same way, the forces between electrons in the object and the electrons in the wall will no longer be synchronous. They will be out of phase, and therefore seen as just random noise. This will allow the object to pass through a wall! Because there is a random residual left over, we may expect there to be a slight force after an object shifts phase in this way.

OBEs

The process of passing through physical walls is similar to the description of people who experience OBEs, out-of-body experiences. When they pass through walls or ceilings, for example, they feel a slight resistance, very slight, which they can penetrate by exerting a small force with their minds. There is a large literature on this subject, but the experience is fairly accurately portrayed in the fictional movie *Ghost*. Patrick Swayze goes through an educational process as he learns how to affect the physical dimension, and he finds that, with a slight force, he can walk through walls. This is consistent with a large body of research on real cases.

For simplicity here, and because I do not have a better understanding of this subject, I am referring to this component as the "soul body," which we also identify with the seat of consciousness, and also with the component which makes up ghosts and astral projections. There are a great many similarities among these manifestations, so for simplicity we will assume that they have a similar origin and makeup. This "soul" substance is of great importance. It may be the key to what makes us alive. It may contain the mystery of what consciousness really is. This important subject, with the evidence as well as theoretical ideas, will be described in much greater detail in Volume III of this series.

But for the moment, we will say only that esoteric traditions, as well as the accounts of healers and those able to "see" subtle energies, describe several layers of such energy surrounding the physical body. These layers of subtle energy are said to be of different types: etheric, astral, causal and mental. They often report that the "soul body" seems to be comprised of elements of the etheric and the astral energy.

The etheric is often described as a "duplicate" to the physical. It is often described as having the same shape, or as being a shadow body. In German this body is referred to as the "Doppelganger." It may be the component of the biophoton radiation field which maintains radiation balance for the body, and enables the biological processes to be so efficient. The etheric body is said to be closely tied to the physical, and may be thought of as a "time-reversed" or "phase-conjugate" mirror image of the physical body.

By comparison, the astral seems to be a higher dimension, not a parallel copy of the physical dimension. These are subtleties and complexities which will be discussed in more detail in later volumes. Western science is just beginning to take its first faltering steps to understand these issues. Any model proposed must be considered extremely hypothetical. At the same time, it is interesting that the "soul body" or "astral body" during an OBE is sometimes reported as resembling the person who is projecting. The Wilmot and Landau OBE cases are good examples of this. At other times the OBE form is seen as a small, rapidly moving orb. Is it possible that these two forms of appearance are related to the presence of the two kinds of energy? Is it possible that the etheric energy may preserve and project the physical appearance of the individual, while his astral form may appear more as a moving orb?

Physics Of Meditation And Prayer -The Power of the Phased Array

Meditation is often considered to be a "quieting of the mind," because the talking part of the mind becomes quiet. The verbal and analytical processes cease. But brain wave (EEG) studies show that actually the brain becomes more "coherent" in meditation. This means that the firings of the billions of neurons in the brain occur more "in step" with one another. The electrical impulses from all the cells become less random, less independent. It is as though they begin to march in step with one another.

This state of mind has enormous power to affect reality, based on the synchronized 4-D holographic model we have presented. In order to affect reality, we must send a coherent, "in step" pattern of photons into the future and into the past. This pattern must be so clear that when it interacts with the distant matter and refocuses, it retains the desired image.

The DNA in our cells can naturally produce waves of this type, which contain both forward-time traveling waves and matching backward-time traveling waves. Matched waves of this type are called "phase-conjugate" waves. In the last decade laser scientists have learned to make and control these waves for certain applications. But the double helix structure of DNA suggests that our cells may have been making such waves for a much longer time. They are ideally suited for generating coupled photons which radiate out along the axis of the double helix in both directions (see Figure 13.30).

DNA DOUBLE HELIX IS IDEAL FOR CREATING PAIRS OF PHASE CONJUGATE PHOTONS

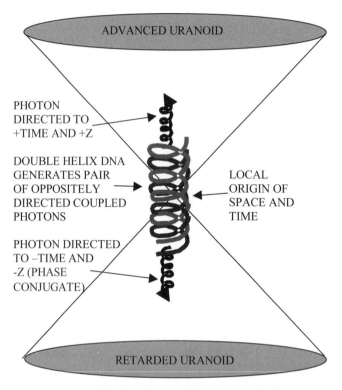

KEY TO PSYCHOKINESIS
GENERATION OF PAIRED "ENTANGLED" PHOTONS
(PHASE CONJUGATE)

Figure 13.28. The double helix of DNA has been shown to be capable of both receiving and transmitting coherent photons (laser-like light). It has been speculated that its structure might be ideal for generating a pair of photons, phase conjugate to one another. If so, this would be an effective means to generate 4-D holographic type signals, and might explain how individual cells are capable of what Backster has called "primary communication."

If this is the case, then each cell is a tiny radio transmitter which is capable of sending phase conjugate waves into the past and into the future. This is probably why individual cells have been shown able to send and receive ESP messages, as in the Backster Effect (Chapter 4). But to send a complex message, or to achieve a more impressive result like teleportation, requires that a great many cells act in unison. The real power of DNA and the use of phase–conjugate waves, which is just a matching pattern of advanced and retarded waves, occurs when millions or billions of cells transmit in phase. When this happens, the strength of the pattern increases as the <u>square</u> of the number of cells which are acting in unison. Therefore, a million cells transmitting their desired visualization in unison will have a <u>thousand billion</u> times more power than a single cell.

It is this power of coherence, of synchronization, which enables some gifted individuals to achieve astounding paranormal feats. A million DNA cells broadcasting at random just produces noise. All the signals cancel out. But a million DNA cells broadcasting coherently and in unison generates a power that turns "ordinary" humans into supermen.

One of the goals, or at least one of the by-products, of the education of the adept is to develop control over the mind and body, so this kind of synchronization of the cells can be achieved at will. Entering deep meditation states causes a synchronization of the vibrations of the DNA in the body, and it is very likely that this is one of the keys to "psychic superpowers." This is why meditation is a central element in all esoteric practices, whether it be a Buddhist monk, a yogi, a *qi-gong* martial artist, or an energy healer.

As we will see in later volumes, this form of synchronization also gives the adept access to other dimensions, including the subtle dimensions such as the astral plane, which are not accessible in the normal consciousness state. The high degree of synchronization which comes from deep meditation makes it possible to access those domains. This opens up entire realms of physics and new phenomena which are familiar to adepts, but are closed to the rest of us. The ability to access these domains, which cut across the "stack of paper" of parallel universes illustrated in Figure 13.18, enables the adept to perceive and act from a higher perspective.

When the remote viewer moves his focus in space and time, his consciousness moves in this higher dimension. It can easily see the future and the past from this perspective. By synchronizing vibrations differently across planes, it is possible to bring energy into our physical plane. This is one of the secrets of PK. It explains why and how the "random quantum background" can be changed by meditation. It explains how radioactive decay can be altered by visualization. It also has applications in so-called "free-energy" devices which can tap this energy across these planes to generate abundant clean, cheap energy.

Ever since the Cold War of the 1950's, huge radar stations have towered above the prairie in the upper Midwest of the United States. The antennas of these radars resemble huge curved walls many stories high. Protruding from these walls are thousands of smaller antennas arranged in a regular grid-like pattern. These structures are called "phased array" radars. The walls do not move. The radar shifts the direction of its beam by varying the <u>phase</u> of the radar signal as it is fed into each of the thousands of tiny antennas. Each antenna radiates a small signal, similar to the DNA of a single cell. But the phases are designed so that all of the radiations from all of the antennas add up coherently in a particular direction. In that direction, the radar beam will be strongest. By varying the phases of each antenna, the radar beam can be rapidly swept across the horizon in a search for incoming Intercontinental Ballistic Missiles, which the radar is designed to detect.

It is likely that the DNA molecules of each cell can be brought into coherence in a similar way. This would enable the brain, when it is quiet and coherent, to combine together the signals of many DNA molecules. In this way, the desired image, which is being visualized, can be brought into being. This is probably one of the reasons that positive visualization works. It may also be one of the keys to the success of prayer, distant energy healing, distant PK, and teleportation. If the 4-D image which is being created is not a physical object, but an idea or a thought, then "thought-balls" can be transmitted this way. Therefore, this is one type of ESP. When there is a receiving brain at the other end (see Figure 13.29), where the energy is focused, then this illustrates the reception of an "idea." The "Eureka" experience, when a flash of insight suddenly hits, may correspond to the reception of one of these patterns.

Summary

We have described here just a few of the ideas which make up the "Synchronized Universe Model" (SUM). Any model in physics must be reduced to mathematics, and must undergo a rigorous process of testing and comparison to data, before it can be considered a successful theory. The SUM is only at the beginning stages of such a process, and must be considered as a collection of interesting and promising ideas which have not yet been proven.

The model seeks to describe the Universe at a deeper level than Quantum Mechanics. At very small scales the electron has no mass and zips around at the speed of light, buffeted by photons from other electrons throughout the universe. Because of the "tunnel vision" of

271

electrons traveling at light speed, they only see one another when their velocities point directly at one another . This leads to a mutual interaction across great distances. As the electrons throughout the universe interact in this way, they take up periodic orbits due to their collective interaction. Thus each electron resembles a tiny atom, with a center and a periodic orbit. This is the origin of the basic frequency every particle has. It explains one of the more puzzling features of quantum mechanics: why a particle has a self-frequency proportional to its mass. In the SUM model, this arises naturally from a fundamental physical idea.

One group of electrons will become synchronized to a particular phase and frequency. These will "see" each other and interact. They form the basis of what we call "our physical universe." We have offered the analogy that the resulting motions of the particles can be described as moving on a single sheet of paper within a stack. But there are many other sets of electrons and other particles which find different phases and frequencies at which *they* couple together. Consequently they form parallel universes which do not interact with ours except randomly. They provide the "quantum noise" so familiar to physicists. Because they are out of sync with "our universe" we see no pattern to this noise.

But when processes occur which cut across the parallel universes, which synchronize them in some way, as consciousness does, then it affects the quantum noise. It changes it. This has been seen in all of the consciousness experiments involving random event generators (REGs). It is one of the ways in which consciousness affects quantum physics.

This model provides a beginning for understanding the subtle energies. In the SUM model, they consist of modes of vibration of the distant matter which cut across the various parallel, synchronized universes. They couple together different "dimensions," different "sheets of paper," as we illustrated in Figure 13.18. Because of this, the subtle energies will have effects which violate the predictions of conventional physics.

Energy forms of this kind have been known and described in Eastern medicine for thousands of years. They are called "prana" or "chi" and are basic to all life. This model also provides a way of understanding "higher" energy forms, such as the "astral" energy which is central to the out-of-body experience, and which may be key to understanding the soul. Our scientific understanding of these energies will be described in greater detail in later volumes.

Since this is a physical model, we should be able to use it to predict and understand the kinds of subtle energies which can exist. We need not wave our hands and retreat into vague generalities. The model may also be useful in understanding the other important physical forces, such as nuclear forces and quarks, and it may help us to understand their relationship to the subtle energies.

At the core of the SUM model is the synchronous interaction of particles across great distances and times. If this idea is correct, then it can be used to explain how paranormal effects can be seemingly immune to time and space displacements. It may help us understand how two minds can be linked when separated by vast distances of space and time. And it offers a way to connect paranormal effects to changes in quantum noise, which is one of the central mysteries facing the new physics.

Most importantly, the model offers a way to understand consciousness. Paranormal research and consciousness studies suggest that our consciousness is not limited to the physical brain. It can leave the body and travel in space and time. When it does, we say "we" travel with it. The experiencer describes the event from where his consciousness is, not where his body is. And physical experiments, such as those of Drs. Karlis Osis, Keith Harary, and Janet Mitchell, show that there are measurable physical effects in the presence of consciousness. We provisionally call this the "soul" although this may be an oversimplification. But whatever it is, it seems to be the essence of a human. It is not the body. It is this consciousness or soul where awareness takes place. "We are much more than our physical bodies," as Robert Monroe used to say. This places us on the threshold of awareness of the much larger universe which is out there, and a much grander conception of who we are as humans.

*****

ABOUT THE AUTHOR

The author, Claude Swanson, grew up in a small town in southern Virginia. He became interested in science after attending a science summer program for High School students, in which he met and worked with his first "real" scientist, Dr. John Mrgudich. As the program ended, he and his advisor applied for a patent on a device which they developed.

Encouraged by this early success, and always curious about understanding the world at a deeper level, Swanson attended MIT, where he graduated in "Course VIII," physics. During these years he worked at the MIT Science Teaching Center and Brookhaven National Laboratory in the summer. He attended Princeton University for Graduate School, where he received his Ph.D. in physics. He was awarded a National Science Foundation Fellowship and a Putnam Fellowship during his time there.

He research at Princeton was in the "Gravity Group," which focuses on experimental cosmology and astronomy, and was headed by Professor Robert Dicke. His thesis advisor was Dr. David Wilkinson, who later became chairman of the physics department. Swanson conducted postgraduate work at Princeton and Cornell Universities, and then began work for Aeronautical Research Associates of Princeton, a consulting company. He later formed his own consulting company, which carried out studies in applied physics for commercial and governmental agencies, including DuPont, United Technologies, the U.S. Army and Navy, DARPA and the CIA, among many others.

During these years, Dr. Swanson's professional work included analyzing and modeling new phenomena and devices in many areas of applied science: optics, radar, fluid dynamics, high speed mechanics, materials properties, thermodynamics, and related subjects. This often involved constructing theoretical models and computer simulations of complex phenomena and new devices.

For the last twenty years, interspersed with his conventional professional career in applied physics, Dr. Swanson has pursued investigations into "unconventional physics" to determine which aspects of it may be genuine, and how it impacts our deeper understanding of physics. He carried out extensive literature searches, conducted interviews with working scientists in these fields, attended conferences, and pursued direct experiments and investigations, as well as theoretical analyses to understand how such paranormal phenomena might be incorporated into modern physics theory.

This research "on the side" has involved underwater research in Bimini, scientific measurements in haunted houses, experiments in remote viewing and psychokinesis, and testing of unconventional devices, among many other investigations. This book is the first of a series summarizing what he has learned from this fascinating adventure.

He has two grown children, Alexandra and William, and currently lives in Colorado.

REFERENCES

A-

Abbot, Edwin A., *Flatland, A Romance of Many Dimensions*, Penguin USA (1998)

Adler, Stephen L., and Horwitz, Lawrence P., "Structure and Properties of Hughston's Stochastic Extension of the Schroedinger Equation," IASSNS-HEP-99/83, LANL eprint: arXiv:quant-ph/9909026 v1 8 Sept 1999, September (1999)

Alexander, John B., "The New Mental Battlefield: 'Beam Me Up, Spock' ", *Military Review*, pp. 47-54, December (1980)

Allais, Maurice F.C., (1959a) "Should the Laws of Gravitation be Reconsidered? Part I-Abnormalities in the Motion of a Paraconical Pendulum on an Anisotropic Support", *Aero/Space Engineering*, September (1959)

Allais, Maurice F.C., "Should the Laws of Gravitation be Reconsidered? Part II, *Aero/Space Engineering*, October (1959b)

Anonymous, "Use of Psychics in Law Enforcement", Criminal Information Bulletin [State of California Department of Justice], p. 26, February 7 (1979)

Arp, Halton, "What Has Science Come To?," *Journal of Scientific Exploration*, Vol. 14, No. 3 (2000)

Atwater, F. Holmes, "Accessing Anomalous States of Consciousness with a Binaural Beat Technology," *Journal of Scientific Exploration*, Vol. 11, No. 3 (1997)

Atwater, P.M.H., *Coming Back to Life: The After-Effects of the Near-Death Experience*, Ballantine Books, New York (1988)

Atwater, P.M.H., *Beyond the Light*, Avon Books, New York (1994)

Atwater, P.M.H., *Future Memory*, Birch Lane Press, Carol Publishing Group, New York (1996)

Atwater, P.M.H., *Children of the New Millennium*, Three Rivers Press, New York (1999)

Ayling, Keith, the Editors of Fate Magazine, *Strange World of the Occult*, Paperback Library, Inc. New York (1968)

B-

Backster, Cleve, "Evidence of a Primary Perception in Plant Life", *International Journal of Parapsychology*, vol. 10, no, 4, Winter, pp. 329-348 (1968)

Backster, Cleve, "Evidence of a Primary Perception at a Cellular Level in Plant and Animal Life", unpublished. Backster Research Foundation, Inc. (1973)

Backster, Cleve, and White, "Biocommunication Capability at a Distance Between Human Donors and In Vitro Oral Leukocytes", *Int. J. of Biosoc. Res.*, Vol. 7(2), pp. 132-46, 1985; presented at the Meeting of the Orthomolecular Medical Society, San Francisco, CA Nov. 18 (1985)

Backster, Cleve, *Primary Perception: Biocommunication with Plants, Living Foods, and Human Cells*, (Franci Prowse, editor) W. R. M. Press c/o Anza Sanctuary of Healing Arts, Anza, California (2002)

Beaumont, Dr. Roger A., "C[nth]?: On the Strategic Potential of ESP," *Signal: Journal of the Armed Forces Communications and Electronics Association."*, pp. 39-45, January (1982)

Becker, Robert O., M.D., and Selden, Gary, *The Body Electric*, William Morrow & Company, New York (1985)

Belinfante, Frederik J., "The Casimir Effect Revisited," *Am. J. Physics,* Vol. 55, No. 2, p. 134, (1987)

Bell, J.S. *Physics,* Vol. 1, p. 195 (1964)

Bell, J.S., *Review of Modern Physics*, Vol. 38, p. 447 (1966)

Bentley, Molly, "World Warming in 2002 'Near Record'", *BBC News Online in Nice*, http://news.bbc.co.uk/2/hi/science/nature/2935883.stm (2002)

Benveniste, Jacques, 18th Meeting of the Society for Scientific Exploration, June 5, 1999 (see several dozen additional supporting references and papers by various groups on Benveniste's website: http://www.digibio.com) (1999)

Benveniste, Jacques, "Specific Remote Detection of Bacteria Using an Electromagnetic/Digital Procedure," *FASEB Journal*, Vol. 13, p. A852 (1999b)

Benveniste, J., Aissa, J., and Guillonnnet, D., "Digital Biology: Specificity of the Digitized Molecular Signal," FASEB Journal, Vol. 12, p. A412 (1998)

Berlitz, Charles, *Charles Berlitz's World of Strange Phenomena*, pp.29-30, Fawcett Crest, New York (1988)

Bierman, D. J., "Exploring Correlations between Local Emotional and global emotional events and the behavior of a random number generator", *Journal of Scientific Exploration* **10**:363-74 (1996)

Bierman, D. J., and Radin, D. I., "Anomalous Anticipatory Response on Randomized Future Conditions," *Perceptual & Motor Skills*, Vol. 84, pp. 689-90 (1997)

Blaine, David, *Fearless*, 110 minute Videotape, Buena Vista Home Entertainment, Inc. (2001)

BLS, Bureau of Labor Statistics, U. S. Government, http://data.bls.gov/servlet/SurveyOutputServlet (2003)

Bohm, David, *Quantum Theory*, Prentice-Hall, Englewood Cliffs, New Jersey (1951)

Bohm, D., and Aharonov, Y., *Physical Review*, Vol. 108, p. 1070 (1957)

Boyer, T. H., "Derivation of Blackbody Radiation Spectrum without Quantum Assumptions", *Phys. Rev.*, **182**, 1374 (1969).

Boyer, T. H., "Retarded van der Waals Forces at All Distances Derived from Classical Electrodynamics with Classical Electromagnetic Zero-Point Radiation", *Phys. Rev. A*, **7**, no. 6, 1832 (1973).

Boyer, T. H., "Random Electrodynamics: The Theory of Classical Electrodynamics with Classical Eelctromagnetic Zero-Point Radiation", *Phys. Rev. D*, **11**, p790 (1975).

Boyer, T. H., "Temperature Dependence of Van der Waals Forces in Classical Electrodynamics with Classical Electromagnetic Zero-Point Radiation", *Phys. Rev. A*, **11**, 5, 1650 (1975)

Boyer, T. H., "Thermal Effects of Acceleration for a Classical Dipole Oscillator in Classical Electromagnetic Zero-Point Radiation", *Phys. Rev. D*, **29**, 6, 1089 (1984).

Boundary, http://boundaryinstitute.org/randomness.htm (2001)

Braud, William G., and Schlitz, Marilyn J., "Consciousness Interactions with Remote Biological Systems: Anomalous Intentionality Effects," *Subtle Energies*, Vol. 2, No. 1, pp. 1-46 (1991)

Brinkley, Dannion, with Perry, Paul, *Saved By The Light*, Harper Spotlight/Harper Collins, New York (1994)

Brinkley, Dannion, in *The Eclectic Viewpoint Newsletter*, http://www.eclecticviewpoint.com/evbrink3.html (describes TV appearance of Dr. Raymond Moody on the Joan Rivers Show, in which she described this event, also seen by the author) (1994a)

Brinkley, Dannion, with Perry, Paul, *At Peace in the Light*, HarperCollins, New York (1995)

Brody, D.C., and Hughston, L.P., "Stochastic Reduction in Non-Linear Quantum Mechanics, *Proc. Roy. Soc. London A*, V. 458, pp. 1117-1127 (2002)

Brown, Lee, "Excerpts from a talk at the 1986 Continental Indigenous Council", Fairbanks, Alaska, http://www.dreamscape.com/morgana/atlas.htm (1998)

Brown, Courtney, Ph.D., *Cosmic Voyage*, Dutton, Penguin Group, New York (1996)

Browning, Norma Lee, *The Psychic World of Peter Hurkos*, Doubleday, New York (1970)

Bruce, Robert, *Astral Dynamics*, Hampton Roads Publishing Company, Charlottesville (1999)

Brunton, Paul, *A Search in Secret Egypt*, Weiser, York Beach, ME (1973)

Brunton, Paul, *A Search in Secret India,* E.P.Dutton and Company, New York (1935)

Brunton, Paul, *The Quest of the Overself*, Samuel Weiser, York Beach, ME (1970)

Bruyere, Rosalyn L., *Wheels of Light-Chakras, Auras, and the Healing Energy of the Body*, A Fireside Book, Simon and Shuster, New York (1994)

Byrd, Eldon, private communication (1992)

Bywater, Hector C., *Sea Power in the Pacific: A Study of the American-Japanese Naval Problem* (Constable, London, 1921; also Houghton, Mifflin, Boston and New York (1921)

Bywater, Hector C., *The Great Pacific War: A History of the Japanese-American Campaigne, 1931-1933.*, Constable, London, 1925. This book was also translated into Japanese as *Taiheiyo no Soha-sen*, 1931-1933, translated by Kyoji Kitagami (Ha-kuho-sha, Tokyo, 1925) See also: *Life,* 12/22/1941. A condensation of Bywater's book, published posthumously (1925)

Bywater, Hector C., *The Great Pacific War: A Historic Prophecy Now Being Fulfilled,* Houghton-Mifflin, Boston (1942)

C-

Cannon, Dolores, *Conversations with Nostradamus*, Volumes 1, 2 and 3, Ozark Mountain Publishers, Huntsville, AR (1989)

Cannon, Dolores, *Legacy From the Star*s, Ozark Mountain Publishers (1996)

Carrington, Hereward, *Laboratory Investigations into Psychic Phenomena*, Ayer Company Publishers, Inc. (1975)

Cayce, Edgar Evans, and Cayce, Hugh Lynn, *The Outer Limits of Edgar Cayce's Power*, Association for Research and Enlightenment, Virginia Beach, Virginia (1971)

Citro, M., Endler, P.C., Pongratz, W., Vinattieri, C., Smith, C.W., and Schulte, J., "Hormone Effects by Electronic Transmission," *FASEB Journal* (9: A392: 2271 (abs)) (1995)

Clark, Adrian V., *Psychokinesis-Moving Matter with the Mind*, Parker Publishing Company, West Nyack, New York (1973)

Clark, Fay Marvin*, Into the Light*, Pyramid Publishers of Iowa, Perry, Iowa, 1988, ISBN #0-945543-01-8 (1988)

Clauser, J.F., and Horne, M.A., *Phys. Rev. D*, Vol. 10, p. 526 (1974)

Clynes, M., "Spatial Visual Evoked Potentials as Physiologic Language Elements of Color and Field Structure," *Electroencephalogr. Clin. Neurophysiol.*, Suppl. 26, pp. 82-96, (1967)

Clynes, Manfred, Ph.D. (1977), *Sentics-The Touch of the Emotions*, Doubleday & Company, New York (1977), reprinted by Prism Press, Dorset, UK (1989)

Cockell, Jenny, *Past Lives, Future Lives*, Fireside, Simon and Shuster, New York (1996)

Cockell, Jenny, *Across Time and Death,* Fireside, Simon and Shuster, New York (1993)

Conybeare, F. C., *Philostratus-The Life of Apollonius of Tyana*, William Heineman, London (1912)

Corliss, William, "Strange Minds: A Sourcebook of Unusual Mental Phenomena", Volume P-1, *The Sourcebook Project*, Glen Arm, Maryland (1976)

Cosgrove, William, Press Release, "Number of Killer Storms and Droughts Increasing Worldwide," Secretariat of the 3rd World Water Forum, Tokyo Japan, Feb. 27 (2003)

Cramer, John G., "Generalized Absorber Theory and the Einstein-Podolsky-Rosen Paradox," *Physical Review D*, Vol. 22, No. 2, pp. 362-376 (1980)

Cramer, John G., "The Arrow of Electromagnetic Time and Generalized Absorber Theory," *Foundations of Physics*, Vol. 13, p. 887 (1983)

Cramer, John G., "The Transactional Interpretation of Quantum Mechanics," *Reviews of Modern Physics, Vol 58*, pp. 647-687, July (1986)

Cramer, John G., "An Overview of the Transactional Interpretation," *The International Journal of Theoretical Physics*, Vol. 27, p. 227 (1988)

Cramer, John G., "Quantum Nonlocality and the Possibility of Superluminal Effects," *NASA Breakthrough Propulsion Physics Workshop,* Cleveland, Ohio, August 12-14 (1997)

Crookes, W., "Notes of an Inquiry into the Phenomena Called Spiritual, During the Years 1870-73". *The Quarterly Journal of Science, and Annals of Mining, Metallurgy Engineering, Industrial Arts, Manufacturing and technology,* London, Volume Number XLI, January (1874)

Crookes, Sir William, "Researches in Spiritualism," Reproduced by *The Soucebook Project*, P.O.Box 107, Glen Arm, MD 21057 (1976)

D-

Dean, D., "The Plethysmograph as an Indicator of ESP," *Journal of the Society for Psychical Research*, Vol. 41, pp. 351-353 (1962)

Dean, D., "Plethysmograph Recordings as ESP Responses," *International Journal of Neuropsychiatry*, Vol. 2, pp. 439-446 (1966)

Denning, Melita and Phillips, Osborne, *Astral Projection-The Out-of-Body Experience*, Llewellyn Worldwide, Ltd., St. Paul, Minnesota, USA (1990)

Devyatkov, N.D., amd Golant, M.B., "Prospects for the Use of Millimeter-Wave Electromagnetic Radiation as a Highly Informative Instrument for Studying Specific Processes in Living Organisms," *Sov. Tech. Phys. Lett.*, **12** (3), p. 118, March (1986)

Dong, Paul, *The Four Major Mysteries of Mainland China*, Prentice-Hall, Englewood Cliffs, NJ (1984).

Dong, Paul, and Raffill, Thomas E., *China's Super Psychics*, Marlowe and Company, New York (1997)

Dossey, Larry, M.D., *Space, Time and Medicine*, New Science Library, Boston and London (1985)

Dossey, Larry, M.D., *Healing Words: The Power of Prayer and the Practice of Medicine*, Harper, San Francisco (1993)

Dossey, Larry, M.D., "Healing, Energy and Consciousness: Into the Future or a Retreat to the Past?," *Subtle Energies*, Vol. 5, No. 1, p. 1 (1994)

Dossey, Larry, M.D., (1996a) Dialogue, *Subtle Energies*, Vol. 5, No. 3, p. 264, 1996
Druckman, Daniel and Swets, John A., Editors, *"Enhancing Human Performance-Issues, Theories and Techniques,"* National Academy Press, Washington, D.C. 1988. This is a report prepared by the Committee on Techniques for the Enhancement of Human Performance, Commission on Behavioral and Social Sciences, National Research Council (1996a)

Dubrov, A.P., *The Geomagnetic Field and Life*, Plenum Press, New York (1977)

Dunne, Brenda J., and Jahn, Robert G., *Experiments in Remote Human/Machine Interaction*, Journal of Scientific Exploration, Vol. 6, No. 4, pp. 311-332 (1992)

Dunne, Brenda J., and Jahn, Robert G., "Consciousness and Anomalous Physical Phenomena," PEAR Lab Technical Note – PEAR 95004, May (1995)

E-

Eadie, Betty, *Embraced by the Light*, Bantam, New York (1992)

Eddington, A.E., "*Space, Time and Gravitation*", originally printed in 1920, reprinted by Cambridge University Press, Cambridge (1987)

Edward, John, "Crossing Over," Jodere Group (2001)

Edwards, Frank, "*Strange People*", Lyle Stuart Popular Library, New York (1961)

Einstein, A., Podolsky, B., and Rosen, N., *Physical Review*, Vol 47, p. 777 (1935)

Einstein, Albert, *Out of My Later Years*, Philosophical Library, New York (1950)

Einstein, A., Podolsky, B., and Rosen, N., *Phys. Rev.* Vol. 47, p. 777 (1935)

Einstein, Albert, http://www.rsrch.com/saturna (1932)

Eisenbud, Jule, M.D., *The World of Ted Serios*, William Morrow, New York (1967)

Eisenbud, Jule, "Paranormal Photography," Part IV, Chapter 4 in *Handbook of Parapsychology*, Wolman, Benjamin B., editor, Littleton Educational Publishing, Van Nostrand Reinhold Company, New York (1977)

Eisenbud, Jule, Pratt, J.G., and Stevenson, Ian, "Distortions in the Photographs of Ted Serios," *Journal of the American Society for Psychical Research*, Vol. 75, April, (1981)

Endler, P.C., Pongratz, W., van Wijk, R., Waltl, K., Hilgers, H., and Brandmaier, R., "Transmission of Hormone Ingformation by Non-Molecular Means," *FASEB Journal* (8: A400 (abs)) (1994)

EPRI (1994): (1) Okamoto, M., Yoshinaga, Y., Aida, M., and Kusunoki, T. "Excess Heat Generation, Voltage Deviation, and Neutron Emission in D_2O-LiOD Systems," Proc. ICCF4, Lahaina, Maui, dec. 6-9, 1993. EPRI TR104188-V2 (1994), p. 3; also *in Transactions of Fusion Technology* (Proceedings of the ICCF4), Vol. 26, 4T, Part 2, December 1994, pp. 176-179; (2) Storms, E., "Some Characteristics of Heat Production Using the 'Cold Fusion' Effect," Proc. ICCF4, Lahaina, Maui, Dec. 6-9, 1993. EPRI TR-104188-V2, p. 4 (1994)

d'Espagnat, B., *Phys. Rev. D.,* Vol. 11, p. 1424 (1974)

d'Espagnat, B., *Phys. Rev. D.,* Vol. 18, p. 349 (1978)

Eysenck, H. J., *Sense and Nonsense in Psychology*, New York, Penguin (1957)

F-

Farish, Lucius, "The UFO Newsclipping Service", Route 1-Box 220, Plumerville, Arkansas, 72127 (1995)

Farr, Sidney Saylor, *What Tom Sawyer Learned from Dying*, Hampton Roads Publishing Company, Inc., Charlottesville, Virginia (1993)

Feynman, R.P.,in: Wheeler, J.A., and Feynman, R.P., "Interaction with the Absorber as the Mechanism of Radiation", *Rev. Mod Phys*, **17**, no. 2, p157 (1945).

Feynman, R.P., *The Feynman Lectures in Physics*, Volume II, Addison-Wesley, New York (1970)

Fiore, Edith, Ph.D., *You Have Been Here Before*, Ballantine, New York, (1978)

Fiore, Edith, Ph.D., *The Unquiet Dead: A Psychologist Treats Spirit Possession*, Ballantine Books, New York (1987)

Ford, Arthur, *Unknown But Known - My Adventure into the Meditative Dimension*, Harper and Row, New York (1968)

Frohlich, H., "Long Range Coherence and Energy Storage in Biological Systems," Int. J. Quantum Chem. Vol. 2, pp: 641-49 (1968)

Frey, A.H., "Electromagnetic Field Interactions with Biological Systems," *FASEB Journal* (7: 272-28) (1993)

Frohlich, H., "The Biological Effects of Microwaves and Related Questions," *Advances in Electronics and Electron Physics*, Vol. 53, pp. 85-152, Academic Press (1980)

Frohlich, H., "Coherence in Biology," in *Coherent Excitations in Biological Systems*, Springer Verlag, Berlin-Heidelberg (1983)

G-

Geller, Uri, and Playfair, Guy Lyon, *The Geller Effect*, Henry Holt and Company, New York (1986)

Gersi, Douchan, *Faces in the Smoke-An Eyewitness Experience of Voodoo, Shamanism, Psychic Healing and Other Amazing Powers*, Jeremy P. Tarcher, Los Angeles (1991)

Green, E.E., et al., "Voluntary Controls Project: Swami Rama, Preliminary Report," Menninger Foundation, 6 June (1970)

Green, E.E., Parks, P.A., Guyer, P.M., Fahrion, S.L., and Coyne, L., "Anomalous Electrostatic Phenomena in Exceptional Subjects," *Subtle Energies*, Vol. 2, p. 69 (1993)

Green, Elmer, and Green, Alyce, *Beyond Biofeedback*, Dell, New York (1977)

Greenhouse, Herbert B., *The Astral Journey*, Avon Books, New York (1974)

Grimes, Dale, *Electromagnetism and Quantum Theory*, Academic Press, New York, (1969)

Gris, Henry and Dick, William, *The New Soviet Psychic Discoveries*, Prentice-Hall, Englewood Cliffs, New Jersey (1978)

Guthrie, Julian, *Tapping Our Psychic Powers*, San Francisco Examiner, Dec. 24 (1995)

H-

Hall, Manly P. *The Secret Teachinge of All Ages,* 19th Edition, Philosophical Research Society, Los Angeles, California (1973)

Hall, Manley Palmer, *The Adepts in the Esoteric Classical Tradition, Part One, The Initiates of Greece and Rome*, The Philosophical Research Society, Los Angeles (1981)

Hall, Manley Palmer, *The Adepts in the Esoteric Classical Tradition, Mytics and Mysteries of Alexandria*, The Philosophical Research Society, Los Angeles (1988)

Hall, Manley Palmer, *The Phoenix, An Illustrated Review of Occultism & Philosophy*, Philosophical Research Society, Inc., Los Angeles (1983)

Hall, Manley Palmer, *Orders of the Quest – The Holy Grail*, Philosophical Research Society, Inc., Los Angeles (1949)

Haish, B. and Rueda, A., "An Electromagnetic Basis for Inertia and Gravitation: What are the Implications for 21st Century Physics and Technology?", *Space Technology and Applications International Forum-1998*, ed by Mohammed S. El-Genk, DOE CONF-980103 (1998)

Haish, B. and Rueda, A., "The Zero-PointField and the NASA Challenge to Create the Space Drive", *NASA Breakthrough Propulsion Physics Workshop*, NASA Lewis Research Center, Aug. 12-14 (1997a)

Haish, B., and Rueda, A., "The Zero-Point Field and Inertia", presented at *Causality and Locality in Modern Physics & Astronomy: Open Questions and Possible Solutions*, A Symposium to Honor Jean-Pierre Vigier, York Univ., Toronto, Aug. 25-29 (1997b)

Hameroff, S.R., "Quantum Coherence in Microtubules: a Neural Basis for Emergent Consciousness?" *Journal of Consciousness Studies*, Vol. 1, pp. 98-118 (1994)

Harary, Keith, Ph.D., and Weintraub, Pamela, *Have an Out-of-Body Experience in 30 Days*, St. Martin's Press, New York (1989)

Harmon, Willis, "Review Essay: The Acentric Labyrinnth: Giordano Bruno's Prelude to Contemporary Cosmology," *Noetic Sciences Review #36*, p. 37, Winter, 1995, http://www.instituteofnoeticsciences.com/Ions/publications/review_archives/36/issue36_37.html (1995)

Hausdorf, Hartwig, *The Chinese Roswell*, New Paradigm Books, Boca Raton, FL (1998), originally published in German as *Die Weisse Pyramide*, by Albert Langen/George Muller Verlag in der F.A. Herbig Verlagsbuchhandlung GmbH, Munich (1994)

Henslow, G., *The Proofs of the Truth of Spiritualism*, Dodd, Mead, New York (1919)

Herbert, B., "Report on Nina Kulagina", *Parapsychology Review*, **3**, pp. 8-10 (1972)

Hill, Douglas and Williams, Pat, *The Supernatural*, Hawthorn Books, New York (1965)

Ho, Mae-Wan, Ph.D., *The Rainbow and the Worm – The Physics of Organisms*, (second edition) World Scientific Publishing Company Pte. Ltd., Singapore (1998)

Ho, Mae-Wan, Ph.D., and Knight, David P., "The Acupuncture System and the Liquid Crystalline Collagen Fibres of the Connective Tissues-Liquid Crystal Meridians," *American Journal of Complementary Medicine* (in press), *Institute of Science in Society* (2003), http://www.i-sis.org.uk

Honorton, C., "Rhetoric over Substance: The impoverished state of skepticism", *Journal of Parapsychology*, **57**:191-214 (1993)

Honorton, C., (1975) "Has Science Developed the Competence to Confront Claims of the Paranormal?." in *Research in Parapsychology* 1975, ed. J. Morris, W. Roll, and R. Morris, pp. 199-223, Scarecrow Press, Metuchen, NJ (1976)

Houck, Jack, "Researching Remote Viewing and Psychokinesis", *TREAT V Conference Proceedings*, (1993), Santa Fe, New Mexico, 17-21 March, 1993, also found at webpage: http://www.tcom.co.uk/hpnet/houck1.htm (1993)

Houck, Jack, "First Archaeus Congress Firewalk-A Technical Report", ARTIFEX, Vol. 5, No. 1, February-March 1986, pp. 3 (1986)

Howard, E. Lee, *My Adventure in Spiritualism*, MacMillan, New York (1935)

Holden, C., "Identical Twins Reared Apart", *Science*, Vol. 207, 1323-1328 (1980)

Holbert, Joe, personal communication (2000)

Hone, Harry, *The Light at the End of the Tunnel*, A Limited Manuscript Edition, American Biographical Center, Williamsburg, Virginia, Library of Congress Number 79-55362 (1986)

Honan, William H., *Visions of Infamy-The Untold Plans of How Journalist Hector C. Bywater Devised the Plans that Led to Pearl Harbor*, St. Martin's Press, New York (1991)

Hubbard, G. Scott, May, E.C., and Puthoff, H.E., "Possible Production of Photons During a Remote Viewing Task: Preliminary Results," SRI International, in D.H.Weiner and D.I.Radin (eds.) *Research in Parapsychology* 1985, Scarecrow Press, Metuchen, NJ, pp. 66-70 (1986)

Hughston, L.P., Proc. Roy. Soc. Lond. A, Vol. 452, p. 953 (1996)

Hunt, Valerie V., *Project Report: A Study of Structural Integration from Neuromuscular, Energy Field, and Emotional Approaches*. Boulder, Colorado: Rolf Institute of Structural Integrtion (1977)

Hunt, Valerie V., *Infinite Mind-The Science of the Human Vibrations*, Malibu Publishing Company, Malibu, California 90265 (1995)

Hunt, Valerie V., *Infinite Mind-Science of the Human Vibrations of Consciousness*, Malibu Publishing Company, Malibu, California 90265 (1996)

Hyman, R., "Scientists and Psychics," in G.O.Abell and B. Singer (Eds.) *Science and the Paranormal: Probing the Existence of the Supernatural*, pp. 119-141, Scribners, New York (1981)

Hyman, R., 1982 Parapsychological Association Convention (1982)

Hyman, R., "Evaluation of Program on Anomalous Mental Phenomena," University of Oregon, September 11, 1995, http://www.mceagle.com/remote-viewing/refs/science/air/hyman.html. [For two years this document was hosted on the Universe of Oregon website, where Dr. Hyman is on the faculty.] (1995)

Hyman, R., "Evaluation of a Program on Anomalous Mental Phenomena, *Journal of Scientific Exploration*, Vol. 10, pp. 31-58 (1996)

I-

Inyushin, V.M., and Chekurov, P.R., *Biostimulation Through Laser Radiation and Bioplasma*, translated by Scott Hill and T.D. Ghoshal, Danish Society for Psychical Research, Copenhagen (1977)

Inyushin, V.M., "The Concept of Biological Plasma," in *Bioenergetics Questions (Material of the Scientific Methodological Seminar in Alma-Ata)*, Edited by B.A.Dombrovsky, G.A.Sergeyev, B.M.Inyushin, Southern California Society for Psychical Research, Beverly Hills, California (1972)

Ivanenko, K.K., "Structures of Algorithms in the Statistical Processing of Bioplasmograms," in *Bioenergetics Questions (Material of the Scientific Methodological Seminar in Alma-Ata)*, Edited by B.A.Dombrovsky, G.A.Sergeyev, B.M.Inyushin, Southern California Society for Psychical Research, Beverly Hills, California (1972)

Iverson, Jeffrey, In Search of the Dead-A Scientific Investigation of Evidence for Life After Death, Harper, San Francisco (1992)

J-

Jackson, D.D., "Reunion of Identical Twins, Raised Apart, Reveals Some Astonishing Similarities", *Smithsonian*, pp. 48-56, October (1980)

Jahn, Robert G., "The Role of Consciousness in the Physical World," *AAAS Selected Symposium*, Westview Press, Inc., Boulder, Colorado (1981)

Jahn, R.G., and Dunne, B.J., "On the Quantum Mechanics of Consciousness, with Application to Anomalous Phenomena", *Foundations of Physics*, **16,** p721 (1986).

Jahn, R.G., and Dunne, B.J., *Margins of Reality*, Harcourt Brace Jovanovich, New York (1987a)

Jahn, R.G., Dunne, B.J., and Nelson, R.D., "Engineering Anomalies Research," *Journal of Scientific Exploration*, Vol. 1, No. 1, pp.21-50 (1987b)

Jahn, Robert, in Press Release by *Society for Scientific Exploration*, December 15, 1992, http://www.jse.com/PR_Princeton_92.html (1992)

Jonsson, Olof, "Can We Really Receive ESP Signals From the Moon?", *Argosy*, June (1971)

Jung, Carl, *Psychological Reflections: A Jung Anthology*, 15, 143 (1942)

K-

Kaznacheyev, V.P., "Informational Function of Ultraweak Light Flows in Biological Systems," in *Problems in Biophysics*, pp. 7-18, Novosibirsk (1967)

Kaznacheyev, V.P., Mikhailova, L.P., *Ultraweak Radiation in Intercellular Interactions* (Novosibirsk, 1981) [in Russian; English translation: Washington Research Center, San Francisco, (1982)

Kaznacheyev, V.P., "Electromagnetic Bioinformation in Intercellular Interactions", *Psi Research*, Vol. 1, No. 1, March 1982, p. 47-82 (1982)

Kaznacheyev, V.P., Mikhailova, L.P., Sudarev, V.N., Shurin, S.P., "Distant Intercellular Interactions Caused by UV-radiation," in *Photobiology of a Living Cell*, Leningrad, 1979, pp. 221-223 [in Russian] (1979)

Kaznacheyev, V.P., Mikhailova, L.P., Kadayeva, D.G., Dranova, M.P., "Conditions Necessary for Appearance of Distant Intercellular Interactions After UV-radiation," *Bulleten Experimetalnoy Biologii i Meditsiny.*, No. 5, 1979, pp. 468-471 [in Russian] (1979)

Kaznacheyev, V.P., Mikhailova, Shurin, S.P., "Distant Intercellular Interactions in a System of Two Tissue Cultures Connected by Optical Contact" in *Regulation of Biosynthesis and Biophysics of Populations*, Krasnoyarsk, 1969, pp. 372-374 [in Russian] (1969)

Klintman, H., "Is There a Paranormal (Precognitive) Influence in Certain Types of Perceptual Sequences? Part I," *EJP*, Vol. 5, pp. 19-49 (1983)

Klintman, H., "Is There a Paranormal (Precognitive) Influence in Certain Types of Perceptual Sequences? Part II," *EJP*, Vol. 5, pp. 125-40 (1984)

Kolodny, Lev, "When Apples Fall," *Moscow Pravda,* March 17, 1968. Partial translation *Journal of Paraphysics*, Vol. 2, No. 4, Downton, Wiltshire, England (1968)

Kozyrev, N. A., "Possibility of Experimental Study of the Properties of Time," *JPRS*: 45238, translation, U.S. Department of Commerce, from Russian, Pulkovo, O VOZMOZHNOSTI EKSPERIMENTAL'NOGO ISSLEDOVANIYA SVOYSTV VREMENI, pp. 1-49, September (1967)

Kozyrev, N.A., in *Flare Stars* [in Russian], pp. 209-226, Erevan (1977)

Kozyrev, N. A., and Nasonov, V.V., in *Astronomy and Celestial Mechanics*, Moscow, Leningrad (1978)

Kozyrev, N. A., and Nasonov, V.V., in *Manifestations of Cosmic Factors on Earth and in the Stars* [in Russian], Moscow-Leningrad (1980)

Kozyrev, N. A., in *Physical Aspects of Modern Astronomy* [in Russian], Moscow-Leningrad (1985)

Kress, Kenneth A., "The Kress Report-Parapsychology in Intelligence-A Personal Review and Conclusions," [originally classified SECRET and published in the Winter 1977 edition *of Studies in Intelligence*, an in-house CIA publication, reprinted here from *The Psychic Battlefield* by Mandelbaum (Mandelbaum, 2000)] (1977)

Krippner, Stanley and Rubin, Daniel, *Galaxies of Life*, Gordon and Breach, New York (1973)

Kroy, Walter, "The Use of Optical Radiation for Stimulation Therapy", in *Electromagnetic BioInformation*, Popp, E.A., ed., Urban & Schwartzenberg, Munchen-Wien-Baltimore (1989)

Kuhn, Thomas, *The Structure of Scientific Revolution*, U. of Chicago Press (1962)

Kulagin, V.V., "Nina S. Kulagina", *Journal of Paraphysics*, 5, 54-62 (1971)

Kulin, Yevgeniy T., *Bioelectretic Effect*, Washington Research Center, 3101 Washington Street, San Francisco, California, translated from original Russian, published by Science and Technics, Minsk, USSR (1980)

Kubler-Ross, E., *On Death and Dying: What the Dying Have to Teach Doctors, Nurses, Clergy, and Their Families*, Burdett, NY: Larson (reprint) (1997)

Kurtz, Paul, Nienhuys, Jan Willem, and Sandhu, Ranjit, "Is the 'Mars Effect' Genuine?", *Journal of Scientific Exploration*, Vol. 11, No. 1, pp. 19-39 (1997)

Kurz, O., "The Hranice Case," *Journal of Paraphysics*, Vol. 2, No. 5. (Downton, Wiltshire, England) (1968)

Kurz, O., and Rejdak, Z., "About Telekinesis," *Pravda* (Czech) June 14 and 21 (1968)

L-

LaMothe, John D., *Controlled Offensive Behavior-USSR*, Defense Intelligence Agency Task No. T72-01-14 (ST-CS-01-169-172), July (1972)

Landau, L., "An Unusual Out-Of-Body Experience," *Journal of the Society for Psychical Research*, Vol. 42, pp. 126-128 (1963)

Lloyd, D.H., M.D., Objective Events in the Brain Correlating with Psychic Phenomena," *New Horizons*, Vol. 1, No. 2, Summer (1973)

van Lommel, P., van Wees, R., Meyers, V., and Elfferich, I., "Near-Death Experience in Survivors of Cardiac Arrest: A Prospective Study in the Netherlands," *The Lancet*, Vol. 358, pp. 2039-2045 (2001)

Lorenz, Edward N., "Deterministic Non-Periodic Flow," *Journal of Atmospheric Sciences*, Vol. 20, pp. 130-141 (1963)

Lorenz, Edward, *Essence of Chaos*, U. of Washington Press, ISBN: 0295975148 (1993)

Lorenz, K. "Les Fondements de l'ethologie", *Nouvelle Biblioteque Scientifique*, p. 338, Flammarion (1978)

Lynes, Barry, *The Cancer Cure That Worked!*, Marcus Books, 1987; (see also Nexus, Oct-Nov. '93; http://medicaltruth.com/RoyalRife.html (1987)

Lyons, Arthur, and Truzzi, Marcello, Ph. D., *The Blue Sense-Psychic Detectives and Crime*, The Mysterious Press, New York (1991)

M-

MacDougall, Duncan, M.D., "Hypothesis Concerning Soul Substance Together with Experimental Evidence of the Existence of Such Substance", *American Medicine*, April, 1907; also in *Journal of the American Society for Psychical Research*, Vol. 1, pp. 237-244 (1907)

Maire, Louis F. III, and LaMothe, J.D., *Soviet and Czechoslavakian Parapsychology Research*, Defense Intelligence Agency Task PT-1810-12-75 (DST-18105-387-75) September (1975)

Mallove, Eugene, Ph.D., "Cold Fusion: The 'Miracle' is No Mistake," *Analog Magazine*, July/August (1997)

Mandelbaum, W. Adam, *The Psychic Battlefield*, St. Martin's Press, New York (2000)

Margolis, Jonathan, *Uri Geller-Magician or Mystic?,* Welcome Rain, New York [532 LaGuardia Place, New York, N.Y. 10012; ISBN 1-56649-025-1] (1999)

Maxwell, James Clerk, *The Aether* (1876)

Maxwell, James Clerk, "To the Committee of the Caylay Portrait Fund", referenced on www.enterprisemission.com (1887)

May, Edwin and Spottiswood, James, *Global Consciousness Project: An Independent Analysis of the 11 September 2001 Events*, Laboratories for Fundamental Research, 2001, http://www.boundaryinstitute.org/articles/May-Spot_Sep11.pdf (2001)

McCulloch, J., and Etkin, D. eds. *Proceedings of a Workshop on Imprioving Responses to Atmospheric Extremes: The Role of Insurance and Compensation*. Environment Canada, Downsview, Ontario (1993)

McDougall, W., "Fourth Report on a Lamarckian Experiment," *British Journal of Psychology*, Vol. 28, pp. 321-45 (1938)

McMoneagle, J., *Mind Trek: Exploring Consciousness, Time and Space Through Remote Viewing*, Hampton Roads Publishing Company, Charlottesville (1993)

McMoneagle, J., *The Ultimate Time Machine*, Hampton Roads Publishing Company, Charlottesville (1998)

McMoneagle, J., address to the *Project Awareness Conference* in Clearwater, Florida, on November 14 (1999)

McMoneagle, Joe, personal communication during lecture at the Monroe Institute (1997)

Mead, G. R. S., *Apollonius of Tyana,* Ares Publishers, Chicago, originally published in 1819 (1980)

Medwick, Cathleen, *Teresa of Avila-The Progress of a Soul*, Alfred A, Knopf, New York (1999)

Mendoza, Ramon, *The Acentric Labyrinth*, Harper Collins (1995)

Millis, Mark G., "NASA Breakthrough Propulsion Physics Program", A White Paper, www.lerc.nasa.gov/WWW/bpp/WhitePaper.htm, 2/5/99 (1999)

Milton, J., "Ordinary State ESP Meta-Analysis," in *Proceedings of Presented Papers, 36th Annual Parapsychological Association,* M.J. Schlitz ed., pp. 87-104, Parapsychological Association, Fairhaven (1993)

Mitchell, Edgar, in "UFOs: 50 Years of Denial", airing on *The Learning Channel*, March 4 (1999)

Mitchell, Edgar, *The David Frost Show*, 16 March 1971, quoted in (LaMothe, 1972) (1971)

Mitchell, Edgar D., *Psychic Exploration, A Challenge for Science*, ed.by John White, Perigee Books, published by G.P.Putnam & Sons, New York (1974)

Mitchell, Edgar, and Williams, Dwight, *The Way of the Explorer*, Putnam, New York (1996)

Mitchell, Edgar, "An ESP Test From Apollo 14," *Journal of Parapsychology*, Vol. 35, pp. 89-107 (1971)

Mitchell, Janet Lee, Ph.D., *Out of Body Experiences-A Handbook*, Ballantine Books, New York (1987)

Motoyoshi, Akio, "Teleportation Without Resorting to Bell Measurement", *Physics Letters A*, **270**, PP. 293-295 (2000)

Moody, Raymond A., with Paul Perry, *"The Light Beyond"*, Bantam, New York (1988)

Moody, Raymond A., Jr. *Life After Life,* Mockingbird Books, Covington, Georgia (1975)

Moody, Raymond A., Jr. *Reflections on Life After Life*, Bantam Books, New York (1978)

Monroe, Robert, *Journeys Out of the Body*, Anchor/Doubleday, New York (1971)

Monroe, Robert, *Far Journeys*, Doubleday, New York (1985)

Monroe, Robert, *Ultimate Journey*, Doubleday, New York (1994)

Morehouse, David, *Psychic Warrior-Inside the CIA's Stargate Program*, St. Martin's Press, New York (1996)

Morse, Melvin, M.D., with Paul Perry, *Closer to the Light-Learning from the Near-Death Experiences of Children*, Ivy Books, published by Ballantine Books, division of Random House, New York (1990)

Morse, Melvin, M.D., with Paul Perry, *Transformed by the Light*, Villard Books, New York (1992)

Morse, Melvin, M.D., with Paul Perry, *Where God Lives*, Harper Collins, New York (2000)

Mishlove, Jeffrey, *"The PK Man: A True Story of Mind Over Matter*," Hampton Roads Publishing Company, Hampton Roads, Virginia (2000)

Merritt, Grace E., "Moving Time with Light," *The Hartford Courant*, Friday, July 27 (2001)

Morris, R.L., Harary, S.B., Janis, J., Hartwell, J., and Roll, W.G., "Studies of Communication during Out-of-Body Experiences," *Journal of the American Society for Psychical Research*, Vol. 72, pp. 1-21 (1978)

Muldoon, Sylvan, *The Case for Astral Projection*, Aries Press, Chicago (1936)

Muldoon, Sylvan, and Carrington, Hereward, *The Projection of the Astral Body,* Samuel Weiser, York Beach, Maine (1973)

Murphy, Michael, *The Future of the Body: Explorations into the Further Evolution of Human Nature,* Putnam Publishing Group, New York (1992)

N-

Nelson, J.H., "Shortwave Radio Propagation Correlation with Planetary Positions", *RCA Review* (Princeton, NJ), March (1951)

Nelson, J.H., "Planetary Position Effect on Short-Wave Signal Quality", conference paper recommended by the AIEE Subcommittee on Energy Sources and presented at the AIEE Winter General Meeting, New York, N.Y., January 21-25 (1952)

Nelson, R.D., "Wishing for Good Weather: A Natural Experiment in Group Consciousness". Technical Note PEAR 96001 (June). Princeton Engineering Anomalies Research Laboratory, Princeton University School of Engineering/Applied Science (1996)

Nelson, R.D., Bradish, J., Dobyns, Y.H., Dunne, B.J., and Jahn, R.G., 1996. "Field REG Anomalies in Group Situations", *Journal of Scientific Exploration*, **10**:111-42 (1996)

Nelson, R.D., Dobyns, Y.H., Dunne, B.J., and Jahn, R.G., "Analysis of Variance of REG Experiments: Operator Intention, secondary parameters, database structure." *Technical Note* PEAR 91004, Princeton Engineering Anomalies Research Laboratory, Princeton University School of Engineering/Applied Science (1991)

Nelson, R.D., Dunne, B.J., and Jahn, R.G., "An REG Experiment with Large Database Capability, III: Operator related anomalies." *Technical Note* PEAR 84003 (September), . Princeton Engineering Anomalies Research Laboratory, Princeton University School of Engineering/Applied Science (1984)

Nelson, R. D., "Extended Analysis: September 11 2001 in Context," http://noosphere.princeton.edu/terror1.html (2001)

Nelson, R.D., *Global Harmony* on Global Consciousness Project webpage, http://noosphere.princeton.edu/groupmedit.html (2003)

News (1971), "Apollo ESP Test Told", *Washington Daily News*, Feb. 22 (1971)

Newton, Michael, Ph.D. *Journey of Souls: Case Studies of Life Between Lives*, Llewellyn Publications, St. Paul, Minnesota (1995)

O-

O'Leary, Brian, *Exploring Inner and Outer Space-A Scientist's Perspective on Personal and Planetary Transformation*, Copyright 1989, North Atlantic Books, Berkeley, California (1989)

Orme-Johnson, D., M.C. Dillbeck, Wallace, R.K., and Landrith III, G.S., "Intersubject EEG Coherence: Is Consciousness a Field?" *International Journal of Neuroscience* **16**:203-9 (1982)

Orme-Johnson, D., Alexander, C.N., Davies, J.L., Chandler, H.M., and Larimore, W.E., "International Peace Project in the Middle East: The Effects of the Maharishi Technology on the Unified Field", *Journal of Conflict Resolution*, **32**: 776-812 (1988)

Osis, Karlis, M.D., and Haraldson, E., M.D., *At the Hour of Death*, Avon Books, New York (1977)

Osis, K. and McCormick, D., "Kinetic Effects at the Ostensible Location of an Out-of-Body Projection during Perceptual Testing," *Journal of the American Society for Psychical Research*, Vol. 74, pp. 319-329 (1980)

Ostrander, Sheila and Schroeder, Lynn, *Psychic Discoveries Behind the Iron Curtain*, Bantam Books, New York (1970)

Ostrander, Sheila and Schroeder, Lynn, *Superlearning*, Delta/The Confucian Press (1979)

Ostrander, Sheila and Schroeder, Lynn, *The ESP Papers-Scientists Speak Out Behind the Iron Curtain*, Bantam Books, New York (1976)

Ostrander, Sheila and Schroeder, Lynn, *Handbook of Psi Discoveries*, Berkeley Publishing Company, distributed by Putnam, New York (1974)

Ostrander, Sheila and Schroeder, Lynn, *Psychic Discoveries*, Marlowe and Company, New York (1997)

P-

Pavlova, L.P., (1967) "Results and Discussions of Experiments with the Nedra-20." Paper presented at *Seminar of Technical Parapsychology Section affiliated All-Union Engineering Institute*, Moscow, August 4, 1967; also: "Some Electroencephalographic Indices in Experimental Research in Bio-telecommunication," Moscow (1967)

Pearsall, Paul, *The Heart's Code-Tapping the Wisdom and Power of Our Heart Energy*, Broadway Books, New York (1998)

Penrose, R., *The Emporer's New Mind*, Oxford Press, New York (1989).

Penrose, R., *Shadows of the Mind*, Oxford University Press, Oxford (1994)

Penrose, R., and Hameroff, S. "What Gaps? Reply to Grush and Churchland," *Journal of Consciousness Studies*, Vol. 2, No. 2, pp. 98-111 (1995)

Peoc'h, Rene (1988a), "Action Psychocinetique des Poussins sur un Generateur Aleatoire", *Revue Francaise de Psychotronique*, **1**, 11-24 (1988)

Peoc'h, Rene, (1988b), "Chicken Imprinting and the Tachyscope: an ANPSI Experiment", *Journal of the Society for Psychical Research*, **55**, 1-9 (1988)

Peoc'h, Rene (1988c), "Psychokineitc Action of Young Chicks on the Path of an Illuminated Source", *Journal of Scientific Exploration*, **9**, 223-29 (1995)

Perkins, John, *PsychoNavigation-Techniques for Travel Beyond Time*, Destiny Books, Rochester, Vermont (1990)

Picknett, Lynn, *Flights of Fancy? 100 Years of Paranormal Experiences*, Ballantine, New York (1987)

Pope, Nick, *Open Skies, Closed Minds,* Penguin USA (1999)

Popp, F..A., "Photon Storage in Biological Systems, " in *Electromagnetic Bioinformation,* Proceedings of the Symposium, Marburg, September 5, 1977, published by Munchen-wien-Baltimore (1979)

Popp, F. A., ed., *Electromagnetic Bioinformation*, Urban & Schwartzenberg, Munchen-Wien-Baltimore (1989)

Popp, F. A., Li, K.H., and Gu, Q., *Recent Advances in Biophoton Research and Its Applications*, Tech. Ctr. Kaiserslautern, Int'l Inst. of Biophysics, (2003)

Pratt, J.G., Rhine, J.B., Smith, B.M., Stuart, C.E., and Greenwood, J.A., 1966. *Extrasensory Perception after sixty years*., Bruce Humphies, Boston. Originally published in (1940).

Pribram, Karl, "The Neurophysiology of Remembering," in *Physiological Psychology*, Jan, 1969, pp. 387-398 (1969)

Pressman, A.S., *Electromagnetic Fields and Living Nature* (Moscow, 1968) [English translation: "Electromagnetic Fields and Life", Plenum, New York (1970)

PRC, Chinese Academy of Sciences, High Energy Institute, Special Physics Research Team, "Exceptional Human Body Radiation," *PSI Research*,Vol. 1, No. 2, June, pp. 16-25, (1982)

Prigogine, Ilya, *From Being to Becoming*, W.H.Freeman and Company, New York (1980)

Prigogine, Ilya, *Order Out of Chaos*, Bantam Doubleday Dell, New York (1989)

Puthoff, Harold E., Targ, Russell, and May, Edwin C., "Experimental Psi Research: Implications for Physics*,"* in *The Role of Consciousness in the Physical World*, ed. by Robert G. Jahn, AAAS Selected Symposium, Westview Press, Inc. Boulder, Colorado (1981)

Puthoff, Harold, and Targ, Russell, *Physics, Entropy and Psychokinesis,* in *Proc. Conf. Quantum Physics and Parapsychology*, p. 129-144, Parapsychology Foundation, New York (1975)

Puthoff, H. E., "CIA-Initiated Remote Viewing Program at Stanford Research Institute", *Journal of Scientific Exploration*, **10**, p. 63 (1996).

Puthoff, H.E., "Information Transmission Under Conditions of Sensory Shielding," *Nature*, Vol. 251, No. 18 (October) pp. 602-607 (1974)

Puthoff, H.E., "A Perceptual Channel For Information Transfer Over Kilometer Distances: Historical Perspective And Recent Research," *Proceedings of the IEEE*, Vol. 64, March (1976)

Puthoff, H. E. "Source of Vacuum Electromagnetic Zero-Point Energy", *Phys. Rev. A*, **40**, 9, 4857 (1989b).

Puthoff, H.E., "Zero Point Fluctuations of the Vacuum as the Source of Atomic Stability and the Gravitational Interaction", *Proc. Brit. Soc. Phil Sci*, September (1988).

Puthoff, H.E., "Gravity as a Zero-Point Fluctuation Force", *Phys. Rev. A,* **39**, No. 5, 2333 (1989a).

Puthoff, H.E., "Ground State of Hydrogen as a Zero-Point-Fluctuation-Determined State", *Phys. Rev. D*, 35, no. 10, p3266 (1987).

Puthoff, Harold E., Ph.D., and Targ, Russell, *The Record: Eight Days with Uri Geller*, Stanford Research Institute, Menlo Park, California, posted at http://www.tcom.co.uk/hpnet/g4.htm (1999)

Puthoff, Harold, and Targ, Russell, "Psychic Research and Modern Physics," in (Mitchell, 1974)

Puthoff, H.E., Ph.D., "Can the Vacuum be Engineered for Spaceflight Applications? Overview of Theory and Experiments," Presented at the NASA Breakthrough Propulsion Physics Workshop, August 12-14, 1997, NASA Lewis Research Center, Cleveland, OH, reprinted in *Infinite Energy,* p. 72, July-November (1997)

Q-

Quigley, Joan, *What Did Joan Say? My Seven Years as White House Astrologer to Nancy and Ronald Reagan,* A Birch Lane Press Book, published by Carol Publishing Group, New York (1990)

R-

Radin, Dean I., Rebman, Jannine M., and Cross, Maikwe P., "Anomalous Organization of Random Events by Group Consciousness: Two Exploratory Experiments", *Journal of Scientific Exploration,* Vol. 10, No. 1, pp. 143-168 (1996)

Radin, Dean, *The Conscious Universe*, Harper Collins, New York (1997).

Radin, Dean I., "Unconscious Perception of Future Emotions: An Experiment in Presentiment," *Journal of Scientific Exploration*, Vol. 11, No. 2, pp. 163-180 (1997a).

Radin, Dean, "Global Consciousness Project Analysis for September 11, 2001," Institute of Noetic Sciences, 2001, http://noosphere.princeton.edu/dean/wtc0921.html (2001)

Radin, Dean, "Extended Analysis, September 11, 2001 in Context," Institute of Noetic Sciences, 2001, http://noosphere.princeton.edu/terror1.html (2001a)

Radin, Dean, "Terrorist Disaster, September 11, 2001," Institute of Noetic Sciences, 2001, http://noosphere.princeton.edu/terror.html (2001b)

Radin, Dean, Ph.D., Machado, Fatima Regina, and Zangari, Wellington, "Effects of Distant Healing Intention Through Time & Space: Two Exploratory Studies," *Subtle Energies & Energy Medicine*, Vol. 11, No. 3, p. 207 (2001c)

Radin, D.I., and Rebman, J.M., "Seeking Psi in the Casino," *Journal of the Society for Psychical Research,* Vol. 62, pp. 193-219 (1998)

Raudive, Konstantine, *Breakthrough,* Colin Smith, London (1971), also Zebra Books, New York (1971)

Rejdak, Zdenek, "Psychotronics and Parapsychology," Paper presented: Seminar of Technical Parapsychology Section affilitated All Union Engineering Institue, Moscow, May 1-4 (1967)

Rejdak, Zdenek, "Telekinesis or Fraud?" *Pravda* (Czech) June 21, 1968. Partial translation: *Journal of Paraphysics*, Vol. 1, No. 3, Downton, Wiltshire, England (1968)

Rejdak, Zdenek, "The Kulagina Cine Film," *Journal of Paraphysics*, Vol. 3, No. 3 (1968)

Regan, Donald, (Regan President Ronald Reagan's Chief of Staff), *Washingtonian*, December, 1989, in a review of Nancy Reagan's book *My Turn* (1989)

Regan, Donald, *For The Record: From Wall Street To Washington*, Harcourt Brace Jovanonich, New York (1988); also in "Good Heavens", *Time*, May 16, p. 26 (1988)

Rhodes, Leon S., *"Swedenborg and the Near-Death Experience"*, *in Emmanuel Swedenborg: A Continuing Vision*, ed. by Robin Larson et al., Swedenborg Foundation,New York, 1988, pp. 237-40 (1988)

Ring, Kenneth, *Life at Death: A Scientific Investigation of the Near-Death Experience*, Moment Point Press, Portsmouth, NH (1985a)

Ring, Kenneth, Heading Towards Omega: In Search of the Meaning of the Near-Death Experience, Quill, New York (1985b)

Ring, Kenneth, Ph.D., "*Life at Death*", Quill, New York, (1980)

Ring, Kenneth, Ph.D., *Heading Towards Omega*, Morrow & Company, New York (1984)

Rhine, J.B., *Extrasensory Perception*, Boston Society for Psychical Research, Boston (1934)

Rheingold, Howard, "Tools for Thought," www.rheingold.com/texts/tft/5.html (2000)

Ritchie, G., *Return From Tomorrow,* Chosen Books, Waco, TX (1978)

Ritter, Malcolm, "Beam Me Up – Science Fact: Scientists Achieve 'Star Trek'-Like Feat," Associated Press, New york, 12-10-97 (1997)

Rogo, D. Scott, *Leaving the Body-A Complete Guide to Astral Projection*, Prentice Hall Press, New York (1983)

Roll, W.G., *Research in Parapsychology*, Scarecrow Press (1983)

Rosenthal, R. and Rubin, D.B., "Impersonal Expectancy Effects: The First 345 Studies" in *Behavioural and Brain Sciences* 3:377-415 (1978)

Rueda, A. and Haish, B., "Contribution to Inertial Mass by Reaction of the Vacuum to Accelerated Motion", *Foundations of Physics*, preprint 9802030 v2, 17 Feb (1998)

Rueda, A. "Behavior of Classical Particles Immersed in the Classical Electromagnetic Zero-Point Field", *Phys. Rev.* A, **23**, no. 4 (1981).

Rueda, A., and Haish, B., "Inertia as Reaction of the Vacuum to Accelerated Motion", *Physics Letters* A. in press, preprint physics/9802031 16 Feb. (1998)

Rueda, A., "On the Problem of the Acceleration of Particles by the Zero-Point Field of Quantum Electrodynamics. Exploration with the Quantum Einstein-Hopf Model.", *Nuovo Cim.*, **96B**, no 1, p. 64 (1986)

S-

Saxl, Erwin J., and Allen, Mildred, "1970 Solar Eclipse as 'Seen' by a Torsion Pendulum," *Physical Review D*, Vol. 3, No. 4, 15 Feb 1971, pp 823-825 (1971)

Schnabel, J., *Remote Viewers: The Secret History of America's Psychic Spies*, Dell, New York (1997)

Schreiber, Th., *Atlas of Classical Antiquities*, London (1895)

Schwartz, Gary, Ph.D., *The Afterlife Experiments - Breakthrough Scientific Evidence of Life after Death,* Pocket Books, New York (2002)

Schroedinger, E., *What is Life?*, Cambridge University Press, Cambridge, U.K. (1967)

Schmidt, Helmut, "Mental Influence on Random Events," *New Scientist*, June, p. 757, 1971); also in "Evidence for Direct Interaction Between the Human Mind and External Quantum Processes," in (Tart, 1979) (1971)

Schmidt, H., "PK Tests with Pre-Recorded and Pre-inspected Seed Numbers. *Journal of Parapsychology*, **45**:87-98 (1981)

Schmidt, H., and Schlitz, M.J., "A Large Scale Pilot PK Experiment with Pre-recorded Random Events", In RIP 1988, ed. By L.A.Henkel and R.E. berger, 6-10. Metuchen, NJ: Scarecrow Press. (1989)

Schmidt, H., Morris, R., and Rudolph, L., "Channeling Evidence for a PK Effect to Independent Observers", *Journal of Parapsychology*, **50**:1-16 (1986)

Schmidt, Helmut, "Non-Causality as the Earmark of Psi," *Journal of Scientific Exploration*, Vol. 7, No. 2, pp/ 125-132 (1993)

Schmeidler, Gertrude, "Psychokinesis: Recent Studies and a Possible Paradigm Shift", in *Advances in Parapsychological Research*, Vol. 5, Krippner, Stanley, ed., McFarland and Company, Jefferson NC and London (1987)

Schroedinger, E., "My View of the World", Cambridge: Cambridge University Press, (1964). Sergeyev, Gennady A., "Perspectives for Using Automatic Processes for Controlling the Brain during Telepathy." Paper presented: Seminar of Technical Parapsychology Section affiliated All Union Engineering Institute, Moscow, Feb. 11 (1967)

Senekowitsch, F., Endler, P.C., Pongratz, W., and Smith, C.W., "Hormone Effects by CD Record/Replay," *FASEB Journal* (9: A392: 2270 (abs)) (1995)

Sergeyev, Gennady A., "On the Nature of the Experimental Research of Dr. Zdenek Rejdak," Paper presented: Seminar of Technical Parapsychology Section affiliated All Union Engineering Institute, Moscow, Dec. 3 (1967)

Sergeyev, G., Pavlova, L and Romankenko, A., *Statitical Method of Rsearch of the Human EEG*, Leningrad: Academy of Science, USSR, Science Publishing (1968)

Sergeyev, Gennady A., Shushkov, G.D., and Griasnuhin, E.G., "A New Detector for Registering the Physiological Functions of the Organism," in *Bioenergetics Questions (Material of the Scientific Methodological Seminar in Alma-Ata)*, Edited by B.A.Dombrovsky, G.A.Sergeyev, B.M.Inyushin, Southern California Society for Psychical Research, Beverly Hills, California (1972)

Sergeyev, Gennady A., and Kulagin, V.V., "The Interaction of Bioplasmic Fields of Living Organisms with Light Photon Sources," in *Bioenergetics Questions (Material of the Scientific Methodological Seminar in Alma-Ata)*, Edited by B.A.Dombrovsky, G.A.Sergeyev, B.M.Inyushin, Southern California Society for Psychical Research, Beverly Hills, California (1972a)

Sergeyev, Gennady A., and Kulagin, V.V., "Characteristics of Bioplasmic Energy," in *Bioenergetics Questions (Material of the Scientific Methodological Seminar in Alma-Ata)*, Edited by B.A.Dombrovsky, G.A.Sergeyev, B.M.Inyushin, Southern California Society for Psychical Research, Beverly Hills, California (1972b)

Sergeyev, G.A., (1972c) "Principles of Mathematical Modeling for Bioplasmic Radiation in a Living System," p. 9-1, in (Dombrovsky, 1972)

Sergeyev, G.A., (1972d) "The Method of Registration and Statistical Processing of the Bioplasmogram,"p. 17-1, in (Dombrovsky, 1972)

Sheldrake, Rupert, *A New Science of Life-Morphic Resonance*, Publishers Group West (PGW),

Toronto, (1995)

Sheldrake, Rupert, *Seven Experiments that Could Change the World-A Do-It-Yourself Guide to Revolutionary Science*, Fourth Estate, London (1994)

Sheldrake, Rupert, *Dogs That Know When Their Masters Are Coming Home*, Three Rivers Press, New York (1999)

Sheldrake, Rupert, and Smart, Pam, "A Dog That Seems to Know When His Owner is Coming Home: Videotaped Experiments and Observations", *Journal of Scientific Exploration*, Vol. 14, No. 2, pp. 233-255 (2000)

Sheldrake, R. and Smart, P., "Psychic Pets: A Survey in Northwest England*", Journal of the Society for Psychical Research* **61**, 353-64 (1997)

Sheldrake, R. and Smart, P., "A Dog That Seems to Know When Its Owner Is Returning: Preliminary Investigations*", Journal of the Society for Psychical Research* **62**, 220-32 (1998)

Shoup, Richard, "EGG Salad," Boundary Institute http://www.boundaryinstitute.org/articles/EGG_Salad.pdf (2001)

Skousen, W. Cleon, *Prophecy and Modern Times*, Desert Book Company, Salt Lake City (1939)

Smith, Sister Dr. Justa, "Significant Results in Enzyme Activity from Healer's Hands," *Newsletter of the Parapsychology Foundation*, Jan-Feb (1969)

Spottiswood, James, *Journal of Scientific Exploration*, Vol. 11, No. 2, pp. 109-122 (1997)

Stanford, R.G., and Stein, A.G., "A Meta-Analysis of ESP Studies Contrasting Hypnosis and Comparison Conditoin", *Journal of Parapsychology* **58**, (3): 235-70 (1994)

Statistics, http://www.boundaryinstitute.org (2001)

Steiger, Brad, *Mysteries of Time and Space-Amazing Proof that We Are Not Alone*, Dell Publishing (1973)

Steiger, Brad, *The Psychic Feats of Olof Jonsson*, Prentice-Hall, NJ (1971)

Steiger, Brad, *Mysteries Beyond Space and Time*, Shiffer Publishing, Ltd. (1997)

Stemman, Roy, *Spirits and Spirit Worlds*, The Danbury Press, copyright Aldus Books, Ltd., London (1975)

Stevenson, Ian, "The Evidence for Survival from Claimed Memories of Former Incarnations," *Journal of the American Society for Psychical Research,* Vol. **54**, 51-71, 95-117 (1960)

Stevenson, Ian, "Reincarnation: Field Studies and Theoretical Isues," *Handbook of Parapsychology*, Ed. Benjamin B. Wolman, Van Nostrand Reinhold Company, New York (1977)

Stevenson, Ian, *Cases of the Reincarnation Type, Vol. I, Ten Cases in India*, University Press of Virginia, Charlottesville (1975)

Stevenson, Ian, *Twenty Cases Suggestive of Reincarnation*, University Press of Virginia, Charlottesville (1966)

Stevenson, Ian, "Birthmarks and Birth Defects Corresponding to Wounds on Deceased Persons",

Journal of Scientific Exploration, Vol. 7, No. 3, p. 403 (1993)

Stevenson, Ian, "Six Modern Apparitional Experiences," *Journal of Scientific Exploration*, Vol. 9, No. 3, pp.351-366 (1995)

Stevenson, I. (1997*) "Reincarnation and Biology: A Contribution to the Etiology of Birthmarks and Birth Defects",* 2 Vols, Praeger, Westport, CT. (1997)

Stevenson, Ian, "Unusual Play in Young Children Who Claim to Remember Previous Lives," *Journal of Scientific Exploration,* Vol. 14, No. 4, pp. 557-570 (2000)

Stone, Robert B., Ph.D*., The Secret Life of Your Cells*, Whitford Press, A Division of Shiffer Publishing Ltd., Atglen, PA, USA (1989)

Sugrue, T., *There is a River: The Story of Edgar Cayce*, A.R.E. Press, Virginia Beach (1942).

Summer Rain, Mary, *Spirit Song - The Visionary Wisdom of No-Eyes*, Donning Company Publishers (1985)

Summer Rain, Mary, *Phoenix Rising*, Hampton Roads Publishing Company, Norfolk, Virginia (1987)

Swanson, Claude, *The Synchronized Universe,* Poseidia Press, Tucson, AZ (2003)

Swanson, Claude, *Life Force: The Scientific Basis*, Poseidia Press, Tucson, AZ (2009)

Swedenborg, Emmanuel*, The Universal Human and Soul-Body Interaction*, ed. and trans. By George F. Dole, Paulist Press, New York (1984)

Szpak, S., and Mosier-Ross, P.A., "Thermal and Nuclear Aspects of the Pd/D2O System," Technical Report 1862, Vol. 1 and 2, U.S.Navy SPAWAR Systems Center, San Diego California, February (2002)

T-

Talbot, Michael, *The Holographic Universe*, Harper Perennial, New York (1991).

Targ, Russell and Puthoff, Harold E., *Mind-Reach: Scientists Look at Psychic Ability*, Delacorte Press (1977)

Targ, Russell and Harary, Keith, *The Mind Race*, Ballantine Books, New York (1984)

Targ, R., "Remote Viewing at Stanford Research Institute in the 1970s: A Memoir.", *Journal of Scientific Exploration,* Vol.10 (I), p77 (1996).

Tart, Charles T., Puthoff, Harold E., and Targ, Russell*, Mind At Large: Institute of Electrical and Electronic Engineers Symposia on the Nature of Extrasensory Perception*, Praeger (1979)

Tart, Charles, "A Psychophysiological Study of Out-of-the-Body Experiences in a Selected Subject," *Journal of the American Society for Psychical Research*, Vol. 62, pp. 3-27 (1968)

Taylor, Albert, *Soul Traveler*, Verity Press, Covina, CA (1996)

Thurston, Mark, *Millenium Prophecies, Predictions for the Century from Edgar Cayce*, Kensington Books, New York (1997)

Thurston, Herbert, *The Physical Phenomena of Mysticism*, London: Burns, Oates (1952)

Tiller, William (1974) "Devices for Monitoring Nonphysical Energies," in (Mitchell, 1974)

Tiller, William, personal communication (1992)

Tiller, William A., Ph.D., *Science and Human Transformation: Subtle Energies, Intentionality and Consciousness*, Pavior Publishing, Walnut Creek, California (1997)

Tiller, William A., Dibble, Walter E., Jr., Kohane, Michael J., *Conscious Acts of Creation - The Emergence of a New Physics*, Pavior Publishing, Walnut Creek, California (2001)

Tiller, William, "Towards a Predictive Model of Subtle Domain Connections to the Physical Domain Aspect of Reality: The Origins of Wave-Particle Duality, Electric-Magnetic Monopoles and the Mirror Principle", *Journal of Scientific Exploration*, Vol. 13, No. 1, p. 41 (1999)

Tiller, William, "Some Energy Field Observations of Man and Nature", in *Galaxies of Life*, ed. by Krippner (Krippner, 1973)

Tiller, W.A., McCraty, R., and Atkinson, M., "Cardiac Coherence: A New Noninvasive Measure of Autonomic Nervous System Disorder," *Alternative Therapies* Vol. 2, pp. 52-65 (1996)

Tiller, William A., Dibble, Walter E., Jr., Kohane, Michael J., "Exploring Robust Interactions Between Human Intention and Inanimate/Animate Systems", *Subtle Energies & Energy Medi*cine, Volume 11, No. 3, p. 265-291 (2002)

Time-Life Books, *Mysteries of the Unknown*, Quality Paperback Club, New York (1987)

Times (2001): Sunday Times of London, November 11 (2001)

Tompkins, Peter and Bird, Christopher, *The Secret Life of Plants*, Harper and Row, New York, (1972)

Tredgold, A.F., *A Textbook of Mental Deficiency*, Wood, Baltimore (1937)

Twyman, James, *Emissaries of Light-A Vision of Peace*, Warner Books, New York (1996)

Twyman, James, http://www.emissariesoflight.com (2003)

U-

Ullman, Montague, "Symposium: Psychokinesis on Stable Systems: Work in Progress-PK in the Soviet Union", *Parapsychology Research 1973*, pp. 121-125 (1973)

Utts, Jessica, "An Assessment of the Evidence for Psychic Functioning", *Journal of Scientific Exploration*, Vol. 10, No. 1, pp. 3-30 (1996)

Utts, Jessica, in "An Evaluation of the Remote Viewing Program," American Institute of Research (AIR) Report, 9/95, (1995) quoted in (Mandlebaum, 2000)

V-

Van Dusen, Wilson, *The Presence of Other Worlds*, Swedenborg Foundation, New York (1974)

Vellinga, P., and Verseveld, W.J. Van, *Climate Change and Extreme Weather Events*, Institute for Environmental Studies, Free University, Amsterdam, September (2000)

Von Braun, Werner, *Neues Europa*, 1 January (1959)

Vogel, Marcel, Ph.D., "Man-Plant Communication," pp. 289-313, in *Psychic Exploration*, ed. by John White, Putnam's Sons, New York (1976)

W-

Waters, J. Frank, *Book of the Hopi*, Ballantine Books, New York (1963)

Weiss, Brian, M.D., *Many Lives, Many Masters*, Warner Books, New York (1991).

Weiss, Brian, M.D., *Only Love is Real-A Story of Soulmates Reunited*, Warner Books, New York (1996)

Weiss, Brian, M.D., *Messages from the Masters-Tapping into the Power of Love*, Warner Books, New York (2000)

Wheeler, J.A., and Feynman, R.P., "Interaction with the Absorber as the Mechanism of Radiation", *Rev. Mod Phys*, **17**, no. 2, p157 (1945).

White, John and Krippner, Stanley, eds. *Future Science: Life Energies and the Physics of Paranormal Phenomena*, pp. 420-430, Doubleday Anchor, (1977)

White, John, ed, and Mitchell, Edgar D., *Psychic Exploration, A Challenge for Science*, Perigee Books, published by G.P.Putnam & Sons, New York (1974)

White, John, *Pole Shift*, A.R.E. Press (1988)

Whiteman, J.H.M., *The Mystical Life*, Faber & Faber, London (1961)

Whitton, J. L., "Ramp Functions in EEG Power Spectra during Actual or Attempted Paranormal Events," *New Horizons*, Vol. 1, pp. 174-183 (1974)

Whitton, Joel and Fisher, Joe, *Life Between Life,* Doubleday, New York (1986)

Williams, Kevin, "Near-Death Experiences and the Afterlife," http://www.near-death.com/experiences/evidence10.html (2003)

Wilson, Colin, *Mysterious Powers*, The Danbury Press, Division of Grolier (1975)

Wilson, Colin, *Spirits and Spirit Worlds*, The Danbury Press, Division of Grolier (1975a)

Wirkus (2003) website for Wirkus Bioenergy and Mietek Wirkus: http://www.mietekwirkus.com

Wirkus, M. et. al., *Subtle Energies*, Vol. 3, No. 1, pp. 19-52 (1992)

Wiston, William, translator, *The Works of Flavius Josephus*, J.Grigg, Philadelphia (1835)

X-

Y-

Yan, Xin, et al, "Certain Physical Manifestation and Effects of External Qi of Yan Xin Life Science Technology", *Journal of Scientific Exploration*, Vol. 16, No. 3, pp. 381-411 (2002)

Yan, X., Li, S., Yu, J., and Lu, Z., "Laser Raman Observation on Tap Water, Saline, Glucose and Medemycine Solutions Under the Influence of External Qi," *Ziran Zashi* (The Nature Journal), Vol. 11, p. 567 (1988)

Yan, X., Lu, Z., and Zhu, R., "The Influence of External Qi of Qi-Gong on the Half-life of Radioactive Isotope ^{241}Am," *Chinese Journal of Somatic Science*, Vol. 10, 3-12 (2000)

Yogananda, Paramahansa, *Autobiography of a Yogi,* Self-Realization Fellowship, Los Angeles (1946)

Yonjie, Zhao and Hongzhang, Xu, "EHBF Radiation: Special Features of the Time Response," Institute of High Energy Physics, Beijing, Peoples Republic of China, *PSI Research*, December (1982)

Yukteswar, Swami Sri, *The Holy Science*, Self-Realization Fellowship, Los Angeles, California, (1949)

INDEX

twins, identical 85-86

U-
UFOs 12
unemployment 211
unified field theory 7
Utts, Jessica 15

V-
vegetative nervous system 85
voltage during kundalini 140
voltage, high, effect on OBE 175-177
vacuum of space 240

W-
Wilmot OBE 170-171
Wirkus, Mietek 10-11
Wisdom Schools (see Mystery Schools)
witch doctor 130
World Trade Center attack 96-100
wormwood 219

Y-
Yukteswar, Sri 122, 129
Yogananda, Paramahansa 108-109, 121-123, 135
yogi 108-109, 121-124, 130, 136, 151
Yonjie 6

Z-
zero-point energy 234-237
Zhang Baosheng 115, 117

GIVE THE GIFT OF *THE SYNCHRONIZED UNIVERSE*
TO YOUR FRIENDS AND COLLEAGUES
CHECK YOUR LOCAL BOOKSTORE OR ORDER HERE

☐ YES, I want ____ copies of *The Synchronized Universe*, for US $23.95 each.

☐ YES, I am interested in having Dr. Swanson speak or give a seminar to my organization. Please send me information.

Include $3.95 shipping and handling for one book, and $1.95 for each additional book. Colorado, Ohio and New York Residents must include applicable sales tax. Canadian orders must include payment in US funds, with 7% GST added. For overseas destination outside the United States, add US $18.00 for shipping and handling.

My check or money order for $_____ is enclosed.

Name _____

Organization_____

Address _____

City/State/Zip _____

Phone_____ Email_____

Card #_____

Exp. Date_____ Signature _____

Make your check payable to

Poseidia Press

7320 North La Cholla, Suite #154-304

Tucson, AZ 85741

For credit card orders:

Order on-line at

www.synchronizeduniverse.com

or on Amazon.com

307